Evolution: The Fossils Still Say NO!

Duane T. Gish, Ph.D.

Institute for Creation Research
El Cajon, California

Evolution: The Fossils Still Say NO!
1st Edition

Copyright © 1995

A revision of *Evolution: The Challenge of the Fossil Record*
Copyright © 1985

Institute for Creation Research
P. O. Box
El Cajon, California 92021

Library of Congress Catalog Card Number 85-06257C
ISBN 0-89051-112-8

Cataloging in Publication Data

Gish, Duane Tolbert, 1921-
Evolution: The Fossils Still Say NO!

1. Creation 2. Evolution 3. Paleontology

GH369.G54 575

Printed in the United States of America

Cover: Design and photos by Marvin Ross

ABOUT THE AUTHOR

DUANE T. GISH, Ph.D. (Biochemistry, University of California, Berkeley) is Senior Vice President and Professor of Natural Science at the Institute for Creation Research, Santee, California 92071. He spent 18 years in biochemical research at Cornell University Medical College, the Virus Laboratory of the University of California, Berkeley, and The Upjohn Company, Kalamazoo, Michigan. He is the author or co-author of numerous technical articles in his field and a well-known author and lecturer on creation/evolution. He is a member of the American Chemical Society and a Fellow of the American Institute of Chemists.

iii

DEDICATION

This book is dedicated to the late Sidney J. Jansma, one of the outstanding lay leaders of America in the cause of scientific creationism.

PREFACE

This book constitutes one of the most devastating critiques of the evolutionary philosophy one could find. It goes right to the stronghold of the supposed scientific evidence for evolution and demolishes its central bastion.

The fossil record must provide the critical evidence for or against evolution, since no other scientific evidence can possibly throw light on the actual history of living things. All other evidence is circumstantial and can be more effectively explained in terms of the creation model. The time scale of human observation is far too short to permit documentation of real evolutionary change from lower to higher kinds of organisms at the present time. The vital question, therefore, is: "Does the record of past ages, now preserved in the form of fossils, show that such changes have occurred?" The answer, unequivocally, is: "The fossils say no!" There has been no evolution in the past any more than in the present. This important fact is conclusively demonstrated and documented by Dr. Gish in this book.

Dr. Duane T. Gish is a careful scientist of impeccable academic credentials. He has successfully defended creationism before numerous university and scientific audiences and in formal debates with many of the nation's leading evolutionary scientists.

This book (under its original title, *Evolution: The Challenge of the Fossil Record*) has gone through several printings and has already been eminently successful in its mission of convincing men of the truth of creationism. In this new enlarged and revised edition with a new

v

title to emphasize the powerful nature of the evidence for creation, it is still more convincing, and will, no doubt, have a greater acceptance than ever before. Anyone who reads this book and who then still rejects creationism in favor of evolutionism must at least acknowledge that he *believes* in evolution in *spite* of the massive witness of the fossil record *against* it!

Henry M. Morris, Ph.D., President
Institute for Creation Research
Santee, California 92071

Contents

Credits

The Author wishes to thank Connie Horn and Ruth Richards for assistance in typing the manuscript and especially Mary Morris Smith for typing, editing, and preparing the manuscript in final form for publication.

Chapter I

Evolution—A Philosophy, Not a Science

The general theory of organic evolution, or the evolution model, is the theory that all living things have arisen by a materialistic evolutionary process from a single source, which itself arose by a similar process from a dead, inanimate world. This theory may also be called the molecule-to-man theory of evolution.

The creation model, on the other hand, postulates that all basic animal and plant types (the created kinds) were brought into existence by acts of a supernatural Creator using special processes which are not operative today.

Most scientists accept evolution, not as a theory, but as an established fact. The late Theodosius Dobzhansky, geneticist and widely-known evolutionist, formerly Professor of Zoology at Columbia University and visiting Professor at the University of California, Davis, has said that "the occurrence of the evolution of life in the history of the earth is established about as well as events not witnessed by human observers can be."[1] Richard B. Goldschmidt, a Professor at the University of California before his death, has stated that "Evolution of the animal and plant world is considered by all those entitled to judgment to be a fact for which no further proof is needed."[2] Almost all science books and school and university texts present evolution as an

---

[1] T. Dobzhansky, *Science* 127:1091 (1958).
[2] R. B. Goldschmidt, *American Scientist* 40:84 (1952).

established fact. These considerations alone convince many people that molecule-to-man evolution has actually occurred.

The proponents of evolution theory adamantly insist that special creation be excluded from any possible consideration as an explanation for origins on the basis that it does not qualify as a scientific theory. On the other hand, they would view as unthinkable the consideration of evolution as anything less than pure science. In fact, as already mentioned, most evolutionists insist that evolution must no longer be thought of as a theory, but must be considered to be a fact. However, evolution does not even qualify as a scientific theory, according to a strict definition of the latter.

What criteria must be met for a theory to be considered as scientific in the usually accepted sense? George Gaylord Simpson has stated that "it is inherent in any definition of science that statements that cannot be checked by observation are not really about anything . . . or at the very least, they are not science."[3] A definition of science given by the Oxford Dictionary is:

> A branch of study which is concerned either with a connected body of *demonstrated truths* or with *observed fact* systematically classified and more or less colligated by being brought under general laws, and which includes trustworthy methods for the discovery of new truth within its own domain. (Emphasis added.)

Thus, for a theory to qualify as a scientific theory, it must be supported by events, processes, or properties which can be repeatedly observed, and the theory must be useful in predicting the outcome of future natural phenomena or laboratory experiments. An additional limitation usually imposed is that the theory must be capable of falsification. That is, it must be possible to conceive some experiment, the failure of which would disprove the theory.

It is on the basis of such criteria that most evolutionists insist that creation be refused consideration as a possible explanation for origins. Creation has not been witnessed by human observers, it cannot be tested experimentally, and as a theory it is nonfalsifiable.

The general theory of evolution also fails to meet all three of these

---

[3] G. G. Simpson, *Science* 143:769 (1964).

criteria, however. It is obvious, for example, that there were no human observers to the origin of the universe, the origin of life, the conversion of a fish into an amphibian, or an ape into a man. No one, as a matter of fact, has ever observed the origin of a species by naturally occurring processes. Evolution has been *postulated*, but it has never been *observed*.

This was affirmed by both Dobzhansky and Goldschmidt, who, as it has been noted, were wholly committed to faith in evolution. In the quotation cited earlier in this chapter, Dobzhansky clearly stated that *evolution has not been witnessed by human observers*.

Goldschmidt, after outlining his postulated systemic mutation, or "hopeful monster" mechanism for evolution, stated:

> Such an assumption is violently opposed by the majority of geneticists, who claim that the facts found on the subspecific level must apply also to the higher categories. Incessant repetition of this unproved claim, glossing lightly over the difficulties, and the assumption of an arrogant attitude toward those who are not so easily swayed by fashions in science, are considered to afford scientific proof of the doctrine. It is true that nobody thus far has produced a new species or genus, etc., by macromutation. It is equally true that nobody has produced even a species by the selection of micromutations.[4]

A macromutation is a change in a gene or other genetic change which produces a drastic and thus obvious change in the organism and is very often lethal. A micromutation is a genetic change which produces an effect that is generally so slight the effect, although harmful, may be difficult to detect.

Later on in this same paper, he stated: "Neither has anyone witnessed the production of a new specimen of a higher taxonomic category by selection of micromutants."[5] Goldschmidt has thus affirmed that, in the molecules-to-man context, only the most trivial change, or that at the subspecies level, has actually ever been observed.

Since evolution has not been observed in nature, and even a species

[4] Goldschmidt, *American Scientist* 40:94 (1952).
[5] *Ibid.*, p. 97.

cannot be produced by the selection of mutants, it is apparent that evolution is not subject to experimental test. This was admitted by Dobzhansky when he said:

> These evolutionary happenings are unique, unrepeatable, and irreversible. It is as impossible to turn a land vertebrate into a fish as it is to effect the reverse transformation. The applicability of the experimental method to the study of such unique historical processes is severely restricted before all else by the time intervals involved, which far exceed the lifetime of any human experimenter. And yet it is just such impossibility that is demanded by anti-evolutionists when they ask for "proofs" of evolution which they would magnanimously accept as satisfactory.[6]

Dobzhansky thus stated that the applicability of the experimental method to evolution is an "impossibility." One reason given by Dobzhansky and other evolutionists for rejecting creation as a possible explanation for origins is because it is not subject to the experimental method. At the same time, however, they consider it wholly unreasonable for creationists to place the same demand on evolution theory!

It can be seen that evolutionists seek to excuse the fact that evolution cannot be observed or tested experimentally on the basis that real evolutionary events require great lengths of time for their consummation. Yes, it is true that the evolutionary process postulated would require more time than we have available for human observation. But then, it is obvious that evolution can never be more than just a postulate.

Macbeth, who was by no means a creationist, has flatly stated that "Darwinism is not science."[7] Birch and Ehrlich state that the theory of evolution "is 'outside of empirical science' but not necessarily false. No one can think of ways in which to test it."[8]

After stating that the neo-Darwinian theory of evolution is based on axioms (concepts that can be neither proved nor tested), evolution theorist Harris proclaims:

---

[6] T. Dobzhansky, *American Scientist* 45:388 (1957).

[7] N. Macbeth, *American Biology Teacher* (November 1976), p. 496.

[8] L. C. Birch and P. R. Ehrlich, *Nature* 214:349 (1967).

The axiomatic nature of the neo-Darwinian theory places the debate between evolutionists and creationists in a new perspective. Evolutionists have often challenged creationists to provide experimental proof that species have been fashioned *de novo*. Creationists have often demanded that evolutionists show how chance mutations can lead to adaptability, or to explain why natural selection has favored some species but not others with special adaptations, or why natural selection allows apparently detrimental organs to persist. We may now recognize that neither challenge is fair. If the neo-Darwinian theory is axiomatic, it is not valid for creationists to demand proof of the axioms, and it is not valid for evolutionists to dismiss special creation as unproved so long as it is stated as an axiom.[9]

Matthews, British biologist and evolutionist, in his introduction to a 1971 publication of Darwin's *Origin of Species*, says:

The fact of evolution is the backbone of biology, and biology is thus in the peculiar position of being a science founded on an unproved theory—is it then a science or a faith? Belief in the theory of evolution is thus exactly parallel to belief in special creation—both are concepts which believers know to be true but neither, up to the present, has been capable of proof.[10]

While evolutionists deny the miraculous in the origin of living things, the evolutionary process, given enough time, supposedly produces miracles. Thus,

$$\text{FROG} \xrightarrow[t = instantaneous]{} \text{PRINCE} = \text{NURSERY TALE}$$

but

$$\text{FROG} \xrightarrow[t = 300\ million\ years]{} \text{PRINCE} = \text{SCIENCE}$$

---

[9] C. Leon Harris, *Perspectives in Biology and Medicine* (Winter 1975), p. 183.

[10] L. Harrison Matthews, Introduction to C. Darwin, *The Origin of Species* (reprint, London: J. M. Dent and Sons, Ltd., 1971), p. XI.

Furthermore, the architects of the modern synthetic theory of evolution have so skillfully constructed their theory that it is not capable of falsification. The theory is so plastic that it is capable of explaining anything. This is the complaint of Olson[11] and of several participants in the Wistar Institute symposium on mathematical challenges to the neo-Darwinian interpretation of evolution.[12]

Murray Eden, one of the mathematicians, put it this way with reference to falsifiability:

> This cannot be done in evolution, taking it in its broad sense, and this is really all I meant when I called it tautologous in the first place. It can, indeed, explain anything. You may be ingenious or not in proposing a mechanism which looks plausible to human beings and mechanisms which are consistent with other mechanisms which you have discovered, but it is still an unfalsifiable theory.[13]

In addition to scientists who are creationists, a growing number of other scientists have expressed doubts that modern evolution theory could explain more than just trivial change. Eden became so discouraged after computerized calculations showed that the probability of certain evolutionary changes occurring (according to mechanisms postulated by modern evolutionists) was essentially zero that he proclaimed, "an adequate scientific theory of evolution must await the discovery and elucidation of new natural laws—physical, phsyicochemical, and biological."[14] Salisbury has similarly stated his doubts based on probabilistic considerations.[15]

The attack on modern formulations of the theory by French scientists has been intense in recent years. A review of the French situation stated:

---

[11] E. C. Olson, in *Evolution After Darwin*, vol. 1; *The Evolution of Life*, ed. Sol Tax (Chicago: University of Chicago Press, 1960).

[12] P. S. Moorhead and M. M. Kaplan, eds., *Mathematical Challenges to the Neo-Darwinian Interpretation of Evolution* (Philadelphia: Wistar Institute Press, 1967), pp. 47, 64, 67, 71.

[13] Murray Eden, *Mathematical Challenges to Interpretation*, p. 71.

[14] *Ibid.*, p. 109.

[15] F. Salisbury, *Nature* 224:342 (1969).

This year saw the controversy rapidly growing, until recently it culminated in the title "Should We Burn Darwin?" spread over two pages of the magazine *Science et Vie*. The article, by the science writer Aime Michel, was based on the author's interviews with such specialists as Mrs. Andree Tetry, professor at the famous *Ecole des Hautes Etudes*, and a world authority on problems of evolution; Professor Rene Chauvin and other noted French biologists; and on his thorough study of some 600 pages of biological data collected, in collaboration with Mrs. Tetry, by the late Michael Cuenot, a biologist of international fame. Aime Michel's conclusion is significant: "The classical theory of evolution in its strict sense belongs to the past. Even if they do not publicly take a definite stand, almost all French specialists hold today strong mental reservations as to the validity of natural selection."[16]

E. C. Olson, one of the speakers at the Darwinian Centennial Celebration at Chicago, made the following statement on that occasion:

There exists, as well, a generally silent group of students engaged in biological pursuits who tend to disagree with much of the current thought, but say and write little because they are not particularly interested, do not see that controversy over evolution is of any particular importance, or are so strongly in disagreement that it seems futile to undertake the monumental task of controverting the immense body of information and theory that exists in the formulation of modern thinking. It is, of course, difficult to judge the size and composition of this silent segment, but there is no doubt that the numbers are not inconsiderable.[17]

Fothergill refers to what he calls "the paucity of evolutionary theory as a whole."[18] Erhlich and Holm have stated their reservations in the following way:

Finally, consider the third question posed earlier: "What accounts for the observed patterns in nature?" It has

---

[16] Z. Litynski, *Science Digest* 50:61 (1961).
[17] Olson, *Evolution After Darwin*, p. 523.
[18] P. G. Fothergill, *Nature* 191:340 (1961).

become fashionable to regard modern evolutionary theory as the *only* possible explanation of these patterns rather than just the best explanation that has been developed so far. It is conceivable, even likely, that what one might facetiously call a non-Euclidean theory of evolution lies over the horizon. Perpetuation of today's theory as dogma will not encourage progress toward more satisfactory explanations of observed phenomena.[19]

Sometimes the attacks are openly critical, such as Danson's letter which appeared in *New Scientist* and stated, in part:

> The Theory of Evolution is no longer with us, because neo-Darwinism is now acknowledged as being unable to explain anything more than trivial change, and in default of some other theory we have none . . . despite the hostility of the witness provided by the fossil record, despite the innumerable difficulties, and despite the lack of even a credible theory, evolution survives. Can there be any other area of science, for instance, in which a concept as intellectually barren as embryonic recapitulation could be used as evidence for a theory?[20]

Macbeth has published an especially incisive criticism of evolution theory.[21] He points out that although evolutionists have abandoned classical Darwinism, the modern synthetic theory they have proposed as a substitute is equally inadequate to explain progressive change as the result of natural selection, and, as a matter of fact, they cannot even define natural selection in nontautologous terms. Inadequacies of the present theory and failure of the fossil record to substantiate its predictions leave macroevolution, and even microevolution, intractable mysteries according to Macbeth. Macbeth suggests that no theory at all may be preferable to the existing one.

In a recent book,[22] Pierre Grassé, one of France's best-known scientists, has severely criticized modern evolution theory.

---

[19] P. R. Ehrlich and R. W. Holm, *Science* 137:655 (1962).

[20] R. Danson, *New Scientist* 49:35 (1971).

[21] N. Macbeth, *Darwin Retried* (Boston: Gambit, Inc., 1971).

[22] P. Grassé, *L'Evolution du Vivant* (Paris: Editions Albin Michel, 1973).

Dobzhansky, in his review[23] of that book, stated:

> The book of Pierre P. Grassé is a frontal attack on all kinds of "Darwinism." Its purpose is "to destroy the myth of evolution, as a simple, understood, and explained phenomenon," and to show that evolution is a mystery about which little is, and perhaps can be known. Now one can disagree with Grassé but not ignore him. He is the most distinguished of French zoologists, the editor of the 28 volumes of *Traite de Zoologie*, author of numerous original investigations, and ex-president of the Academie des Sciences. His knowledge of the living world is encyclopedic.

Grassé ends his book with the sentence, "It is possible that in this domain biology, impotent, yields the floor to metaphysics."

Kenneth Hsu, while not a creationist, was moved to make the following observations in his article in the *Journal of Sedimentary Petrology*:

> We all have heard of *The Origin of Species*, although few of us have had time to read it; I did not secure a copy until two years ago. A casual perusal of the classic made me understand the rage of Paul Feyerabend (1975). He considers science an ideology. Feyerabend wrote that "all ideologists must be seen in perspective. One must read them like fairy tales which have lots of interesting things to say but which contain wicked lies." I do not want to follow his lead to lend "three cheers to fundamentalists in California who succeeded in having a dogmatic formulation of the theory of evolution removed from the textbooks and an account of Genesis included" (p. 163). Nevertheless, I agree with him that Darwinism contains "wicked lies"; it is not a "natural law" formulated on the basis of factual evidence, but a dogma, reflecting the dominating social philosophy of the last century.[24]

It must be added that while the effort to place the theory of evolution in a tentative position rather than dogma in California

---

[23] T. Dobzhansky, *Evolution* 29:376 (1975).
[24] K. J. Hsu, *Journal of Sedimentary Petrology* 56(5): 729-730 (1986).

schools was at least a temporary success, an account of Genesis was
not placed in the textbooks, nor was any effort made to do so.
Nevertheless, Hsu has stated plainly his view that Darwinism is an
ideological dogma rather than natural law, as its adherents would have
us believe.

More and more evolutionists have come to doubt the modern
neo-Darwinian theory of evolution so prevalent today. They realize
that the fossil record does not produce the evidence of gradual change
demanded by Darwinism and they have sought to devise new ideas
about the mechanism of evolution. This has generated fierce
opposition from the old guard, the defenders of neo-Darwinism, and
intense controversy within evolutionary circles has resulted. This fact
was revealed in the article, "Science Contra Darwin" by Sharon
Begley, which appeared in *Newsweek*. She states:

> The great body of work derived from Charles Darwin's
> revolutionary 1859 book, *On the Origin of Species,* is under
> increasing attack—and not just from creationists. . . . So
> heated is the debate that one Darwinian says there are
> times when he thinks about going into a field with more
> intellectual honesty: the used-car business.[25]

Michael Denton is neither a Christian nor a professing creationist.
He holds both an M.D. and a Ph.D. from British universities. No one
can accuse him of being a fundamentalist out on the lunatic fringe.
Nevertheless, he has published a devastating critique of modern
evolutionary theory.[26] On every count, according to Dr. Denton,
evolution strikes out. His book is one of the most incisive, thoroughly
documented, and comprehensive books that describes the vast amount
of scientific evidence that refutes evolutionary theory. On the flap of
the book published in 1985 are recorded the following comments:

> The theory of evolution, as propounded by Darwin and
> elaborated into accepted "fact"' by biologists, is in serious
> trouble. This sober, authoritative, and responsible book by a
> practicing scientist presents an accurate account of the

---

[25] Sharon Begley, *Newsweek*, 8 April 1985, p. 80.

[26] Michael Denton, *Evolution: A Theory in Crisis* (London: Burnett
Books, 1985), available from Woodbine House, 5615 Fishers Lane,
Rockville, MD 20852, and the Institute for Creation Research.

rapidly accumulating evidence which threatens to destroy almost every cherished tenet of Darwinian evolution. Although the theory has proved to be right about the relatively minor phenomenon of speciation, its larger claims to account for the relationship between the classes and orders, let alone the origin of life, appear to be based on very shaky scientific foundations indeed. Not only has paleontology failed spectacularly to come up with the fossil "missing links" which Darwin anticipated, but hypothetical reconstructions of major evolutionary developments—such as that linking birds to reptiles—are beginning to look more and more like science fiction fantasies than serious conjectures. Even the currently fashionable theory of "punctuated equilibrium" cannot adequately fill in the very real gaps we face when envisaging how major groups of plants and animals arose.

Most important of all, the discoveries of molecular biologists, of whom Michael Denton is one, far from strengthening Darwinian claims, are throwing more and more doubt upon the correctness of the whole theory. When the amino acid sequences, the basic evidence of a cell's hereditary antecedents, of supposedly related species are examined the results point, not towards the Darwinian picture of a nature linked by the genetic descent of one class from another, but towards the typological model of nature which Darwinism usurped. At a fundamental level of molecular structure, each member of a class seems equally representative of that class and no species appears to be in any real sense "intermediate" between two classes. Nature, in short, appears to be profoundly discontinuous. Furthermore, advances in biochemistry are making the existence of a "prebiotic soup"—the supposed primordial broth in which life began on Earth—look highly unlikely if not completely absurd.

Søren Løvtrup is a well-known Swedish biologist. He is a totally committed evolutionist, but nevertheless he completely rejects the neo-Darwinian theory of evolution. He maintains that mutations and natural selection have had little, if anything, to do with evolution. He is an advocate of the view that macromutations, generating large jumps in evolution, provided the mechanism of evolution. He refers to the modern neo-Darwinian theory of evolution, the theory that is currently being taught as dogma in practically all of the textbooks in use in secondary schools, colleges, and universities in the U.S., as the "Darwinian myth." In 1987 he published a book entitled *Darwinism: The Refutation of a Myth.*[27] In this book Løvtrup reviews the history of Darwinism from its beginning up to its present-day formulation. He describes his objections to the theory, and presents his own ideas about evolutionary theory. Among his conclusions we find the following statements (p. 422):

> I suppose that nobody will deny that it is a great misfortune if an entire branch of science becomes addicted to a false theory. But this is what has happened in biology: for a long time now people discuss evolutionary problems in a peculiar "Darwinian" vocabulary—"adaptation, "selection pressure," "natural selection," etc.—thereby believing that they contribute to the *explanation* of natural events. They do not, and the sooner this is discovered, the sooner we shall be able to make real progress in our understanding of evolution.
>
> *I believe that one day the Darwinian myth will be ranked the greatest deceit in the history of science.* (Emphasis added.)

What an astounding situation! What is being taught in our schools and universities as established truth, a dogma not to be questioned, Løvtrup denounces as the greatest deceit ever perpetuated in the history of science! Creation scientists maintain that not only is modern Darwinian theory the greatest deceit in the history of science, but the very notion of evolution itself is the greatest deceit ever to gain currency in scientific circles. Not that evolutionists are deliberately dishonest, but they have been deceived or have deceived themselves to believe something that is totally false.

In view of the above, it is incredible that most leading scientists dogmatically insist that the molecules-to-man evolution theory be

---

[27] Søren Løvtrup, *Darwinism: The Refutation of a Myth* (New York: Croom Helm, 1987).

taught as a fact to the exclusion of all other postulates. Evolution in this broad sense is unproven and unprovable and thus cannot be considered as fact. It is not subject to test by the ordinary methods of experimental science—observation and falsification. It thus does not, in a strict sense, even qualify as a scientific theory. It is a postulate and may serve as a model within which attempts may be made to explain and correlate the evidence from the historical record, that is, the fossil record, and to make predictions concerning the nature of future discoveries.

Evolutionists, however, insist that evolution is fact, not theory. Philosopher Tom Bethell describes the true situation when he states:

> Evolution is perhaps the most jealously guarded dogma of the American public philosophy. Any sign of serious resistance to it has encountered fierce hostility in the past, and it will not be abandoned without a tremendous fight. The gold standard could go (glad to be rid of that!), Saigon abandoned, the Constitution itself slyly junked. But Darwinism will be defended to the bitter end.[28]

Creation is, of course, unproven and unprovable and thus cannot be considered as fact. It is not subject to test by the ordinary methods of experimental science—observation and falsification. It thus does not, in a strict sense, qualify as a scientific theory. It is a postulate and may serve as a model within which attempts may be made to explain and correlate the evidence from the historical record, that is, the fossil record, and to make predictions concerning the nature of future discoveries.

It is often stated that there are no reputable scientists who do not accept the theory of evolution. This is just one more false argument used to win converts to the theory. While it is true that creationists among scientists definitely constitute a minority, there are many creation scientists, and their number is growing. Among these may be numbered such well-established scientists as Dr. A. E. Wilder-Smith, of Einigen am Thunersee, Switzerland, who has earned doctorates from three European universities and is the author or co-author of more than fifty technical publications; the late Dr. W. R. Thompson, world-famous biologist and former Director of the Commonwealth

---

[28] Tom Bethell, *The American Spectator* (July 1994), p. 17.

Institute of Biological Control of Canada; Dr. Melvin A. Cook, winner of the 1968 E. G. Murphee Award in Industrial and Engineering Chemistry from the American Chemical Society and also winner of the Nobel Nitro Award, now president of the Ireco Chemical Company, Salt Lake City; Dr. Henry M. Morris, for thirteen years Professor of Hydraulic Engineering and Head of the Civil Engineering Department at Virginia Polytechnic Institute and University, one of the largest in the U.S., now President of the Institute for Creation Research, San Diego; Dr. Walter Lammerts, geneticist and famous plant breeder; the late Dr. Frank Marsh, Professor of Biology at Andrews University until his retirement; the late Dr. J. J. Duyvene De Wit, Professor of Zoology at the University of the Orange Free State, South Africa, at the time of his death; Dr. Thomas G. Barnes, Professor Emeritus of Physics at the University of Texas at El Paso; Dr. Dmitri Kouznetsov, M.D., Ph.D., D.Sc., winner of the Komsomol Lenin Prize in 1983 as one of the two most promising young scientists in the Soviet Union, and winner of the Council of Ministries Prize of the USSR in 1986 for his research in biochemistry; and Professor Leonid Korochkin, one of Russia's leading geneticists and Head of the Department of Molecular Biology at the Russian Academy of Sciences Institute for Developmental Biology.

To these names may now be added those of Sir Fred Hoyle, famous British astronomer, and Dr. Chandra Wickramasinghe, Professor and Chairman of the Department of Applied Mathematics and Astronomy, University College, Cardiff, Wales. Neither Sir Fred Hoyle nor Professor Wickramasinghe accept the Genesis account of creation, but each maintains that wherever life occurs in this universe, it had to be created. They further reject Darwinian evolution itself.

The Creation Research Society, an organization of Christian men and women of science, all of whom hold advanced degrees and are fully committed to the acceptance of creation as opposed to evolution, now numbers about 600 in membership.[29] There is yet a vastly larger number of scientists who do not accept the theory but choose to remain silent for a variety of reasons.

Why have most scientists accepted the theory of evolution? Is the evidence really that convincing? This seems to be the clear implication.

---

[29] Creation Research Society, P.O. Box 969, Ashland, OH 44805-0969.

On the other hand, is it possible that that many scientists could be wrong? The answer is an emphatic "YES!" Consider for a moment some historical examples. For centuries the accepted scientific view was that all planets revolved around the earth. This was the Ptolemaic geocentric theory of the universe. Only after a prolonged and bitter controversy did the efforts of Copernicus, Galileo, and others succeed in convincing the scientific world that the Ptolemaic system was wrong and that Copernicus was right in his contention that the planets in the solar system revolved around the sun.

At one time most people with scientific training who rejected creation accepted as fact the idea that life spontaneously arose from nonlife. Thus, frogs supposedly spontaneously arose from swamps, decaying matter generated flies, and rats were brought to life out of matter found in debris, etc. A series of carefully designed and executed experiments by Redi, Spallanzani, and Pasteur spanning 200 years were required to put to rest the theory of the spontaneous generation of life.

In recent times, a theory dealing with weak interaction of atomic particles became so widely accepted by physicists that it won the status of a law, the Law of Parity. During the 1950s, two brilliant Chinese-American scientists performed a series of experiments that disproved the theory and deposed the "Law."

In all of the above examples, the vast majority of scientists were wrong and a small minority were right. No doubt, strong preconceived ideas and prejudices were powerful factors in accounting for the fact that scientists were reluctant to give up the geocentric theory of the universe and the theory of the spontaneous generation of life.

The effects of prejudice and preconceived ideas are of overwhelming importance in the acceptance of the theory of evolution. The reason most scientists accept evolution has nothing to do, primarily, with the evidence. The reason that most scientists accept the theory of evolution is that most scientists are unbelievers, and unbelieving, materialistic individuals are forced to accept a materialistic, naturalistic explanation for the origin of all living things. Watson, for example, has referred to the theory of evolution as "a theory universally accepted not because it can be proved by logically coherent evidence to be true, but because the only alternative, special creation, is clearly incredible."[30] That this is

---

[30] D. M. S. Watson, *Nature* 124:233 (1929).

the philosophy held by most biologists has been emphasized by Dobzhansky. In his review of Monod's book, *Chance and Necessity*, Dobzhansky said, "He has stated with admirable clarity, and eloquence often verging on pathos, the mechanistic materialist philosophy shared by most of the present 'establishment' in the biological sciences."[31]

The late Sir Julian Huxley, British evolutionist and grandson of Thomas Huxley, one of Darwin's strongest supporters when he first published his theory, has said that "Gods are peripheral phenomena produced by evolution."[32] What Huxley meant was that the idea of God merely evolved as man evolved from lower animals. Huxley had hoped to establish a humanistic religion based on evolution. Humanism has been defined as "the belief that man shapes his own destiny. It is a constructive philosophy, a nontheistic religion, a way of life."[33] This same publication quotes Huxley as saying:

> I use the word "Humanist" to mean someone who believes that man is just as much a natural phenomenon as an animal or plant; that his body, mind, and soul were not supernaturally created but are products of evolution, and that he is not under the control or guidance of any supernatural being or beings, but has to rely on himself and his own powers.

The inseparable link between this nontheistic humanistic religion and belief in evolution is evident.

The late Dr. George Gaylord Simpson, Professor of Vertebrate Paleontology at Harvard University until his retirement and one of the world's best-known evolutionists, has said that the Christian faith, which he calls the "higher superstition" (in America and Africa), is intellectually unacceptable.[34] Simpson concludes his book, *Life of the Past*,[35] with what Sir Julian Huxley has called "a splendid assertion of the evolutionist view of man."[36] Simpson writes:

---

[31] T. Dobzhansky, *Science* 175:49 (1972).

[32] J. Huxley, *The Observer*, 17 July 1960, p. 17.

[33] *What is Humanism?* A pamphlet published by The Humanist Community of San Jose, California 95106.

[34] G. G. Simpson, *Science* 131:966 (1960).

[35] G. G. Simpson, *Life of the Past* (New Haven: Yale University Press, 1953).

[36] J. Huxley, *Scientific American* 189:90 (1953).

Man stands alone in the universe, a unique product of a long, unconscious, impersonal material process with unique understanding and potentialities. These he owes to no one but himself, and it is to himself that he is responsible. He is not the creature of uncontrollable and undeterminable forces, but his own master. He can and must decide and manage his own destiny.

Thus, according to Simpson, man is alone in the universe (there is no God), he is the result of an impersonal, unconscious process (no one directed his origin or creation), and he is his own master and must manage his own destiny (there is no God who is man's Lord and Master and who determines man's destiny). That, according to Simpson and Huxley, is the evolutionist's view of man.

Dr. Phillip Johnson is the Jefferson E. Peyser Professor of Law at the University of California, Berkeley. He has published an excellent critique of the creation/evolution controversy in his book, *Darwin on Trial*.[37] Following his use of a quotation from George Gaylord Simpson which concludes with the statement, "Man is the result of a purposeless and natural process that did not have him in mind," Johnson states (p. 114):

Because the scientific establishment has found it prudent to encourage a degree of confusion on this point, I should emphasize that Simpson's view was not some personal opinion extraneous to his scientific discipline. On the contrary, he was merely stating explicitly what Darwinists mean by "evolution." The same understanding is expressed in countless books and articles, and where it is not expressed it is pervasively implied. Make no mistake about it. In the Darwinist view, which is the official view of mainstream science, God had nothing to do with evolution.

Naturalism is not something about which Darwinists can afford to be tentative, because their science is based upon it. As we have seen, the positive evidence that Darwinian evolution either can produce or has produced important biological innovations is non-existent. Darwinists know that

[37] P. E. Johnson, *Darwin on Trial* (Washington, D.C.: Regency Gateway, 1991).

the mutation-selection mechanism can produce wings, eyes, and brains not because the mechanism can be observed to do anything of the kind, but because their guiding philosophy assures them that no other power is available to do the job. The absence from the cosmos of any Creator is therefore the essential starting point for Darwinism.

As Johnson so well describes in his book, the basic position of modern evolutionists, as it was with Darwin, is pervasive naturalism—the absolute insistence that only naturalistic, mechanistic processes be utilized to explain origins, along with total refusal to even consider the possibility of a theistic supernatural origin of the universe and the living things it contains.

No doubt a large majority of the scientific community embraces the mechanistic materialistic philosophy of Simpson, Huxley, Monod, and Darwinists in general. Many of these men are highly intelligent, and they have woven the fabric of evolution theory in an ingenious fashion. They have then combined this evolution theory with humanistic philosophy and have clothed the whole with the term, "science." The product, a nontheistic religion, with evolutionary philosophy as its creed under the guise of "science," is being taught in most public schools, colleges, and universities of the United States. It has become our unofficial state-sanctioned religion.

The evolutionist's view of man as expressed by Simpson and Huxley is in direct contrast to the Biblical view of man, found, for example, in Psalm 100, verse 3: "Know ye that the Lord He is God: it is He that hath made us and not we ourselves; we are His people and the sheep of His pasture." The Bible does indeed reveal that there is a living God who has created us and who controls our destiny.

Furthermore, a God who is great enough to create and control this universe is great enough, once having given His revelation to man, to preserve that revelation free from error. This preservation was not dependent upon man, but succeeded in spite of man. In this revelation, found in the first two chapters of Genesis in the Bible, the account of creation is recorded in a grand but concise fashion.

Not all evolutionists are materialistic atheists or agnostics. Many evolutionists believe in God, and some even believe the Bible to be the Word of God. They believe that evolution was God's method of creation, that God initiated the process at the molecular level and then allowed it to follow its natural course. The Biblical and scientific evidence, however, tells just as strongly against theistic evolution as it does against any other form of evolution.

The first two chapters of Genesis were not written in the form of parables or poetry, but present the broad outlines of creation in the form of simple historical facts. These facts directly contradict evolution theory. The Bible tells us that at one time in history there was a single human being upon the earth—a male by the name of Adam. This is in basic contradiction to evolution theory, because, according to that theory, populations evolve, not individuals. After God had formed Adam from the dust of the ground, the Bible tells us that He used some portion from Adam's side (in the King James Version, this is translated as "rib") to form Eve. This, of course, cannot be reconciled with any possible evolutionary theory concerning the origin of man.

The New Testament Scriptures fully support this Genesis account. For example, in I Corinthians 11:8 we read, "Man is not of the woman, but the woman of the man." By any natural reproductive process, man is always born of a woman. We all have mothers. This Biblical account can, therefore, be referring only to that unique time in history when God created woman from man, just as described in Genesis 2:21, 22.

It is apparent that acceptance of creation requires an important element of faith. Yes, it is true, creationists do have faith, and that faith is vitally important. In Hebrews 11:6 we read: "But without faith it is impossible to please Him, for he that cometh unto God must believe that He is, and that He is a rewarder of them that diligently seek Him." This faith is an intelligent faith, supported both by Biblical revelation and the revelation found in nature. While the *theories* and *opinions* of some scientists may contradict the Bible, there is no contradiction between the *facts* of science and the Bible.

Of course, belief in evolution also requires a vitally important element of faith. According to one of the most popular theories on the origin of the universe, all energy and matter of the universe was once contained in a plasma ball of electrons, protons, and neutrons and other subatomic particles (how it got there, no one has the faintest notion). This huge cosmic egg then exploded—and here we are today, several billion years later, human beings with a three-pound brain composed of twelve billion neurons each connected to about ten thousand other neurons in the most complicated arrangement of matter known to man. (There are thus 120 trillion connections in the human brain.)

If this is true, then what we are and how we came to be were due solely to the properties inherent in electrons, protons, and neutrons. To believe *this* obviously requires a tremendous exercise of faith. Evolution theory is indeed no less religious nor more scientific than creation.

The vast majority of evolutionists reject all notions that God had anything to do with evolution. They *believe* this. It is their *faith*. Dr. William Provine teaches the philosophy and history of science at Cornell University. He is an atheist, totally committed to a naturalistic explanation of origins. He believes that establishing evolution as a fact would be sufficient to prove the non-existence of God, and any attempt to link God with evolution is foolishness in the extreme. Recently he published a critical review[38] of the two-volume set by Wendell Bird, *The Origin of Species: The Theories of Evolution and Abrupt Appearance*.[39] In this review, he states "The real question his book raises is naturalism vs. supernaturalism."[40] While admitting that "Naturalism is indeed a faith," he maintains that the leap of faith required to believe in evolution by descent through natural causation is very small compared to that required to believe in supernatural origins. He makes several very interesting statements in this article. Although a committed evolutionist, he believes teachers in our schools and universities should openly encourage discussion of alternatives to evolution theory, including supernatural creation. This is in direct conflict with the evolutionists who dominate and control our scientific and educational establishments. Provine says:

> Evolutionists have worked hard to keep alternative theories of origins out of the science classrooms. I think this is a tactical mistake.

> Evolutionists fear that students will believe creationism rather than evolution, and that only evolution should be

---

[38] William B. Provine, *Biology and Philosophy* 8:11-124 (1993).

[39] W. R. Bird, *The Origin of Species Revisited*, vols. I and II (New York: Philosophical Library, 1989).

[40] Provine, *Biology and Philosophy* 8:123 (1993).

taught. How interesting, indeed, that evolutionists might think that the evidence for creationism is more compelling to students than the evidence for evolution, or that the teachers of biology are incapable of presenting evolution convincingly, the solution of which is suppression of creationism. I think the better solution is to let creationism and evolutionism fight it out in the science classrooms everywhere.[41]

Teachers and school boards in public schools are already free under the Constitution of the USA to teach about supernatural origins if they wish in their science classes.[42]

And I have a suggestion for evolutionists. Include discussion of supernatural origins in your classes, and promote discussion of them in public and other schools. Come off your high horse about having only evolution taught in science classes. The exclusionism you promote is painfully selfserving and smacks of elitism. Why are you afraid of confronting the supernatural creationism believed by the majority of persons in the USA and perhaps worldwide? Shouldn't students be encouraged to express their beliefs about origins in a class discussing origins by evolution?[43]

Provine is, of course, confident that when students have an opportunity to hear all of the evidence on both sides of the creation/evolution question, the majority will accept evolution. Actually, precisely the opposite seems to be true. Creationists have engaged evolutionists in debates throughout the USA and many other countries (this author has been personally involved in about 300 debates). These debates usually involve about two and one-half hours of an exchange of views, followed by thirty to sixty minutes of questions from the audience. Each side thus has adequate time to present its case. Most of the debates have taken place on university campuses, and almost always both sides are represented by scientists who hold doctorates. Evolutionists have admitted that the creationists

[41] *Ibid.*, p. 113.
[42] *Ibid.*, p. 124.
[43] *Ibid.*

have won practically every debate.[44] Two ardent evolutionist biology professors on the faculty of San Diego State University, confident that evolutionary theory would carry the day, offered a special creation/evolution course at that university. They invited scientists from the Institute for Creation Research to participate, giving them thirteen of the twenty-six lectures. After about three years the ICR scientists were informed that henceforth they would be given only nine of the twenty-six lectures. After another year or so, the class was switched to evening sessions of three hours each, and the ICR scientists were informed that they would be given only two of the fifteen sessions! The next year the ICR scientists were informed that the class had been canceled, "due to lack of interest." The creation scientists were left with a deep and abiding suspicion that these evolutionist professors found out they weren't winning with equal time, nor with two-thirds of the time, and even with 13/15 of the time, so the class was canceled.

Even when students are taught evolution with no opportunity to hear the evidence supporting special creation, the results sometimes appear to discourage belief in evolution. In an article published in the *Journal of Research in Science Teaching*,[45] Bishop and Anderson report some results obtained in their class in which they were teaching the principles of evolution and natural selection to students who were non-biology majors but who had an average of nearly two years of biology. A pretest showed that in answer to the question, "Do you believe the theory of evolution to be truthful?" Fifty-nine percent said yes, eleven percent replied no, and thirty percent were unsure. At the close of the class these students were given a posttest. This test now showed that believers in evolution had slipped to forty-nine percent, nonbelievers had increased to twenty-six percent, while twenty-seven percent were still unsure! While these professors may claim that the change in student opinion was relatively minor, yet in spite of the fact that only evolution was being taught, the shift in opinion was toward disbelief in evolution! What would have been the results if the teaching of evolutionary theory had been coupled with an opportunity to hear the scientific evidence for creation?

[44] Niles Eldredge, *The Monkey Business* (New York: Washington University Press, 1982), p. 17; Roger Lewin, *Science* 214:1102 (1981).
[45] Beth A. Bishop and C. W. Anderson, *Journal of Research in Science Teaching* 27:415-427 (1990).

The question is, then, who has more evidence for his faith, the creationist or the evolutionist? The scientific case for special creation, as we will show in the following pages, is much stronger than the case for evolution. The more I study and the more I learn, the more I become convinced that evolution is a false theory and that special creation offers a much more satisfactory interpretive framework for correlating and explaining the scientific evidence related to origins.

Chapter II

The Creation and Evolution Models

Much evidence could be drawn from the fields of cosmology, chemistry, thermodynamics, mathematics, molecular biology, and genetics in an attempt to decide which model offers a more plausible explanation for the origin of living things. In the final analysis, however, what actually *did* happen can only be decided, scientifically, by an examination of the historical record, that is, the fossil record. Thus, W. Le Gros Clark, the well-known British evolutionist, has said:

> That evolution actually *did* occur can only be scientifically established by the discovery of the fossilized remains of representative samples of those intermediate types which have been postulated on the basis of the indirect evidence. In other words, the really crucial evidence for evolution must be provided by the paleontologist whose business it is to study the evidence of the fossil record.[1]

Pierre Grassé is the most distinguished of all French zoologists. It has been said that his knowledge of the living world is encyclopedic. He sharply rebukes the claim that the fossil record is unimportant as support for evolution. He states:

> Naturalists must remember that the process of evolution is revealed only through fossil forms. A knowledge of paleontology is, therefore, a prerequisite; only paleontology can provide them with the evidence of evolution and reveal

---

[1] W. Le Gros Clark, *Discovery* (January 1955), p. 7.

its course or mechanisms. Neither the examination of present beings, nor imagination, nor theories can serve as a substitute for paleontological documents. If they ignore them, biologists, the philosophers of nature, indulge in numerous commentaries and can only come up with hypotheses.[2]

Evolutionists Glenister and Witzke state:

The fossil record affords an opportunity to choose between evolutionary and creationist models for the origin of the earth and its life forms.[3]

Douglas Futuyma, in his anti-creationist book, declares that:

Creation and evolution, between them, exhaust the possible explanations for the origin of living things. Organisms either appeared on the earth fully developed or they did not. If they did not, they must have developed from preexisting species by some process of modification. If they did appear in a fully developed state, they must indeed have been created by some omnipotent intelligence.[4]

Thus, it is evident that the fossil record is of supreme importance in the search for the answer to the question of the origin of living organisms, including man, on the earth, and that record specifically provides the evidence that enables one to choose between the alternatives of creation and evolution.

The history of life upon the earth may be traced through an examination of the fossilized remains of past forms of life entombed in the rocks. If life arose from an inanimate world through a mechanistic, naturalistic, evolutionary process and then diversified by a similar process via increasingly complex forms into the millions of species that

---

[2] Pierre Grassé, *Evolution of Living Organisms* (New York: Academic Press, 1977), p. 4.

[3] B. F. Glenister and B. J. Witzke, "Interpreting Earth History," in *Did the Devil Make Darwin Do It?* ed. D.B. Wilson (Ames: Iowa State University Press, 1983), p. 58.

[4] D. J. Futuyma, *Science on Trial* (New York: Pantheon Books, 1983), p. 197.

have existed and now exist, then the fossils actually found in the rocks should correspond to those predicted on the basis of such a process.

On the other hand, if living things came into being by a process of special creation, the broad outlines of which are given in the first two chapters of Genesis, then predictions very different from those based on evolution theory should be made concerning the fossil record. It is our contention that the fossil record is much more in accord with the predictions based on creation than with those based on the theory of evolution, and actually strongly contradicts evolution theory. The purpose of this publication is to document that contention and to demonstrate that all of the facts derivable from the fossil record are readily correlated within a framework of special creation.

Definitions

For the purposes of this discussion, it is very important that it be clearly understood just what we mean by the terms evolution and creation.

Evolution. When we use the term *Evolution*, we are using it in the sense defined by the general theory of evolution. According to the *General Theory of Evolution*, all living things have arisen by a naturalistic, mechanistic, evolutionary process from a single living source which itself arose by a similar process from a dead, inanimate world. This has sometimes been called the "amoeba-to-man" theory, or as I sometimes call it, the "fish-to-Gish" theory.

According to this theory, all living things are interrelated. Man and ape, for example, are believed to have shared a common ancestor. The divergence from this common ancestor has been variously estimated to have occurred from five to twenty million years ago, depending upon who is telling the story. The primates, which include men and apes, are believed to have shared a common ancestor with the horse, and this divergence is believed to have occurred approximately seventy-five million years ago.

Similar relationships are imagined throughout the entire animal and plant kingdoms. The supposed evolutionary relationships of an animal or plant with all other animals or plants is referred to as its phylogeny, and such relationships are portrayed in a so-called phylogenetic tree. One such tree is illustrated in figure 1.

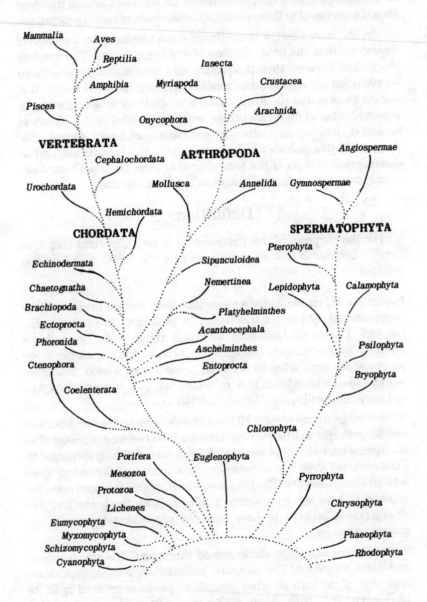

Figure 1. Hypothetical phylogenetic tree.

Equally important to our discussion is an understanding of just what we are *not* talking about when we use the term evolution. We are not referring to the limited variations that can be seen to occur, or which can be inferred to have occurred in the past, but which do not give rise to a new basic type.

We must here attempt to define what we mean by a basic type. A basic animal or plant type would include all animals or plants which were truly derived from a single stock. In present-day terms, it would be said that they have shared a common gene pool. All humans, for example, are within a single basic type, *Homo sapiens*. In this case, the basic type is a single species.

In other cases, the basic type may be at the genus level. It may be, for instance, that the various species of the coyote, such as the Oklahoma Coyote (*Canis frustor*), the Mountain Coyote (*C. lestes*), the Desert Coyote (*C. estor*), and others, are of the same basic type. It is possible, even likely, that this basic kind (which we may call the dog kind) includes not only all coyote species, but also the wolf (*Canis lupus*), the dog (*Canis familiaris*), and the jackals, also of the genus *Canis*, since they are all interfertile and produce fertile offspring.

The Galapagos Island finches provide another example of species, and even genera, which are probably of one basic type. Lammerts has pointed out[5] that these finches, which include various "species" within the "genera," *Geospiza*, *Camarhynchus*, and *Cactospiza*, intergrade completely and should probably be included within a single species, certainly within a single genus, at the very least. These finches apparently have been derived from a parent finch stock, the basic type having been broken up into various forms as a result of rearrangement of their original variability potential. The warbler finches, or *Certhidea*, on the other hand, are distinctive, and may have been derived from a basic stock separate from that which includes the other three finch "genera."

Another example which may be cited, this one from the plant kingdom, is that of the various varieties of corn. These include sweet corn, popcorn, dent corn, starch corn, pod corn, and flint corn, all of which are probably merely varieties of the corn kind.[6]

---

[5] W. E. Lammerts, "The Galapagos Island Finches," *Why Not Creation?* ed. W.E. Lammerts (Philadelphia: Presbyterian & Reformed Publ. Co., 1970), p. 354.

In the above discussion, we have defined a basic type as including all of those variants which have been derived from a single stock. We have cited some examples of varieties which we believe should be included within a single basic kind. We cannot always be sure, however, what constitutes a separate kind. The division into kinds is easier the more the divergence observed. It is obvious, for example, that among invertebrates the protozoa, sponges, jellyfish, worms, snails, trilobites, lobsters, and bees are all different basic types. Among the vertebrates, the fishes, amphibians, reptiles, birds, and mammals are obviously different basic types.

Among the reptiles, the turtles, crocodiles, dinosaurs, pterosaurs (flying reptiles), and ichthyosaurs (aquatic reptiles) would be placed in different kinds. Each one of these major groups of reptiles could be further subdivided into the basic kinds within each.

Within the mammalian class, duckbilled platypuses, opossums, bats, hedgehogs, rats, rabbits, dogs, cats, lemurs, monkeys, apes, and men are easily assignable to different basic types. Among the apes, the gibbons, orangutans, chimpanzees, and gorillas would each be included in a different basic kind.

When we attempt to make fine divisions within groups of plants and animals where distinguishing features are subtle, there is a possibility of error. Many taxonomic distinctions established by man are uncertain and must remain tentative.

Let us now return to our discussion of evolution. According to the general theory of evolution, not only have the minor variations within kinds arisen through natural processes, but the basic types themselves have arisen from fundamentally different ancestral forms. Creationists do not deny the former, that is, the origin of variations within kinds, but they do deny the latter, that is, the evolutionary origin of basically different types of plants and animals from common ancestors.

In our discussion of evolution, therefore, we are *not* referring, for example, to the possible origin of the variations within the dog kind. We *are* referring to the alleged origin of the dog kind and cat kind from a common ancestor. We are *not* referring to the origin of the finches within *Geospiza*, *Camarhynchus*, and *Cactospiza*. We *are* referring to

---

[6] F. L. Marsh, *Creation Research Society Quarterly* 8:13 (1969).

the origin of these finches and, say, the herons, from a common ancestor, and their ultimate origin from an ancestral reptile.

Neither are we referring to "industrial melanism,"[7] a case often cited by evolutionists as proof for evolution. The peppered moth, *Biston betularia*, is normally white with a covering of black spots and stripes. Melanic, or dark-colored, forms, known as the carbonaria form, have always existed, but as rarities.

Before the advent of the industrial revolution and resultant air pollution, the tree trunks in England were light-colored. The peppered moth rests on tree trunks during the day, with wings outspread. The normal, or light-colored, variant is very inconspicuous against such a background. The melanic form, on the other hand, is easily detected under these circumstances. As a result, predators (birds) picked off a much higher percentage of the melanic form, and they thus remained a minor proportion of the total population of peppered moths.

This was the case in 1850 at about the time the industrial revolution in England began. The tree trunks became progressively darker, however, and by 1895, ninety-five percent of these moths in the vicinity of Manchester were of the carbonaria, or melanic, variety. This change had taken place because now the melanic form was inconspicuous against the blackened tree trunks, while the light-colored variant was easily detected when resting against this background.

We wish to emphasize, first of all, that this process did not result in increasing complexity or even anything new. The melanic form of the peppered moth had existed in England many years before the industrial revolution. It was a stable, though minor, fraction of the population. The change brought about by air pollution did decrease detection of this preexisting form by its natural enemies and thus resulted in a shift in populations of the melanic versus the light-colored form.

Of greatest importance to our discussion, however, is the fact that no significant evolutionary change has occurred in these moths. These moths today not only are still moths, *but they are still peppered moths, Biston betularia*. This evidence, therefore, is irrelevant to the questions we seek to answer: Did these lepidopterous insects (the

[7] W. Wickler, *Mimicry in Plants and Animals* (New York: World University Library, 1968), p. 51.

Lepidoptera is an order of insects comprising the butterflies, moths, and skippers, which in the adult state have four membranous wings more or less covered with small scales) arise by a naturalistic, mechanistic process from a nonlepidopterous insect? Did the insects themselves arise from a noninsect form of life?

While no real evolutionary change took place in the shift in populations of the two varieties of the peppered moth, one natural science encyclopedia has recently characterized this event as "the most striking evolutionary change ever to be witnessed by man."[8] If this is the best evidence for evolution that can be produced, then indeed—just as Dobzhansky has admitted—evolution has not been witnessed by human observers, for this is not evolution at all.

The evolutionist assumes that the accumulation of many such minor changes eventually could result in a new basic type and in increasing complexity, but *this is purely an assumption*. What is required is experimental evidence, or, lacking that, hard fossil evidence, or historical evidence, that basic changes of this type actually did take place.

Another form of change which is often cited by evolutionists as evidence for evolution is the origin of domesticated plants and animals by artificial selection and breeding. Evidence of this nature is again irrelevant to our discussion, since nothing new or complex arises, and the change accomplished is always extremely limited.

What artificial selection and breeding actually accomplishes is to rapidly establish the *limit* beyond which no further change is possible. We wish to cite just two examples.[9] In 1800, experiments were begun in France to increase the sugar content of table beets, which at that time amounted to 6%. By 1878, the sugar content had been increased to 17%. Further selection failed to increase the sugar content above that figure.

One worker tried to reduce the number of bristles on the thorax of fruit flies by artificial selection and breeding. In each generation, the average number of bristles became fewer until the twentieth generation. After that, the average remained the same, although he

---

[8] M. Burton and R. Burton, eds., *The International Wildlife Encyclopedia* (New York: Marshal Cavendish Corp., 1970), p. 2706.

[9] W. J. Tinkle, *Heredity* (Houston: St. Thomas Press, 1967), p. 55.

selected as before. Selection was no longer effective; the limit had been reached.

Similar experimental approaches have been used to develop chickens that lay more eggs, cows that give more milk, and corn with increased protein content. In each case, limits were reached beyond which further change has not been possible. Furthermore, the breeders ended up with the same species of chickens, cows, and corn with which they began. No real change had taken place.

It must be strongly emphasized, also, that in all cases these specialized breeds possess reduced viability; that is, their basic ability to survive has been weakened. Domesticated plants and animals do not compete well with the original, or wild type. Thus, Falconer has stated:

> Our domesticated animals and plants are perhaps the best demonstration of the effects of this principle. The improvements that have been made by selection in these have clearly been accompanied by a reduction of fitness for life under natural conditions, and only the fact that domesticated animals and plants do not live under natural conditions has allowed these improvements to be made.[10]

These experiments thus demonstrate that even with the aid of man's inventive genius, which permits the maximum variation in the shortest possible time, the variation achieved is extremely limited and actually results in plants and animals with reduced viability. They survive only because they are maintained in an environment which is free from their natural enemies, food supplies are abundant, and other conditions are carefully regulated.

In summary, by evolution we mean a process which is supposed to have been responsible for converting the most primitive form of life, the hypothetical primordial cell, via innumerable increasingly complex forms of life, into man, the highest form of life. The theory of evolution, then, proposes that basically different types of plants and animals have arisen from common ancestors, which in turn had arisen from more ancient and more primitive forms of life. By evolution, we do not mean limited variations that have taken place within a distinct, separate

---

[10] D. S. Falconer, *Introduction to Quantitative Genetics* (Ronald Press, 1960), p. 331; as quoted by W. J. Tinkle, *Heredity* (Grand Rapids: Zondervan Publishing House, 1970), p. 84.

kind, and which have not led to the origin of a basically different form of life.

Creation. By creation we mean the bringing into being of the basic kinds of plants and animals by the process of sudden, or fiat, creation, an example of which is described in the first two chapters of Genesis. Here we find the creation by God of the plants and animals, each commanded to reproduce after its own kind, using processes which were essentially instantaneous.

We do not know how God created, what processes He used, *for God used processes which are not now operating anywhere in the natural universe.* This is why we refer to divine creation as special creation. We cannot discover by scientific investigations anything about the creative processes used by God. As we have pointed out earlier, evolutionists have not witnessed any real evolutionary changes take place, nor will this be possible in the future. They, likewise, will never be able to know how their postulated evolutionary changes may have taken place.

In our earlier discussion, we have defined what we mean by a basic animal or plant type. During the creation week God created all of these basic animal and plant kinds, and since then no new kinds have come into being, for the Bible speaks of a *finished* creation (Genesis 2:2). The variation that has occurred since the end of the creation work of God has been limited to changes within kinds.

As noted earlier, then, the concept of special creation does not exclude the origin of varieties and species (as sometimes defined by man) from an original created kind. It is believed that each kind was created with sufficient genetic potential, or gene pool, to give rise to all of the varieties within that kind that have existed in the past and those that are yet in existence today.

Each kind was created with a great variety of genes. These genes can be sorted out during the sexual reproductive process in an enormous number of different ways. For instance, there are approximately five billion human beings in the world today, and except for identical twins and other cases of multiple births, no two individuals are exactly alike. None have the same gene combination. This sorting out process has not only given rise to many different individuals but also to distinctively different races. All remain, however, members of one species, *Homo sapiens.*

Another example familiar to all of us is that of the dog. All of the dogs, from the tiny Chihuahua to the Great Dane, and from the bulldog to the greyhound, have been derived from a single species, *Canis familiaris.* The process has been generated by man, of course, through artificial selection and inbreeding.

Many other examples could be cited. In each case the great variety of genes responsible for the variations that have taken place was present in the original created kind. There has merely occurred a sorting out in many different ways. No matter what combinations may occur, however, the human kind always remains human, and the dog kind never ceases to be dog kind. The transformations proposed by the theory of evolution never take place.

It might be added here that Genesis does not have two creation accounts as some have alleged. Chapter 1 is a chronological, or step-by-step, description of creation. Chapter 2 is a recapitulation of the creation, told in such a manner as to emphasize certain features.

When I was in pharmaceutical research, I kept a laboratory notebook in which were recorded daily the experiments I had performed. This, of course, constituted a chronological record of my research. Each year the members of each project team were asked to prepare an annual project summary. In these reports we recapitulated our laboratory results. The sequence of the results reported in this summary was not chronological, but was recorded in such a way as to convey the significance attached to each result. So it is with the Genesis account of creation.

The Evolutionary Mechanism. Before we can evaluate the fossil record for the evidence it can shed on the question of creation and evolution, we must first understand the mechanism by which evolution has supposedly occurred. On the basis of this hypothetical mechanism, we will be able to predict what the fossil record ought to show if evolution actually did occur.

We have noted above the many variations that exist within each kind. Darwin had noted this fact, although he did not understand what was responsible for the origin of this variability. Darwin proposed that changes are constantly taking place within a species.

Darwin was aware of the fact that many more animals are born than actually survive. He envisioned a struggle for existence in which the stronger survive and the weaker are eliminated. Under these conditions any variation that results in a lowered viability (basic ability to survive) or reproductive capacity would cause the elimination of the plant or animal inheriting this variation.

On the other hand, Darwin reasoned, any variation which increased the viability or fertility of a plant or animal would give it an advantage in the struggle for existence. This favored variant and its offspring which inherited this favorable variation would tend to survive at the expense of the unchanged variety. Nature was said to have selected the favored variant, and the evolutionary process was thus said to consist of *variation with natural selection*. The accumulation of many of these small hypothetical favorable changes over a long period of time supposedly was able to accomplish the most profound changes, even converting a microscopic bacterial cell into a human being.

Darwin was ignorant of what produced the variability within species. Gregor Mendel's great work on genetics was published at about the same time as Darwin's *Origin of Species*, but was ignored by Darwin and most other scientists at that time. What Darwin did propose to account for the origin of variability was completely erroneous. He accepted the idea of the inheritance of acquired characteristics, particularly in the later editions of his book, *Origin of Species*. This was the idea that when cells in the tissues (somatic cells) are affected by the environment, hereditary units ("gemmules") are formed. These "gemmules" it was believed, were carried to the germ cells and then passed on to the offspring. The characteristic acquired by the parent was thus supposedly inherited by its offspring.

Today we know that inheritance is controlled by the genes found solely in the germ cells (the eggs, or ova, and the spermatozoa). Only alterations in the genes of the germ cells are inheritable. No such thing as a "gemmule" is formed, and acquired characteristics are not inherited.

Hundreds of thousands of genes are present in the nucleus of every cell of the higher animals. Each gene consists of a long strand of several hundred to several thousand subunits, linked together like the links of a chain. The particular type of complex chemical which constitutes a gene is called deoxyribonucleic acid, or DNA.

There are four different kinds of subunits (nucleotides) in DNA. It is the particular order or sequence of these subunits in the DNA chain which distinguishes one gene from another, just as the specific sequence of the letters of the alphabet distinguishes one sentence from another.

Each characteristic is influenced by at least two genes. The genes of this gene pair are called alleles. One such gene is inherited from each of the parents. Thus, the egg and sperm each have a single set of genes. When fertilization occurs, these two sets of genes combine. The segregation and recombination of the genes which occur during production of the germ cells produce sperm and eggs with a tremendous variety of different gene combinations. These sperm and egg cells in turn, depending upon which sperm fertilizes which egg, can be combined in a great variety of ways. The result is the tremendous variability that we see within each species.

The genes are ordinarily very stable. A particular gene (in the form of its successors) may exist many thousands of years without alteration in its structure. Very rarely, however, the chemical structure of a gene does undergo a change. Such a change is called a mutation. Mutations may be caused by chemicals, X-rays, ultraviolet light, cosmic rays, and other causes. Some may occur during cell reproduction due to copying errors.

Most mutations result in a change in only one of the several thousand subunits in a gene. The change usually is so subtle that it cannot be directly detected by present chemical techniques. The effect on the plant or animal is frequently very drastic, however. Very often a mutation proves to be lethal, and they are almost universally harmful.

The mutations we see occurring spontaneously in nature or those that can be induced in the laboratory always prove to be harmful. It is doubtful that of all the mutations that have been seen to occur, a single one can definitely be said to have increased the viability of the affected plant or animal.[11] Evolutionists claim, however, that a very small fraction (perhaps 1 in 10,000) of these mutations are beneficial. This claim is made, not because we can actually observe such favorable

---

[11] C. P. Martin, *American Scientist* 41:100 (1953).

mutations, but because evolutionists know that unless favorable mutations do occur, evolution is impossible. In the final analysis, all of evolution must be ascribed to mutations.[12]

These hypothetical beneficial mutations supposedly alter the plant or animal in such a way that its ability to compete and survive is enhanced and/or its reproductive capacity is increased. The plants or animals inheriting these mutant genes then would tend to survive at the expense of the unchanged variety. Evolutionists believe that after many thousands of generations eventually the mutant would completely replace the original, unchanged variety. Nature is said to have selected the favored mutant, and the evolutionary process, therefore, is termed *mutation with natural selection*.

Evolutionists, with very few exceptions, believe that these proposed favorable mutations which supposedly contribute to evolution must result in only slight changes. A mutation that would result in more than a slight change would be too disruptive to the organization of the plant or animal for it to survive. Such a mutation would be certain to be lethal or harmful.

Since each one of the mutations which have supposedly contributed to the evolutionary process would have resulted in only a very slight change, it is evident that the evolution of one species into another would require the accumulation of many thousands of these hypothetical favorable mutations. A much more drastic change, such as the conversion of a fish into an amphibian, would require a very large number of favorable mutations in many, many characteristics.

A mutation of any kind in a gene is a rare event. Furthermore, if only one out of 10,000 or less of these mutations is favorable, it can be seen that the occurrence of a favorable mutation is indeed an extremely rare event, assuming that they occur at all. Furthermore, in order to be inheritable, a mutation must occur in the genes of the germ cells. The germ cells make up only a tiny fraction of all the cells of an organism and are generally relatively well-protected from the environment. It is obvious that *the essence of the postulated evolutionary process is slow and gradual change*. The change of a species into a new species is believed to require hundreds of thousands,

---

[12] E. Mayr, in *Mathematical Challenges to the Neo-Darwinian Interpretation of Evolution*, ed. P.S. Moorhead and M.M. Kaplan, (Philadelphia: Wistar Institute Press, 1967), p. 50.

if not millions, of years. A drastic change such as the change of fish into amphibian or reptile into mammal is believed to have required several tens of millions of years.

The interpretation of the evolutionary process as very slow and gradual change due to small mutations, or micromutations, in combination with the sorting out that accompanies sexual reproduction, all influenced by natural selection in accordance with the environment, is termed the neo-Darwinian interpretation of evolution. The essence of Darwinism is retained but Darwin's theories have been modified to accommodate them to the discoveries made since his time in genetics, molecular biology, etc.

Until recently, with few exceptions, all evolutionists were neo-Darwinists, and the neo-Darwinian mechanism is still textbook orthodoxy. In recent years, however, more and more evolutionists have acknowledged that the fossil record gives little or no evidence of gradual change. A new scenario for biological evolution is now being suggested, called "punctuated equilibria," in an attempt to deal with this embarrassing aspect of the fossil record. This will be discussed in some detail in the final chapter of this book. Whether one accepts the neo-Darwinian idea of slow gradual change or the more jerky notion of evolution embodied in the punctuated equilibria scenario, supposedly all forms of life now on earth arose from a single form of life that came into existence more than three billion years ago. Regardless of which process, then, produced the present flora and fauna, we would have preserved as fossils today a record more than adequate to document the changes that have allegedly taken place.

Predictions Based on the Creation Model and the Evolution Model

In the preceding discussion we have defined what is meant by creation and evolution. We have described alleged evolutionary mechanisms and have described all that human knowledge can tell us about the creation process. We are now ready to produce the evidence that must be found in the fossil record based on the creation model on the one hand and the evolution model on the other hand.

Creation Model. On the basis of the creation model, we would predict an explosive appearance in the fossil record of highly complex forms of life without evidence of ancestral forms. We would predict that all of the major types of life, that is, the basic plant and animal forms, would appear abruptly in the fossil record without evidence of transitional forms linking one basic kind to another.

We would thus expect to find the fossilized remains, for example, of cats, dogs, bears, elephants, cows, horses, bats, dinosaurs, crocodiles, monkeys, apes, and men without evidence of common ancestors. Each major kind at its earliest appearance in the fossil record would possess, fully developed, all the characteristics that are used to define that particular kind.

Evolution Model. On the basis of the evolution model, we would predict that the most ancient strata in which fossils are found would contain the most primitive forms of life capable of leaving a fossil record. As successively younger strata were searched, we would expect to see the gradual transition of these relatively simple forms of life into more and more complex forms of life. As living forms diverged into the millions of species which have existed in the past and which exist today, we would expect to find a transition of one form into another.

We would predict that new types would *not* appear suddenly in the fossil record possessing all of the characteristics which are used to define that group but would retain characteristics used to define the ancestral group.

If fish evolved into amphibia as evolutionists believe, we would predict that we would find transitional forms showing the gradual transition of fins into feet and legs. Of course, many other alterations in the anatomy and physiology of fish would have to occur to change an animal adapted to living its entire life span in water to one which spends most of its life outside of water. The fin-to-feet transition would be an easily traceable transition, however.

If reptiles gave rise to birds, then we would expect to find transitional forms in the fossil record showing the gradual transition of the forelimbs of the ancestral reptile into the wings of a bird, and the gradual transition of some structure on the reptile into the feathers of a bird. These again are obvious transitions that could be easily traced in the fossil record. Of course, many other changes would have been taking place at the same time, such as the conversion of the hind feet of the reptile into the perching feet of the bird, reptilian skull into birdlike skull, etc.

In the pterosaurs, or flying reptiles, the wing membrane was supported by an enormously lengthened fourth finger. If the pterosaurs actually evolved from a nonflying reptile, we would predict that the fossil record would produce transitional forms showing a gradual increase in length of the fourth finger, along with the origin of other unique structures.

The fossil record ought to produce thousands upon thousands of transitional forms. It is true that according to evolutionary geology only a tiny fraction of all plants and animals that have ever existed would have been preserved as fossils. It is also true that we have as yet uncovered only a small fraction of the fossils that are entombed in the rocks. We have, nevertheless, recovered a good representative number of the fossils that exist. In fact, our museums contain about 250,000 different fossil species, represented by many millions of catalogued fossils.

Sampling of the fossil record has now been so thorough that appeals to the imperfections in the record are no longer valid. George has stated:

> There is no need to apologize any longer for the poverty of the fossil record. In some ways it has become almost unmanageably rich and discovery is outpacing integration.[13]

It seems clear, then, that after 150 years of intense searching a large number of obvious transitional forms would have been discovered if the predictions of evolution theory are valid.

We have, for example, discovered literally billions of fossils of ancient invertebrates and many fossils of ancient fishes. The transition of invertebrate into vertebrate is believed to have required many millions of years. Populations are supposed to constitute the units of evolution and, of course, only successful populations survive. It seems obvious then, that if we find fossils of the invertebrates which were supposed to have been ancestral to fishes, and if we find fossils of the fishes, we surely ought to find the fossils of the transitional forms.

---

[13] T. N. George, *Science Progress,* 48:1 (1960).

We find fossils of crossopterygian fishes which are alleged to have given rise to the amphibia. We find fossils of the so-called "primitive" amphibia. Since the transition from fish to amphibia would have required many millions of years, during which many hundreds of millions, even billions, of the transitional forms must have lived and died, many of these transitional forms should have been discovered in the fossil record even though only a minute fraction of these animals have been recovered as fossils. As a matter of fact, the discovery of only five or six of the transitional forms scattered through time would be sufficient to document evolution.

So it would be throughout the entire fossil record. There should not be the slightest difficulty in finding transitional forms. Hundreds of transitional forms should fill museum collections. If we find fossils at all, we ought to find transitional forms. As a matter of fact, difficulty in placing a fossil within a distinct category should be the rule rather than the exception.

Summary

The contrast between the two models and the predictions based on each model may be summarized as follows:

Creation Model	Evolution Model
By acts of a Creator.	By naturalistic mechanistic processes due to properties inherent in inanimate matter.
Creation of basic plant and animal types with characteristics complete in first representatives.	Origin of all living things from a single living source which itself arose from inanimate matter. Origin of each kind from an ancestral form by slow gradual change.
Variation and speciation limited within each kind.	Unlimited variation. All forms genetically related.

These two models would permit the following predictions to be made concerning the fossil record:

Creation Model	Evolution Model
Sudden appearance in great variety of highly complex forms.	Gradual change of simple forms into more and more complex forms.
Sudden appearance of each created type with characteristics complete.	Transitional series linking all categories.
Sharp boundaries separating major taxonomic groups. No transitional forms between higher categories.	No systematic gaps.

Chapter III

Geologic Time and the Geologic Column

With few exceptions, such as the La Brea Tar Pits, fossils are found in sedimentary deposits. The formation of sedimentary rocks involves erosion, transportation, deposition, and lithification. The action of wind, freezing and thawing, rain, and flooding have caused rocks to disintegrate. The resultant particles, ranging in size from extremely fine particles to boulders, have been transported by water (some have been transported by wind, glaciers, and other agencies, but these represent exceptional cases) and then deposited when the water reached a quiet area. Through the action of cementing agents and/or pressure, these deposits have become consolidated in the form of sedimentary rocks.

The hard parts of marine organisms may be preserved in marine sediments. Fresh water organisms, land animals, and plants may be entrapped and swept along by moving water and buried with the sediments. As the sediments become compacted into rocks, the bones of animals or the imprint left by the remains of animals and plants may become part of the rocks. These remains are known as fossils. Some sedimentary deposits are a few feet thick, some are hundreds of feet thick, and rarely, some are even a thousand feet or more in thickness.

Several approaches to the interpretation of geologic history have been applied.

Uniformitarianism

The uniformitarian concept of historical geology is accepted by almost all evolutionists. According to this interpretation of earth history, existing physical processes acting essentially at present rates, are sufficient to account for all geological formations. As originally formulated by James Hutton and Charles Lyell, any appeal to catastrophes for the explanation of geologic phenomena is rejected. The phrase "the present is the key to the past" was coined for this concept.

According to this interpretation, the formation of sedimentary deposits hundreds of feet thick would have required millions of years. It was also realized that evolution would have required many millions of years. Accordingly, the age of the earth as estimated by evolutionary geologists began to increase at an astounding rate. The application of certain assumptions with radiometric dating methods finally has allowed present-day geologists to estimate an age of about 4.5 billion years for the earth.

Geologists have classified sedimentary deposits according to the type of fossils found in the deposits. Certain fossils are believed to have been laid down during a restricted time span. These fossils have been designated as "index fossils" and are used by evolutionists to identify and date rocks. For example, rocks containing fossils of certain types of trilobites are designated as Cambrian rocks.

Evolutionists assume that Cambrian sedimentary rocks were deposited during a stretch of approximately five to ten million years beginning about 530 million years ago. This period has been named the Cambrian Period. They assume that other sedimentary deposits have followed in a chronological order, each spanning millions of years. The Cambrian Period is assumed to have been followed by the Ordovician, Silurian, Devonian, Mississippian, etc.

This arrangement of various types of fossiliferous deposits in a supposed time sequence is known as the geological column. Its arrangement is based on the assumption of evolution. Thus, invertebrates are assumed to have evolved first, followed by fish, amphibia, reptiles, and mammals in that order.

This brief description of the uniformitarian concept of historical geology is necessarily sketchy and simplified. Any standard textbook on geology may be consulted for a more thorough description of this system.

Main Divisions of Geological Time		
Eras	**Periods**	**Estimated Years Ago**
Recent	Quaternary:	
	Holocene Epoch	10,000
	Pleistocene Epoch	1,800,000
Cenozoic	Tertiary:	
	Pliocene Epoch	5,000,000
	Miocene Epoch	25,000,000
	Oligocene Epoch	35,000,000
	Eocene Epoch	65,000,000
	Paleocene Epoch	70,000,000
Mesozoic	Cretaceous	70,000,000
	Jurassic	to
	Triassic	200,000,000
Paleozoic	Permian	
	Pennsylvanian	200,000,000
	Mississippian	
	Devonian	to
	Silurian	
	Ordovician	530,000,000
	Cambrian	
Proterozoic		530,000,000 to
		1,000,000,000
Archeozoic		1,000,000,000 to
		1,800,000,000

Modified Uniformitarian Concepts

The Day-Age Theory. Some creationists accommodate the uniformitarian concept of historical geology by assuming that the creation days of Genesis were not literal 24-hour days, but were creative periods of time. It is assumed that God allowed varying periods of time to intervene between successive creations, and that animals and plants were created in the sequence required by the geological column. This concept has severe Scriptural problems as well as scientific difficulties.[1]

The Gap Theory. According to this theory, Genesis 1:1 describes an initial creation spanning geological ages. A great time span then intervened between Genesis 1:1 and Genesis 1:2. The geological column is believed to have formed during this initial period of creation and subsequent time span.

Genesis 1:2 is then translated to read: "And the world became without form and void." Thus God is said to have destroyed His original creation for some reason, perhaps at the fall of Lucifer or Satan. A second creation in six literal 24-hour days is then described in succeeding verses, it is believed.

The gap theory is accepted by many conservative Christians and is an attempt to accommodate both the geological column with its vast time span, and the six 24-hour day creation described in Genesis. This theory also has Scriptural problems as well as serious scientific difficulties.[2]

The Catastrophist—Recent Creation Model

The proponents of this model for interpreting geologic history believe that the correct interpretation of Genesis requires acceptance of a creation spanning six 24-hour days. Furthermore, the genealogies listed in Genesis and elsewhere in the Bible, it is believed, would restrict the time of creation to about ten thousand years (plus or minus a few thousand years).

While present geological processes may have operated at present rates for long periods of time, the advocates of this model contend that it is impossible to account for most of the important geological formations according to uniformitarian principles. These formations include the vast Tibetan Plateau, 750,000 square miles of sedimentary deposits many thousands of feet in thickness and now at an elevation of three miles; the Karoo Supergroup of Africa, which has been estimated by Robert Broom to contain the fossils of 800 billion vertebrate animals;[3] the herring fossil bed in the Miocene shales of

---

[1] H. M. Morris, *Biblical Basis for Modern Science* (Grand Rapids: Baker Book House, 1984), pp. 117-121.

[2] *Ibid*, p. 62.

California, containing evidence that a billion fish died within a four-square mile area;[4] and the Cumberland Bone Cave of Maryland, containing fossilized remains of dozens of species of mammals, from bats to mastodons, along with the fossils of some reptiles and birds—including animals which now have accommodated to different climates and habitats from the Arctic region to tropical zones.[5] Neither has the uniformitarian concept been sufficient to explain mountain building nor the formation of such vast lava beds as the Columbian Plateau in the northwest United States, a lava bed several thousand feet thick covering 200,000 square miles.

It is believed that most of the important geological formations of the earth can be explained as having been formed as a result of the worldwide Noachian flood described in Genesis, along with attendant vast earth movements, volcanic action, dramatic changes in climatic conditions, and other catastrophic events. The fossil record, rather than being a record of transformation, is a record of mass destruction, death, and burial by water and its contained sediments.

Proponents of this interpretation of earth history not only face the unenviable position of being labeled as rank heretics, but a massive reexamination and reinterpretation of geologic data is required. It must be remembered, however, that this situation was explicitly prophesied by the Apostle Peter. For 1,800 years after Peter had written his epistles, the flood of Noah was generally accepted, and up until about 1800 A.D. the interpretation of geology that was taught in the great universities, such as Cambridge, Oxford, Harvard, and Yale, was based on flood geology. About this time, the theories of Hutton, Lyell, and others initiated a revolution in the interpretation of historical geology, and today any such worldwide catastrophe as the Noachian flood is completely discounted in the teaching of geology in all of the world's major universities.

This development fulfills the prophecy of the Apostle Peter found in the Second Epistle of Peter, chapter 3, verses 3–6: "Knowing this first, that there shall come in the last days scoffers, walking after their own lusts, and saying, Where is the promise of His coming? For since the fathers fell asleep, all things continue as they were from the beginning of the creation. For this they are willingly ignorant of, that

---

[3] N. D. Newell, *Journal of Paleontology* 33:492 (1959).
[4] H. S. Ladd, *Science* 129:72 (1959).
[5] G. Nicholas, *Scientific Monthly* 76:301 (1953).

by the word of God the heavens were of old, and the earth standing out of the water and in the water: Whereby the world that then was, being overflowed with water, perished." In these verses the Scriptures make plain that toward the end of this Age scoffers would ridicule the promise of Christ's second coming, claiming that from the beginning of creation conditions have always been as they are now (uniformitarianism) and that the great worldwide flood described in Genesis never actually occurred.

The reinterpretation of geologic data according to flood geology would include a reevaluation of all dating methods, including especially a critical review of radiometric dating methods. Such work is already well under way. It should be realized that there is no *direct* method for determining the age of any rock. While very accurate methods are available for determining the *present* ratios of uranium-lead, thorium-lead, potassium-argon, and other isotope ratios in mineral-bearing rocks, there is, of course, no direct method for estimating the *initial* ratios of these isotopes in the rocks when the rocks were first formed. Radiochronologists must resort to indirect methods which involve certain basic assumptions. Not only is there no way to verify the validity of these assumptions, but inherent in these assumptions are factors that assure that the ages so derived, whether accurate or not, will always range in the millions to billions of years (excluding the carbon-14 method, which is useful for dating samples only a few thousand years old).

Recent publications[6] have exposed weaknesses and fallacies in radiometric dating methods, while some recent publications[7] have

---

[6] J. C. Whitcomb and H. M. Morris, *The Genesis Flood* (Philadelphia: Presbyterian and Reformed Publ. Co., 1964); M. A. Cook, *Prehistory and Earth Models* (London: Max Parrish and Co., Ltd., 1966); H. S. Slusher, *Critique of Radiometric Dating Methods*, rev. ed. (San Diego: Creation-Life Publishers, 1981); S. P. Clementson, *Creation Research Society Quarterly* 7:137 (1970); and M. A. Cook, *Creation Res. Society Quarterly* 7:53 (1970).

[7] Whitcomb and Morris, *The Genesis Flood*; Cook, *Prehistory and Earth Models*; Cook, *Creation Research Society Quarterly* 7:53; R. L. Whitelaw, in *Why Not Creation?* ed. W. E. Lammerts (Philadelphia: Presbyterian and Reformed Publ. Co., 1970), pp. 90, 101; R. Gentry, in *Why Not Creation?* p. 106; H. S. Slusher, *Creation Research Society Quarterly* 8:55 (1971); T. G. Barnes, *Origin and Destiny of the Earth's Magnetic Field* (San Diego: Creation-Life Publishers, 1983); H. S. Slusher, *The Age of the Cosmos* (San Diego: Creation-Life Publishers, 1980).

described many reliable chronometers, or "time-clocks," that indicate a young age for the earth. Discussions of the catastrophist interpretation of historical geology may be found in a number of books and recent publications.[8]

It is this author's belief that a sound Biblical exegesis requires the acceptance of the catastrophist—recent creation interpretation of earth history. If this interpretation is accepted, the evolution model, of course, becomes inconceivable. In order to evaluate evolution as an interpretive model to explain origins, therefore, and to compare the predictive value of this model to that of the creation model, the assumptions of evolutionary geologists concerning the duration of geological ages and the validity of their assumptions concerning the geological column must be used along with the model. Therefore, in the succeeding pages of this book we will write as though the Cambrian, Ordovician, Silurian, and other sedimentary deposits were actually laid down during the time spans generally assumed by evolutionists, and that the arrangement of the geological column in the form of successive geological periods as accepted by evolutionary geologists is correct.

Even when these assumptions are accepted, however, the data from the fossil record do not agree with the predictions of the evolution model. Therefore, whether or not the earth is ten thousand, ten million, or ten billion years old, the fossil record does not support the general theory of evolution.

---

[8]Whitcomb and Morris, *The Genesis Flood*; Cook, *Prehistory and Earth Models*; G. M. Price, *Evolutionary Geology and the New Catastrophism*, (Mountain View, California: Pacific Press Pub. Assoc., 1926); Morris, *Biblical Cosmology and Modern Science*, p. 62; H. W. Clark, *Fossils, Flood, and Fire* (Escondido, California: Outdoor Pictures, 1968); Morris, in *Why Not Creation?* p. 114; H. M. Morris, in *Scientific Studies in Special Creation*, ed. W.E. Lammerts (Philadelphia: Presbyterian and Reformed Publ. Co., 1971), p. 103; N. A. Rupke, in *Why Not Creation?* p. 141; C. L. Burdick, in *Scientific Studies in Special Creation*, p. 125; H. W. Clark, in *Scientific Studies in Special Creation*, p. 156; E. C. Powell, *Creation Research Society Quarterly* 9:230 (1973); Steven A. Austin, *Catastrophe Data Base* (Colorado Springs: Master Books, 1994), software on one 3.5-inch floppy disk; Steven A. Austin, *Catastrophes in Earth History* (El Cajon, California: Institute for Creation Research, 1984); Steven A. Austin, *Grand Canyon: Monument to Catastrophe* (El Cajon, California: Institute for Creation Research, 1994); John D. Morris, *The Young Earth* (Colorado Springs: Master Books, 1994).

Chapter IV

The Fossil Record—From Microorganisms to Fish

Life Appears Abruptly In Highly Diverse Forms

According to evolutionary theory, life first appeared on this planet in the form of a microscopic, single-celled organism. Hundreds of articles and books have been published containing speculations about how this event may have occurred, and critiques of these notions by creation scientists are available.[1] Eventually it is believed by evolutionists, this first form of life not only diverged into the many single-celled organisms that now exist—bacteria, algae, fungi, amoeba—but that the Metazoa evolved from one or more of these single-celled organisms. Just how that occurred and what intermediates were involved is viewed as one of the great, as yet unsolved mysteries of evolution. Metazoans, that is, highly complex multi-cellular creatures with specialized organs, abruptly appear fully-formed in the fossil record. There are no intermediates available from the fossil record that link single-celled organisms to the complex invertebrates that supposedly arose from them.

---

[1]S. Aw, *Chemical Evolution* (San Diego: Master Books, 1982); A. E. Wilder-Smith, *The Creation of Life, A Cybernetic Approach* (San Diego: Master Books, 1970); D. T. Gish, *Speculations and Experiments Related to Theories on the Origin of Life: A Critique* (San Diego: Creation-Life Publishers, 1973); *Creation Research Society Quart*erly, 15:185 (1979); C. B. Thaxton, W. L. Bradley, and R. L. Olsen, *The Mystery of Life's Origin* (New York: Philosophical Library, 1984); available from Lewis and Stanlers, 1316 Midway Road, Suite 500, Dallas, TX 75244. This book is especially recommended.

The first abundant fossil record of complex invertebrates appears in rocks of the so-called Cambrian Period. It is assumed by evolutionists that the sediments which formed the rocks of the Cambrian began to be deposited about 530 million years ago and that the time involved in their deposition stretched over about five to ten million years. In Cambrian rocks are found fossils of clams, snails, trilobites, sponges, brachiopods, worms, jellyfish, sea urchins, sea cucumbers, swimming crustaceans, sea lilies, and other complex invertebrates. The appearance of this great variety of complex creatures is so startlingly sudden that it is commonly referred to as the "Cambrian explosion" in geological literature.

Sedimentary rocks that are believed to have formed prior to the Cambrian Period are assigned to a rather nebulous period called the Precambrian. Rocks of the Precambrian generally underlie (although not always) Cambrian rocks and are believed to have been laid down during several hundreds of millions of years preceding the Cambrian. There are now many reports in the scientific literature of the discovery in Precambrian rocks of fossils of microscopic, single-celled, soft-bodied creatures, such as bacteria and algae. On the basis of these claims, evolutionists are asserting that life arose on earth more than three billion years ago, perhaps as much as 3.5 billion years ago.

It would be well to insert a cautionary note at this point concerning the nature of these reports. Certainly many are questionable and open to dispute. Some papers have suggested uncertainties of such identifications.[2] For example, although they accepted the probability that certain alleged microfossils of Precambrian age were of biological origin, Engel et al. cautioned that

> Establishing the presence of biological activity during the very early Precambrian clearly poses difficult problems . . . skepticism about this sort of evidence of early Precambrian life is appropriate.[3]

In any case, if single-celled creatures gave rise to the vast array of complex invertebrates which abruptly burst upon the scene, and nearly three billion years intervened between the origin of life and this

---

[2] P. Cloud, *Science* 148:27 (1965); M. N. Bramlette, *Science* 158:673 (1967); W. H. Bradley, *Science* 160:437 (1968); A. E. J. Engel et al., *Science* 161:1005 (1968).

[3] Engel et al., *Ibid.*, p. 1008.

"Cambrian explosion" of complicated invertebrates, we must find the record of that evolution somewhere in the rocks of the Precambrian. Ever since Darwin the rocks have been intensely searched for this record, but to evolutionists the results have been agonizingly disappointing. Nowhere on this earth—neither on any continent nor on the bottom of any ocean—have we been able to find the intermediates between single-celled organisms and the complex invertebrates. Wherever or whenever we find them, right from the start jellyfish are jellyfish, trilobites are trilobites, and sea urchins are sea urchins.

Concerning this, Axelrod has stated:

> One of the major unsolved problems of geology and evolution is the occurrence of diversified, multi-cellular marine invertebrates in Lower Cambrian rocks on all the continents and their absence in rocks of greater age.

After discussing the varied types that are found in the Cambrian, Axelrod goes on to say:

> However, when we turn to examine the Precambrian rocks for the forerunners of these early Cambrian fossils, they are nowhere to be found. Many thick (over 5,000 feet) sections of sedimentary rock are now known to lie in unbroken succession below strata containing the earliest Cambrian fossils. These sediments apparently were suitable for the preservation of fossils because they are often identical with overlying rocks which are fossiliferous, yet no fossils are found in them.[4]

George Gaylord Simpson has struggled valiantly but not fruitfully with this problem, being forced to concede that the absence of Precambrian fossils (other than those of micro-organisms) is "the major mystery of the history of life."[5]

It had long been maintained by a significant number of evolutionists, of whom we have already cited Axelrod and Simpson above, that no undoubted multi-cellular fossils had been found in rocks that were unquestionably older than the Cambrian. As recently as

[4] D. Axelrod, *Science* 128:7 (1958).

[5] G. G. Simpson, *The Meaning of Evolution* (New Haven: Yale University Press, 1949), p. 18.

1973, for example, Preston Cloud, an evolutionary geologist, expressed his conviction that there are as yet no records of unequivocal Metazoa in undoubted Precambrian rocks.[6]

In more recent times, however, a collection of mostly soft-bodied metazoan fossils that have come to be known as the Ediacaran Fauna from their first discovery in Australia[7] are believed to be late Precambrian. Representatives are now known from the fossil record that have been found not only in Australia, but also in Newfoundland, England, Siberia, and South Africa. Up until very recently some of these creatures were believed to be very similar to our modern jellyfish, sea pens, worms, and other coelenterates and echinoderms. A few other previously unknown and rather problematical fossil creatures were also noted.

These discoveries do not alleviate the problem for evolution theory. These creatures are in no way intermediate between single-celled organisms and the complex invertebrates previously found in Cambrian rocks. They *are* complex invertebrates. Furthermore, it has been recently established that the creatures of the Ediacaran Fauna are not the same as the worms, coelenterates, and echinoderms of the Cambrian. In fact, they are so basically different that it has been stated unequivocally that they could not possibly have been ancestral to any of the Cambrian animals.[8] It is asserted that a previously unrecognized mass extinction eliminated all of these creatures many millions of years before the Cambrian.

We will now describe the many recent publications that discuss the pervasive, perplexing, and persistent problem for evolutionary theory due to the explosive appearance of a vast array of complex invertebrates in the fossil record with a total absence of ancestors and no trace of transitional forms between the various kinds of invertebrates. Richard Dawkins, the British biologist and evolutionist, states:

> . . . the Cambrian strata of rocks, vintage about 600 million years [evolutionists are now dating the beginning of the Cambrian at about 530 million years], are the oldest in

---

[6] P. Cloud, *Geology,* 1:123 (1973).

[7] M. F. Glaessner, *Scientific American* 204(3): 2–8 (1961).

[8] S. J. Gould, *Natural History* 93(2): 14–23 (1984); J. S. Levinton, *Scientific American* 267:86 (1992); J. W. Valentine, *Paleobiology* 16(1): 94 (1990).

which we find most of the major invertebrate groups. And we find many of them already in an advanced state of evolution, the very first time they appear. It is as though they were just planted there, without any evolutionary history. Needless to say, this appearance of sudden planting has delighted creationists.[9]

Yes, indeed! The sudden appearance of these creatures fully formed does delight creationists. It is precisely what is predicted on the basis of creation. Douglas Futuyma, ardent anti-creationist, in his book on evolutionary biology, states:

> It is considered likely that all the animal phyla became distinct before or during the Cambrian, for they all appear fully formed, without intermediates connecting one form to another.[10]

Thus, Futuyma must confess that *all* the animal phyla (a phylum is the broadest category or taxon of plants and animals; for example, all vertebrates—fish, amphibia, reptiles, birds, and mammals, including man—are placed in the phylum Chordata), at least all the invertebrate phyla have appeared in the fossil record with absolutely no evidence that they arose from preceding forms.

James W. Valentine, geologist-paleontologist at the University of California, Santa Barbara, describes the problem this way:

> Most authorities do agree that metazoan phyla more complex than flatworms have all (or perhaps nearly all) descended at least indirectly from flatworm-like stocks, since they all share many features. However, there is no agreement on the actual pathways of descent; nearly every remotely possible ancestral-descendant combination has been suggested by one or another worker. Again, the nature of forms intermediate between known groups will obviously have been different for one ancestor-descendant pair than for another.

---

[9] Richard Dawkins, *The Blind Watchmaker* (New York: W. W. Norton, 1987), p. 229.

[10] Douglas Futuyma, *Evolutionary Biology*, 2nd ed. (Sunderland, Massachusetts: Sinauer Associates, Inc., 1986), p. 325.

The fossil record is of little use in providing direct evidence of the pathways of descent of the phyla or of invertebrate classes. Each phylum with a fossil record had already evolved its characteristic body plan when it first appeared, so far as we can tell from the fossil remains, and no phylum is connected to any other via intermediate fossil types. Indeed, none of the invertebrate classes can be connected with another class by series of intermediates. The relationships among phyla and classes must be inferred on the basis of their resemblance. However, even the most sophisticated techniques of phylogeny analysis have thus far failed to resolve the great differences of opinion concerning the relationships among phyla (or among many classes as well).[11]

The many invertebrate phyla, such as clams, snails, brachiopods, sea urchins, sponges, jellyfish, trilobites, etc., differ drastically from one another, yet evolutionists believe, as Valentine describes, that all of them have evolved from the same common ancestor—a flatworm-like creature! This is based purely on faith, of course, for as Valentine describes later in the same article, those creatures that developed skeletonized structures (those creatures with hard parts, such as clams, snails, trilobites, corals, etc.) did so independently and without leaving any traces of ancestors or transitional forms. He says:

> Each of the phyla that developed durably skeletonized lineages during this period did so independently, suggesting that the opportunities for epifaunal life were open to a wide array of adaptive types. Furthermore, many of the durably skeletonized phyla appearing in Cambrian rocks are represented by a number of distinctive subgroups, classes, or orders, that appear suddenly without known intermediates.[12]

Taking into account the number of phyla, and the number of classes within each phylum, that appear in Cambrian rocks, Valentine estimates that about 300 creatures with different major body plans and subplans are found in these rocks. Billions times billions of fossils of

[11] J. W. Valentine, "The Evolution of Complex Animals," in *What Darwin Began*, ed. Laurie Godfrey (Boston: Allyn and Bacon, 1985), p. 263.

[12] *Ibid.*, p. 267.

these creatures are entombed in the Cambrian rocks scattered on the face of the earth. These rocks, and the Precambrian rocks, should contain many billions of fossils of the vast number of intermediates that would have existed if evolution is true, yet not one has ever been found!

In 1984 at Chengjiang, in the southern province of Yunnan, China, a spectacular discovery of a vast array of complex invertebrates in Cambrian rocks occurred. The strata in which these fossils were found, according to the paleontologists, constitute the very early Cambrian. The discovery was made by Dr. Hou Xianguang, and a study of these fossils were reported by a Swedish scientist, Dr. Jan Bergstrom.[13] According to Bergstrom[14] "the Cambrian transition was a revolution more than evolution." Referring to what was termed a "riotous proliferation of more advanced life forms," Bergstrom states that "evolution of these creatures seems to have been a sudden and widespread phenomenon." Not only were these the oldest such fossils ever found, according to evolutionists, but their soft body parts were unusually well-preserved. Despite their supposed great age, a majority of these fossil species belong to animal groups that still exist. Thus, these creatures were not tiny, primitive fore-runners of later, more advanced forms as evolutionists should expect. It is reported that one creature stood two feet above the floor of the ocean, another had a large disk with concentric air chambers divided into numerous partitions, and the largest animal found was two feet long with stout segmented arms. Three species of trilobites were found. Trilobites, now believed to be extinct, were just as complex as any invertebrate in existence today.

As more and more discoveries are made, evolutionists are getting squeezed more and more. They used to date the beginning of the Cambrian period at about 600 million years, and assumed that its duration was about 80 million years. Now they are assigning a date of about 530 million years, and possibly as recently as 520 million years, for its beginning, and are being forced to squeeze the origin of the vast array of complex invertebrates into a time span which they believe may encompass no more than ten million years and most likely only

<hr />

[13] Jan Bergstrom, Hou Xianguang, Chen Gunyuan, and Maurits Lindstrom, *Research and Exploration* (1991).

[14] Jan Bergstrom, as quoted by John Noble Wilford, "Spectacular Fossils Record Early Riot of Creation," *New York Times*, 23 April 1991.

five million years.[15] Five million years is just a blink of time on their evolutionary time scale. After all, they believe that single-celled organisms existed on the earth for three billion years before these Cambrian animals emerged from nowhere.

Stefan Bengtson, a Swedish paleontologist, describes the situation in the following way:

> If any event in life's history resembles man's creation myths, it is this sudden diversification of marine life when multicellular organisms took over as the dominant actors in ecology and evolution. Baffling (and embarrassing) to Darwin, this event still dazzles us and stands as a major biological revolution on a par with the invention of self-replication and the origin of the eukariotic cell. The animal phyla emerged out of the Precambrian mists with most of the attributes of their modern descendants.[16]

Yes, indeed, this sudden appearance of complex invertebrates "out of the Precambrian mist" without a trace of ancestors or transitional forms is still baffling and embarrassing to evolutionists today, just as it was to Darwin, because 135 years after Darwin evolutionists are no nearer to a solution of the "mystery" than was Darwin. Bengtson tells us that "If any event in life's history resembles man's creation myths, it is this sudden diversification of marine life. . . ." Again we say, yes, indeed! The explosion of complex living organisms found in the fossil record is precisely what is and must be predicted on the basis of creation. The myth is not creation. The myth is the theory of evolution, a myth invented to explain our origin without God.

S. Conway Morris, a paleontologist of the University of Cambridge who has studied Cambrian fossils extensively, says concerning the origin of these creatures:

> A few principles are widely, but not universally, accepted, but no coherent phylogeny for the roughly 35 metazoan phyla exists. . . . The morphological gaps that, by definition, separate phyla, remain inviolate. We remain uninformed both about the now-extinct intermediates and the

---

[15] Stephen Jay Gould, *Natural History*, 103(2): 14 (1994); R. A. Kerr, *Science*, 261:1274 (1993); S. A. Bowring et al., *Science* 261:1293–1298 (1993).
[16] Stefan Bengtson, *Nature* 345:765 (1990).

evolutionary processes that would have been responsible for the diversification of early multicellular animals into what we now perceive as distinct phyla, each with its own body plan. . . . The "Cambrian explosion" is a real evolutionary event, but its origins are obscure. At least 20 hypotheses have been proposed, and although arguments linking diversification to oxygen levels, predation, faunal provinciality, and ocean chemistry all attract support, it is the case that "The emergence of Metazoa remains the salient mystery in the history of life."[17]

Thus, Morris testifies to the fact that we have no record of the assumed "now extinct intermediates" and we remain ignorant of the evolutionary processes that could have produced this tremendous array of greatly diversified, complex animals.

One of the most thorough discussions of all aspects of the "Cambrian explosion" and its attendant "mysteries" is found in Chapter 1, "Origin and Early Radiation of the Metazoa," authored by paleontologists Philip Signor and Jere Lipps in the book edited by the same authors.[18] They begin their account with the statement:

The complex of historical events encompassing the origin and early evolution of Metazoa is at once the salient feature and the most unresolved bio-historical phenomenon in the history of life. It has been the single most perplexing issue since paleontology emerged as a scientific discipline in the eighteenth and nineteenth centuries. Many of paleontology's heroic figures (W. Buckland, C. Lyell, C. R. Darwin, C. D. Walcott) and modern leaders (P. E. Cloud, B. Runnegar, S. M. Stanley, J. W. Valentine) have offered hypotheses or scenarios to explain or account for events of this critical juncture in the history of life. To date, none of these ideas are widely accepted (pp. 3, 4).

They report that:

The sudden appearance of diverse metazoan skeletal fossils heralds the beginning of the Phanerozoic [the

---

[17]S. C. Morris, *Nature* 361:219–225 (1993).

[18]J. H. Lipps and P. W. Signor, eds., *Origin and Early Evolution of the Metazoa*, (New York: Plenum Press, 1992), pp. 3–23.

Phanerozoic Age includes all of the fossil record from the
Cambrian to the present] . . . there is little evidence that the
capacity to form skeletons was acquired gradually or over a
prolonged period. . . . A wide variety of skeleton types and
most of the major marine invertebrate clades appear
suddenly in the fossil record. . . . The ecological
diversification of animals is equally dramatic. A wide variety
of habitats were occupied by these biotas, from shallow to
deep benthos and to the pelagic realm (pp. 7, 8).

Having outlined the mystery that demands an explanation, they list in
detail the various scenarios suggested to explain this great
contradiction to evolutionary theory. These scenarios fall into two
general classes. The first class suggests a hypothetical long, hidden
history of animals followed by a sudden appearance of the completed
forms. Of course, this is no explanation at all. It is merely claimed that
the ancestors and transitional forms must have existed, regardless of
the total lack of evidence. The second class of scenarios suggests that
there were some critical biological or physical events which might
account for the abrupt appearance of such a vast array of complex
animals. About twenty different varieties of explanations have been
put forth within the two general classes, and Signor and Lipps have
listed them under ten main categories: hidden evolution; skeletons and
animals; oxygen and animals; predators and prey; evolution of large
size; carbonate, phosphate, and ocean chemistry; glaciations, sea level,
and diversity; tectonics; genetic mechanisms; and mechanical
efficiency. Only those that are most often mentioned in the scientific
literature and textbooks will be discussed.

Hidden Evolution. Signor and Lipps point out, for example, that not
even the existence of trace fossils prior to the appearance of complex
invertebrates can be documented. An argument often advanced for a
long period of hidden evolution prior to the Cambrian is the fact that
those creatures that do abruptly appear are very complex and very
diverse. It is pointed out, for example, that fully developed trilobites
appear throughout the world, no primitive intermediate forms have
ever been discovered, and no forms that can be considered
intermediate between "primitive" arthropods and their closest
relatives have ever been found. Many evolutionists assume, of course,
there *had* to be a long period of evolution to produce these creatures,

so obviously they must have had a long period of evolution, whether or not we can find any trace of that history. This scenario is based on nothing more, of course, than the assumption of evolution.

Skeletons and Evolution. Many evolutionists have suggested that no ancestors or transitional forms for the Cambrian animals have been found because these hypothetical ancestors were all soft-bodied, and soft-bodied animals generally produce few fossils. In the first place, all, or practically all, of the Ediacaran Fauna referred to earlier (Signor and Lipps refer to this as the Vendian, this term being synonymous with Ediacaran) were soft-bodied metazoa, and many discoveries of these creatures around the world have been reported. The alleged discoveries of fossils of microscopic, single-celled, soft-bodied bacteria and algae have appeared frequently in scientific literature during the past few decades. If it is possible to find fossils of microscopic bacteria, there should certainly be no trouble in finding fossils of everything between these microscopic creatures and the complex invertebrates of the Cambrian, even if they were all soft-bodied. Furthermore, large numbers of fossils of soft-bodied creatures, such as jellyfish and worms, have been found, many in a remarkable state of preservation.

The notion that skeletonized animals could have evolved directly from soft-bodied creatures is contradicted by the evidence. Signor and Lipps describe the fact that the function of the soft anatomy of brachiopods and bivalve mollusks, for example, is so intimately integrated with the shells of these creatures that these animals would not be viable without the shells. In support they cite publications by Cloud,[19] Stanley,[20] and Valentine and Erwin.[21] They further point out that agglutinated skeletons, which require no biomineralization (they are constructed of detrital particles), first appear at the beginning of the Cambrian. If fossils of organisms prior to the Cambrian fail to appear because they had no mineralized shells, at least agglutinated skeletons should appear in Precambrian rocks. None are found.

Oxygen and Animals. It has been suggested by many evolutionists that the origin of the complex invertebrates became possible only after a sufficient quantity of free oxygen had accumulated in the

[19] P. E. Cloud, *Evolution* 2:322–350 (1949).

[20] S. M. Stanley, *Paleobiology* 2:209–219 (1976).

[21] J. W. Valentine and D. H. Erwin, in *Development as an Evolutionary Process*, (New York: Liss, 1987), pp. 71–107.

atmosphere, and that occurred only shortly before the onset of the Cambrian. That suggestion is still appearing in some current publications. This idea was first advanced when geological evidence was sketchy, and preconceived ideas were accommodating what evolutionists wanted to believe. Most geological research in recent years has established beyond little doubt that the earth has always had an oxygenated atmosphere, certainly since sedimentary rocks first began to form. Dimroth and Kimberley, Canadian geologists, reasoned that the distribution in sedimentary rocks of the minerals of uranium, iron, carbon, and sulfur is determined by the amount of oxygen in the atmosphere. When they compared the distribution of these minerals in sedimentary rocks assumed to be very young to that found in some of the oldest sedimentary rocks available, assumed to be between two and three billion years in age, they found no difference.[22] They declared that this evidence indicated that the earth has had a highly oxygenated atmosphere ever since sedimentary rocks began to form. Other research by Holland, Feakes, and Zbinden,[23] Holland and Buekes,[24] and Clemmey and Badham,[25] suggest from about two billion to nearly four billion years for the presence of relatively high proportions of free oxygen in the earth's atmosphere. It is thus well established that the earth's atmosphere contained plenty of oxygen long before the age commonly accepted by evolutionists for the origin of Metazoa, regardless of the precise timing given to this event. As Signor and Lipps state, ". . . there is no evidence that oxygen was limiting in the late Proterozoic."[26]

Carbonate, Phosphate, and Ocean Chemistry. A number of biologists and geologists have suggested that aspects of ocean chemistry prior to the origin of the complex invertebrates inhibited the formation of skeletons but that changes in this chemistry then aided skeleton formation, beginning about the time, or a short time before, the

---

[22] E. Dimroth and M. M. Kimberley, *Canadian Journal of Earth Science* 13:1161–1186 (1976).

[23] H. D. Holland, C. K. Feakes, and E. H. Zbinden, *American Journal of Science,* 289:362–389 (1989).

[24] H. D. Holland and N. J. Buekes, *American Journal of Science* 290A:1–34 (1990).

[25] H. Clemmey and N. Badham, *Geology* 10(3): 141–146 (1982).

[26] Lipps and Signor, *Origin and Early Evolution of Metazoa,* p. 15.

complex invertebrates made their abrupt appearance in the fossil record. But as Signor and Lipps point out, skeletons of calcium carbonate, calcium phosphate, biogenic silica, and agglutinated skeletons all appeared simultaneously in a great variety of invertebrates. It is thus clear that changes in neither atmospheric conditions nor ocean chemistry could have been responsible for the origin of Metazoa.

Conclusions. Signor and Lipps state:

> The marine biota near the Proterozoic-Phanerozoic boundary shows rapid diversification in nearly all clades, and at different grades of organization, different ecologies, different skeletal types, and different trophic levels.

Their conclusion (p. 17): "the emergence of Metazoa remains the salient mystery in the history of life."

Thus, the mystery of the Cambrian explosion remains. It is an interesting exercise to observe how evolutionists struggle with this contradiction to evolution theory. Eldredge, a paleontologist at the American Museum of Natural History, for example, after discussing the Ediacaran Fauna, goes on to say:

> Then there was something of an explosion. Beginning about six hundred million years ago and continuing for about ten to fifteen million years, the earliest known representatives of the major kinds of animals still populating today's seas made a rather abrupt appearance. This rather protracted "event" shows up graphically in the rock record: all over the world, at roughly the same time, thick sequences of rocks, barren of any easily detected fossils, are overlain by sediments containing a gorgeous array of shelly invertebrates: trilobites (extinct relatives of crabs and insects), brachiopods, mollusks. All of the typical forms of hard-shelled animals we see in the modern oceans appeared, albeit in primitive, prototypical form, in the seas of six hundred million years ago.

> Creationists have made much of this sudden development of a rich and varied fossil record where, just before, there was none. . . .

Indeed, the sudden appearance of a varied, well-preserved array of fossils, which geologists have used to mark the beginnings of the Cambrian Period (the oldest division of the Paleozoic Era) does pose a fascinating intellectual challenge.[27]

Eldredge offers several possible solutions to the problem. He mentions that one recent suggestion is that the level of atmospheric oxygen rose to a critical point so that the oxygen level in the ocean became sufficient to support a large variety of animal life.[28] As just documented, we have seen that such claims are simply false. If, on the evolutionary time scale, oxygen was abundant by two billion years ago, and the Cambrian explosion did not occur until 600 million years ago (a difference of 1.4 billion years), it seems obvious that the sudden appearance of all these complex invertebrates had nothing to do with the oxygen content of the atmosphere.

Eldredge's main argument is that evolution does not necessarily proceed slowly and gradually, but that some episodes in evolution may, geologically speaking, proceed very rapidly.[35] Thus, just before the advent of the Cambrian, for some reason or other, there was an evolutionary burst—a great variety of complex multi-cellular organisms, many with hard parts, suddenly evolved. This evolution occurred so rapidly (perhaps in a mere fifteen to twenty million years, more or less) there just wasn't enough time for the intermediate creatures to leave a detectable fossil record.

This notion of explosive evolution is really not a new idea at all, as it has been employed in the past to explain the absence of transitional forms.[29] This notion will not stand up under scrutiny, however. First, what is the *only* evidence for these postulated rapid bursts of evolution? *The absence of transitional forms!* Thus, evolutionists like Eldredge, Simpson, and others are attempting to snatch away from creation scientists what these scientists consider to be one of the best evidences for creation, that is, the absence of transitional forms, and use it as support for an evolutionary scenario!

What is predicted on the basis of evolution—namely, the *presence* of transitional forms—is not forthcoming, so rather than admitting

---

[27] N. Eldredge, *The Monkey Business: A Scientist Looks at Creationism*, (New York: Washington Square Press, 1982), p. 44.

[28] *Ibid.*, p. 47.

[29] Simpson, *The Meaning of Evolution*, p. 18.

that the evidence falsifies their theory, the new scenario predicts just the opposite—the *absence* of transitional forms. Furthermore, the science of genetics is solidly against the notion of rapid bursts of evolution. As a matter of fact, evolutionists argue that the reason we have never witnessed any really significant evolutionary changes in all of human observation is because evolution moves so slowly. Indeed, the genetic apparatus of a lizard, for example, is totally devoted to producing another lizard, and the idea that there could be processes that somehow overcome this genetic bulwark against change and convert a lizard into a different creature without leaving fossilized intermediates is wishful thinking and contrary to science. Even more incredible is the idea that this could have happened to a whole host of complex creatures. Finally, while fifteen to twenty million years, or even five million years, may seem brief to evolutionists, it *is* a very, very long time—plenty of time to leave a rich fossil record.

Later in the book by Eldredge quoted above, Eldredge suggests the most incredible notion of all to explain away the vast Cambrian explosion. He states:

> We don't see much evidence of intermediates in the Early Cambrian because the intermediates had to have been soft-bodied, and thus extremely unlikely to become fossilized.[30]

It is difficult to believe that Eldredge or any other scientist could have made such a statement. Whatever they were, the evolutionary predecessors of the Cambrian animals had to be complex—a single-celled organism could not possibly have suddenly evolved into a great variety of complex invertebrates without passing through a long series of intermediates of increasing complexity. Surely, if paleontologists are able to find numerous fossils of microscopic, single-celled, soft-bodied bacteria and algae, as Eldredge does not doubt they have, then they could easily find fossils of all the stages intermediate between these microscopic organisms and the complex invertebrates of the Cambrian. Furthermore, in addition to the many reported findings of fossil bacteria and algae, there must be many hundreds of finds of soft-bodied, multi-cellular creatures, such as worms and jellyfish, in the scientific literature. The creatures of the

---

[30] Eldredge, *Monkey Business*, p. 130.

Ediacaran Fauna finds, which have been reported from five continents, are soft-bodied.

Even more incredible is Eldredge's suggestion that all of the ancestors of the creatures that abruptly appear fully-formed in Cambrian rocks were soft-bodied. As Eldredge describes above, the Cambrian animals include a gorgeous array of shelly invertebrates—creatures with hard parts. If, as Eldredge says, *all* of the intermediates were soft-bodied, that means that a great variety of creatures with hard parts suddenly arose directly from soft-bodied creatures. That is simply impossible. As already described, the anatomy, the physiology, the very way of life of an invertebrate with hard parts is intimately intertwined with and dependent on those hard parts. Thus the anatomies of soft-bodied animals are very different from the soft anatomies of animals with hard parts. If invertebrates with hard parts evolved from soft-bodied creatures, that change had to be gradual and there would have been many intermediate stages permitting a gradual acquisition of hard parts and changes in the way of life of these creatures. This gradual acquisition of hard parts by these many creatures should be abundantly documented in the fossil record. Fossils of thousands of these intermediate stages should grace museum displays. None have been found.

Evolutionists believe that the vast array of invertebrates represented in the Cambrian rocks evolved from common ancestors, but, of course, there is not a single fossil of an intermediate to document this notion. Billions times billions of these creatures would have lived and died but no intermediates can be found in paleontological collections. Vast unbridged gaps separate such creatures as jellyfish, sponges, worms, sea urchins, sea cucumbers, trilobites, brachiopods, sea lilies, and others.

This leaves evolutionists with what Simpson calls the major mystery of the history of life. In a review of a recent book on the origin of the major invertebrate groups,[31] Runnegar states that:

> As might be expected, the paleontologists have concentrated on the fossil record and have therefore provided a wealth of information on the early history of a

---

[31] M. R. House, ed., *The Origin of Major Invertebrate Groups*, Systematics Assoc. Special, vol. 12, (New York: Academic Press, 1979).

great variety of invertebrate groups, but little insight into their origins.[32]

Eldredge admits that "The Cambrian evolutionary explosion is still shrouded in mystery."[33] But creation scientists say, **what greater evidence for creation could the rocks give than this abrupt appearance of a great variety of complex creatures without a trace of ancestors?** Thus we see, right from the beginning, on the basis of an evolutionary scenario, the evidence is directly contradictory to predictions based on evolution but is remarkably in accord with predictions based on creation. **This evidence alone is sufficient to establish the fact that evolution has not occurred on the earth.**

The remainder of the history of life reveals a remarkable absence of the many transitional forms demanded by the theory of evolution. There is, in fact, a systematic deficiency of transitional forms between the higher categories, just as predicted by the creation model.

The Fossil Record of Insects Offers Remarkable Support for Creation

The absence of transitional forms leaves any evolutionary origin of insects (members of the Insecta, a subphylum of the Arthropoda phylum) shrouded in mystery. Some fossils are found in Middle Devonian rocks, and they are present in such amazing numbers and varieties in rocks of the Pennsylvanian that the so-called Pennsylvanian Period has been called "The Age of Insects." Fossils of dragonflies in Pennsylvanian rocks with a wingspread of two to three feet are not uncommon. When we first see dragonflies, big or little, they are just that—dragonflies.

What about cockroaches? Dr. Betty Faber, an entomologist with the American Museum of Natural History, in a recent interview stated that:

> Several cockroach fossils . . . from the Carboniferous Period of Earth's history make one thing clear. Even back then, about 350 million years ago, the cockroach looked disgusting. It hasn't changed much since.[34]

---

[32] B. Runnegar, *Journal of Paleontology* 55:1138 (1981).

[33] Eldredge, *Monkey Business*, p. 46.

Some cockroaches were larger in the past. Fossils of cockroaches have been found in Pennsylvanian rocks up to four inches in length. Perhaps present-day cockroaches, then, are not quite as disgusting as in the past.

Although such things as spiders, mites, and centipedes are not insects, they are popularly called insects. At the 1983 annual meeting of the American Association for the Advancement of Science, a fascinating report was given of the discovery of remarkably well-preserved fossils of centipedes, a mite, and spiderlike creatures. The fossils were said to be 380 million years old, some of the oldest ever found, and were discovered by Drs. Patricia Bonamo and J. D. Grierson of the State University of New York at Binghamton.

These scientists state, "these creatures were already highly evolved" and that they bore a "close resemblance to living creatures." What those statements simply mean is that those creatures appeared in the fossil record for the first time already fully-formed and that they haven't changed much to this day, supposedly 380 million years later. One fragment was tentatively identified as a machilid, much like the common silverfish, a true insect. Fossils of some creatures resembling the familiar daddy-longlegs were so exquisitely preserved their sense organs were recognizable. One of the scientists analyzing the fossils remarked that "they looked like they might have died yesterday."[35] All of these facts conform admirably to predictions based on the creation model but are notoriously contradictory to what is expected on the basis of evolution theory.

Evolutionists believe that flying insects evolved from nonflying insects. When insects first appear in the fossil record, however, a great variety of both non-flying and flying insects are included. Wootton and Ellington, for example, state:

> When insect fossils first appear, in the Middle and Upper Carboniferous, they are diverse and for the most part fully winged. There are a few primitively wingless forms, but no convincing intermediates are known. Reconstructing the "protopterygotes"—the immediate ancestors of winged

---

[34] M. Kusinitz, *Science World*, 4 Feb. 1983, pp. 12–19.
[35] New York Times Press Service, *San Diego Union*, 29 May 1983; a later technical report of these findings is found in W. A. Shear et al., *Science*, 224:492–494 (1984).

insects—therefore relies, as it always has, on indirect evidence, drawn mainly from Paleozoic fossils and from primitive forms.

Remarkably, two nineteenth century hypotheses are still in contention.[36]

Please understand that just what constitutes "primitive" and "advanced" forms is very much a subjective decision. While evolutionists believe that "primitive" forms gave rise to "advanced" forms, if the assumed positions of the creatures were reversed, evolutionists could just as easily label the "primitive" forms as "advanced" forms and relegate "advanced" forms to a "primitive" status. There is thus an ongoing argument among evolutionists on just what on a nonflying insect gave rise to wings. If a single intermediate between non-flying insects and flying insects could be found, the controversy would be settled, but as yet not one fossil intermediate has ever been found. Thousands of fossils of flying insects rest on museum shelves. Where are the thousands of intermediates that ought to exist? The most reasonable conclusion is that the transitional forms have never been found because they never existed.

Furthermore, flying insects have two different kinds of wings. At rest the wings of the Paleoptera are held aloft, as in magflies, or at the side, as in dragonflies. Insects of the Neoptera have a flexing mechanism which enables them to fold their wings back into a resting place across the abdomen. No transitional forms between these two kinds of flying insects are known.

In figure 2 is seen a suggested evolutionary tree for flying insects. The solid lines denote where actual fossils are known and the dashed lines represent where intermediate forms ought to exist according to the evolutionary schemes, but where none have been found. What actually exists of this evolutionary tree are the tips of the branches. The trunk and branches are only imaginary.

---

[36] R. J. Wootton and C. P. Ellington, "Biomechanics and the Origin of Insect Flight," in *Biomechanics in Evolution*, ed. J. M. V. Rayner and R. J. Wootton, (Cambridge: Cambridge University Press, 1991), p. 99.

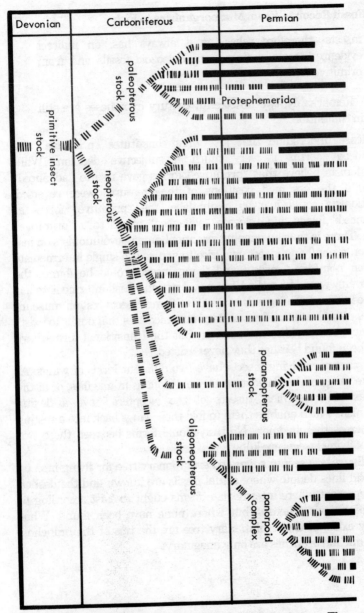

Figure 2. A suggested phylogeny for the flying insects. The solid lines indicate where actual fossils have been found and the dashed lines indicate hypothetical connections only.

Triassic	Jurassic	Cretaceous	Tertiary	Recent
Palaeodictyoptera Megasecoptera Protodonata				
				Odonata
				Ephemeroptera
				Dictyoptera
				Plecoptera
				Zoraptera
Protoperlaria				
				Isoptera
				Embioptera
Protelytroptera				
				Dermaptera
				Grylloblattodea
Protorthoptera Caloneurodea				
	Glosselytrodea			
				Phasmida
				Orthoptera
				Psocoptera
				Mallophaga
				Siphunculata
				Thysanoptera
				Heteroptera
				Homoptera
				Coleoptera
				Hymenoptera
				Neuroptera
	Paratrichoptera			
				Mecoptera
Paramecoptera				
				Siphonaptera
				Diptera
				Trichoptera
				Lepidoptera

The Great Gulf Between
Invertebrate and Vertebrate

The idea that the vertebrates were derived from the invertebrates is purely an assumption that cannot be documented from the fossil record. On the basis of comparative anatomy and embryology of living forms, almost every invertebrate group has been proposed at one time or another as the ancestor of the vertebrates.[37] The transition from invertebrate to vertebrate supposedly passed through a simple, chordate state, that is, a creature possessing a rod-like notochord. Does the fossil record provide evidence for such a transition? Not at all.

Ommanney has thus stated:

> How this earliest chordate stock evolved, what stages of development it went through to eventually give rise to truly fishlike creatures, we do not know. Between the Cambrian when it probably originated, and the Ordovician when the first fossils of animals with really fishlike characteristics appeared, there is a gap of perhaps 100 million years which we will probably never be able to fill.[38]

Incredible! One hundred million years of evolution and no fossilized transitional forms! All hypotheses combined, no matter how ingenious, could never pretend, on the basis of evolution theory, to account for a gap of such magnitude. Such facts, on the other hand, are in perfect accord with the predictions of the creation model.

In contrast to the billions times billions of the transitional forms between invertebrates and vertebrates that must have lived and died as some invertebrate evolved into the fishes (believed by evolutionists to constitute the first vertebrates), and in contrast to the untold billions of fossil fishes entombed in rocks, evolutionists can describe only a single fossil chordate, *Pikaia*, which they suggest as being an intermediate. However, we still have chordates with us today. *Amphioxus* is a chordate that is very much a part of the modern world. As one of the defining characteristics, it has a notochord, a stiff,

---

[37] E. G. Conklin, as quoted by G. E. Allen, *Quart. Rev. Biol.*, 44:173 (1969); A. S. Romer, *Vertebrate Paleontology*, 3rd ed., (Chicago: University of Chicago Press, 1966), p. 12.

[38] F. D. Ommanney, *The Fishes*, Life Nature Library (New York: Time-Life, Inc., 1964), p. 60.

rod-like support above which is a nerve chord and below which is a simple digestive tube. There is no brain or real head in this creature. It has a series of gills that run down along the front of the body. Myotomes, which are a characteristic of chordates, are zig-zag bands of muscles and these extend the entire length of the body. It has a small tail fin and is a capable swimmer. Evolutionary biologists state that *Amphioxus* is a very primitive chordate, and thus must maintain that there has been little, if any, change in chordates since they are believed to have originated in the Cambrian, or even Precambrian "times." Thus evolutionists would have us believe that while some chordate evolved into a fish, which evolved into amphibians, which evolved into reptiles, which evolved into birds and mammals, and lower mammals evolved on up the ladder to humans, all under compelling changes in the environment, chordates have remained unchanged for at least 600 million years! Evolution is a strange phenomenon, indeed.

Some evolutionists boastfully cite a fossil chordate, *Pikaia*, as an intermediate. One single fossil chordate as their "evidence" for the evolution of invertebrate into vertebrate! But if evolution is true, millions of undoubted intermediates showing the gradual evolution of fishes from its invertebrate ancestor should crowd museum shelves and be on display for any doubters to see. How desperate are evolutionists for the *most pitiful* little evidence they can find to bridge the monumental gap between invertebrates and vertebrates!

The fossil *Pikaia* is found in the Burgess Shale of Canada. The Burgess Shale, in which is found a vast array of both soft-bodied and skeletonized invertebrates, every one of which occurs in a fully-formed state, and many in an amazing state of preservation, is assigned by evolutionists to the Middle Cambrian. If, as it is now maintained, the entire Cambrian can be compressed into a mere five million years, one can almost forget about "early," "middle," and "late" Cambrian. On an evolutionary time scale and tempo, there would be no essential differences in time between these divisions. It can certainly not be claimed that *Pikaia* is more primitive than *Amphioxus*. It had the notochord, nerve chord, and myotomes characteristic of chordates. Unlike *Amphioxus*, which has no real head, *Pikaia* had a distinct head. It had a caudal fin wrapped around the posterior end of the tail. Some suggest, however, that its breathing and feeding organs appear to be more primitive than those of *Amphioxus*.

Thus, there you have him! A real fossil of a chordate, a possible intermediate between invertebrates and vertebrates. Enough to make any evolutionist swell with pride as he breathes a great sigh of relief! Now he has something to bridge the 100 million year gap (more or less) between invertebrates and fishes. Now he can slap the faces of those silly creationists with *real* evidence. Strahler, who has written a voluminous anti-creationist book, refers to *Pikaia* as "a winning ace"![39] Incredible! Not only should the fossil record produce billions times billions of fossils of creatures intermediate between invertebrates and vertebrates, but it should also produce a vast number of fossils that reveal the intermediates between the major classes of fishes as they diverged from the ancestral fish. As the next section documents, not one such intermediate has ever been found.

Distinct Separation of Major Fish Classes

A careful reading of Romer's book *Vertebrate Paleontology* seems to allow no other conclusions but that all of the major fish classes are clearly and distinctly set apart from one another with no transitional forms linking them. The first to appear in the fossil record is the class Agnatha. The most ancient of these vertebrates, representatives of the two orders Osteostraci and Heterostraci, were almost always encased in bony or other hard material, and most were equipped with bony armor plates. Concerning their origin, Romer has written:

> In sediments of late Silurian and early Devonian age, numerous fishlike vertebrates of varied type are present, and it is obvious that a long evolutionary history had taken place before that time. But of that history we are mainly ignorant (p. 15).

Concerning the ostracoderms (Osteostraci) he writes: "When we first see these ostracoderms, they already have a long history behind them and are divided into several distinct groups" (p. 16). Of the Heterostraci, Romer writes that they are obviously not closely related to the other forms in the class Agnatha. If they evolved, they also must have had a long evolutionary history. But, like the ostracoderms, they appear suddenly in the fossil record without any evidence of evolutionary ancestors.

[39] A. N. Strahler, *Science and Earth History—The Evolution/Creation Controversy*, (Buffalo: Prometheus Books, 1987), p. 405.

The placoderms are especially troublesome. Within the placoderms were about six major different kinds of weird fishes. Of them, Romer says: "There are few common features uniting these groups other than the fact that they are, without exception, peculiar" (p. 24). Later he says:

> They appear at a time—at about the Silurian-Devonian boundary—when we would expect the appearance of proper ancestors for the sharks and higher bony fish groups. We would expect "generalized" forms that would fit neatly into our preconceived evolutionary picture. Do we get them in the placoderms? Not at all. Instead, we find a series of wildly impossible types which do not fit into any proper pattern; which do not, at first sight, seem to come from any source or to be appropriate ancestors to any later or more advanced types. In fact, one tends to feel that the presence of these placoderms, making up such an important part of the Devonian fish story, is an incongruous episode; it would have simplified the situation if they had never existed! (p. 33).

But they did exist, and their record does not support, but rather strongly contradicts, the evolution model.

The higher "orthodox" fish types, structured along well-recognized plans, with paired fins and well-developed jaws, are placed within two classes, the Chondrichthyes, or cartilaginous fishes, and the Osteichthyes, or higher bony fishes.

Some have argued in the past that the absence of bone in the cartilaginous fishes represents a primitive condition, and that the Chondrichthyes were an evolutionary stage preceding bony fishes. Romer argues strongly against this, pointing out that the sharks were one of the last of the major fish groups to appear in the fossil record. He goes on to say:

> The record, in fact, fits in better with the opposite assumption: that the sharks are degenerate rather than primitive in their skeletal characters; that their evolution has paralleled that of various other fish types in a trend toward bone reduction; and that their ancestry is to be sought among primitive bony, jaw-bearing fishes of the general placoderm type. No well-known placoderms can be identified as the actual ancestors of the Chondrichthyes, but

we have noted that some of the peculiar petalichthyids appear to show morphologically intermediate stages in skeletal reduction. Increasing knowledge of early Devonian placoderms may some day bridge the gap (p. 38).

Earlier, with reference to the placoderms, Romer had said, "we must consider seriously that at least the sharks and chimeras may have descended from such impossible ancestors" (p. 34). Romer insists that special creation is not admissible as a scientific explanation for origins, but he is willing to appeal to "impossible ancestors" to support his own sagging theory! A consideration of the creation model certainly seems more reasonable than an appeal to "impossible ancestors."

Of the typical bony fishes, Romer records the fact that their appearance in the fossil record is a "dramatically sudden one" (p. 52). Later on (p. 53), he states:

> The common ancestor of the bony-fish groups is unknown. There are various features, many of them noted above, in which the two typical subclasses of bony fish are already widely divergent when we first see them. . . .

Errol White, an evolutionist and expert on fishes, in his presidential address on lungfishes to the Linnean Society of London, said:

> But whatever ideas authorities may have on the subject, the lungfishes, like every other major group of fishes that I know, have their origins firmly based in nothing. . . .[40]

Later he went on to say, "I have often thought how little I should like to have to prove organic evolution in a court of law." He closed out his address by stating:

> We still do not know the mechanics of evolution in spite of the over-confident claims in some quarters, nor are we likely to make further progress in this by the classical methods of paleontology or biology; and we shall certainly not advance matters by jumping up and down shrilling "Darwin is God and I, So-and-so, am his prophet"—the recent researches of workers like Dean and Henshelwood (1964) already suggest

---

[40] E. White, *Proc. Linn. Soc. London* 177:8 (1966).

the possibility of incipient cracks in the seemingly monolithic walls of the Neo-Darwinian Jericho.

In his discussion concerning the origin of bony fishes, Todd makes the following remark:

All three subdivisions of the bony fishes appear in the fossil record at approximately the same time. They are already widely divergent morphologically, and they are heavily armored. How did they originate? What allowed them to diverge so widely? How did they all come to have heavy armor? And why is there no trace of earlier intermediate forms?[41]

Indeed, why is there no trace of earlier intermediate forms? Evolutionists may speculate forever but the facts do not change. The predicted evolutionary transitional forms are nowhere to be found.

Even Strahler must concede defeat concerning the effort to find ancestors and transitional forms for the fishes. He must admit that "Origin of the vertebrates is obscure—there is no fossil record preceding the occurrence of fishes in the late Ordovician time."[42] His book includes an extensive critical review of my earlier book on the fossil record and an edition of a later book (1985).[43] This is what he has to say concerning ancestors and transitional forms for fishes:

Duane Gish finds from reading Alfred S. Romer's 1966 treatise, *Vertebrate Paleontology*, that mainstream paleontologists have found no fossil record of transitional chordates leading up to the appearance of the first class of fishes, the Agnatha, or of transitional forms between the primitive, jawless agnaths and the jaw-bearing class Placodermi, or of transition from the placoderms (which were poorly structured for swimming) to the class Chondrichthyes, or from those cartilaginous-skeleton sharklike fishes to the class Osteichthyes, or bony fishes (1978a, pp. 66–70; 1985, pp. 65–69). The evolution of these

---

[41] G. T. Todd, *American Zoology* 20(4): 757 (1980).

[42] Strahler, *Science and Earth History*, p. 316.

[43] D. T. Gish, *Evolution: The Fossils Say No* (El Cajon, California: Master Books, 1978); *Evolution: The Challenge of the Fossil Record* (El Cajon, California: Master Books, 1985).

classes is shown in Figure 43.1. Neither, says Gish, is there any record of transitional forms leading to the rise of the lungfishes and the crossopterygians from the lobe-finned bony fishes, an evolutionary step that is supposed to have led to the rise of amphibians and ultimately to the conquest of the lands by air-breathing vertebrates.

In a series of quotations from Romer (1966), Gish finds all the confessions he needs from the evolutionists that each of these classes appears suddenly and with no trace of ancestors. The absence of the transitional fossils in the gaps between each group of fishes and its ancestor is repeated in standard treatises on vertebrate evolution. Even Chris McGowan's 1984 anticreationist work, purporting to show "why the creationists are wrong," makes no mention of Gish's four pages of text on the origin of the fish classes. Knowing that McGowan is an authority on vertebrate paleontology, keen on faulting the creationists at every opportunity, I must assume that I haven't missed anything important in this area. This is one count in the creationists' charge that can only evoke in unison from the paleontologists a plea of *nolo contendere*.[44]

Nolo contendere is, of course, a guilty plea by a defendant who must admit that he has no defense.

The fossil record has thus not produced ancestors nor transitional forms for the major fish classes. Such hypothetical ancestors and the required transitional forms must, on the basis of the known record, be merely the products of speculation. How then can it be argued that the explanation offered by the evolution model to explain such evidence is more scientific than that of the creation model? In fact, the evidence *required* by evolution theory cannot be found. The evidence, of the other hand, is precisely what would be expected if creation is true.

Summary

In the scientific contest between creation and evolution, the controversy is essentially settled at this point. No further discussion of the fossil record is necessary. In fact, no further discussion of any kind

---

[44] Strahler, *Science and Earth History*, p. 408.

is required. **The evidence from the fossil record discussed in this chapter has established beyond any reasonable doubt that evolution has not taken place on the earth.** The evidence is absolutely clear. All of the complex invertebrates appear fully-formed without a trace of ancestors or transitional forms linking one to another. Many millions of years would have been required for their origin by evolutionary processes. Billions times billions of their fossils lie entombed in rocks all over the world, including all kinds of soft-bodied creatures. Even many published reports of the discovery of fossils of microscopic, single-celled, soft-bodied organisms have appeared in scientific journals. If evolution is true, the rocks should contain billions times billions of fossils of the ancestors of the complex invertebrates. **Yet, not one has ever been found.** It is simply physically impossible to have millions of years of evolution, producing a vastly diverse collection of complex invertebrates, without leaving a trace.

Even more convincing, if that can be said, is the total absence of intermediates between invertebrates and fishes, and the total absence of ancestors and transitional forms for each major class of fishes. Many billions of fossil fishes exist in rocks upon the earth, with very diverse forms of many kinds. The rocks should be full of the fossils documenting the transition of some invertebrate into a fish, and a rich fossil record of the various transitional forms should exist linking the various major types of fishes to each other, if evolution is true. There should be no difficulty whatsoever in finding vast numbers of fossils of the ancestors and transitional forms. Again, **it is physically impossible for millions of years of evolution to take place, producing a great variety of major types of fish, without leaving a trace.**

Just think. Fishes, amphibians, reptiles, birds, and mammals are all vertebrates. The origin of vertebrates would thus have been the greatest event in all of history. Volume after volume should have been written about this momentous event. These volumes should be full of pictures of the various intermediates, documenting the step by step conversion of an invertebrate into a fish, and the many intermediates linking one kind of fish to another. Here would be undoubted proof of the fact of evolution, but what we have instead is a vast void, a total blank. The only thing that evolutionists can offer in an attempt to fill the void is simply pointless speculation, totally devoid of empirical evidence. Here, at this very early point in the consideration of the evidence from the fossil record, evolution theory is left dead in the water.

EVOLUTION? THE FOSSILS SAY NO!

Chapter V

The Fossil Record—From Fish to Reptiles

The Origin of Tetrapods

The tetrapods include all the four-legged animals within the amphibians, reptiles, and mammals. Evolutionists assume that tetrapods evolved from a fish ancestor and that amphibians were the first tetrapods. Which fish was ancestral to the tetrapods is, however, a very controversial subject among evolutionists. The reason the controversy exists is that paleontologists have failed completely to find transitional forms between fish and amphibians. If such transitional forms existed, it would be a rather simple matter to connect ancestor to descendant. Robert L. Carroll assumes that rhipidistian crossopterygian fish (see Glossary for definitions) gave rise to amphibians,[1] yet he freely admits that: "We have no intermediate fossils between rhipidistian fish and early amphibians. . . ."[2] Rosen, Forey, Gardiner, and Patterson reject this suggestion and argue that a lungfish gave rise to amphibians.[3] Thomas Gorr and Traute Kleinschmidt reject both of these suggestions and argue that

---

[1] R. L. Carroll, *Vertebrate Paleontology and Evolution* (New York: W. H. Freeman and Co., 1988), p. 138.

[2] *Ibid.*, p. 4.

[3] D. E. Rosen et al., *Bulletin of the American Museum of Natural History*, 167:159-276 (1981).

amphibians evolved from a coelacanth fish, previously believed to have become extinct about 80 million years ago until a live specimen of the genus *Latimeria* was brought up from the deep sea by fishermen off the east coast of Africa in 1938. Subsequently, about 200 specimens have been taken from the sea. They base this claim on the fact that the hemoglobin molecule of *Latimeria* is closer in amino acid sequence to the Beta-hemoglobin chain of the tadpole of a bullfrog, *Rana catesbeiana*, than that of lungfish, shark, and several teleost fish (teleosts include modern bony fish).[4]

Peter Forey, on the other hand, totally rejects the idea that *Latimeria* could have been ancestral to amphibians. He says:

> The discovery of *Latimeria* raised hopes of gathering direct information on the transition of fish to amphibians, for there was then a long-held belief that coelacanths were close to the ancestry of tetrapods. *Latimeria* was thus heralded as a "missing link," a reputation that rested on the theory that coelacanths and tetrapods were more closely related to each other than either was to any other living group. But studies of the anatomy and physiology of *Latimeria* have found this theory of relationship to be wanting and the living coelacanth's reputation as a missing link seems unjustified.[5]

As one reads critically the massive amount of literature on the origin of major groups, such as the origin of tetrapods, reptiles, and primates, one soon becomes overwhelmed and confused by the many controversial and contradictory notions of evolutionists. Each espouses his supposedly logical argument based on a comparison of the many characteristics that the theorist assumes to be the most important in selecting the creature believed to be the probable ancestor. Carroll, in his book on vertebrate paleontology and evolution, writes as if it were a foregone conclusion that rhipidistian fish were ancestral to amphibians. As we have seen above, other evolutionists insist that lungfish or coelacanths were the most likely ancestors. In an article in the *New York Times* by Malcolm Browne commenting on the paper

---

[4] Thomas Gorr and Traute Kleinschmidt, *American Scientist*, 81(2): 72-82 (1993).

[5] P. L. Forey, *Nature* 336:729 (1988).

by Gorr and Kleinschmidt, mention is made of their ideas supporting the coelacanth as the ancestor of amphibians.[6] Browne also describes research by Axel Meyer and Allan C. Wilson that suggests the lungfish as the best candidate and which rules out the coelacanth as a possible ancestor. Nowhere in the article is there a single word about the possibility that a rhipidistian fish could have been ancestral to amphibians, even though Carroll and many other evolutionists take that for granted. In his article, Browne does state that:

> No one can be certain which group or groups of fishes was the first to make the transition to land, or what their evolutionary pathways may have been . . . the transition from water to land occurred long ago, and various family trees suggested by the fossil record are so tangled that scientists acknowledge they may never be able to sort them out definitively.

Thus Carroll votes for rhipidistian fish, Gorr and Kleinschmidt vote for coelacanth, Rosen et al. vote for a lungfish, and each gives reasons why the other suggestions are invalid. Why such confusion and lack of agreement? As the saying goes today, "It's the lack of transitional forms, stupid!" Just a few transitional forms would reveal what was ancestral to amphibians and what the evolutionary pathway was. Lacking that, all suggestions are mere scenarios and empty rhetoric.

Changing a fish that spends all of its time in the water into a creature that spends much or most of its time on land would require more than simply changing the form or morphology of the ancestors as they evolved into the amphibian. Carroll describes a few of the critically important changes a fish would have to undergo to become an amphibian.[7] These include:

Water Balance: As the proto-amphibian moved from water to dry land, he would have suffered serious loss of water through mouth, lungs, and body surfaces. Significant changes had to occur in these organs and structures to minimize these losses.

---

[6] M. W. Browne, "Biologists Debate Man's Fishy Ancestors," *New York Times*, 16 March 1993, p. C-1.

[7] Carroll, *Vertebrate Paleontology and Evolution*, pp. 164-167.

Sense Organs: How could a fish or the alleged proto-amphibian survive on land before his many sensory structures had undergone extensive reorganization in order to adapt to the physical and chemical differences between water and air? Keep in mind that each sense organ had to function correctly from the very first, each change had to occur in the right sequence and be coordinated with all others, and all of this had to take place via random or accidental changes or mutations of the genes. Many other important physiological changes would have had to take place to enable the nascent amphibian, or part-way amphibian, to survive on land.

Critically important morphological changes would have to take place to convert a fish into an amphibian. The fins of a fish are designed to provide balance, steering, and locomotion in water. The fins could not possibly support the body of the fish in air where there is no buoyancy provided by water. The pelvic bone of a fish is loosely embedded in muscle, with no connection to the vertebral column. None is needed. The fins do not support the weight of the body. In what is supposed to be one of the earliest amphibians, *Ichthyostega* (figure 3), it is seen that the pelvic bone is very large and firmly attached to the vertebral column. This is the type of anatomy required

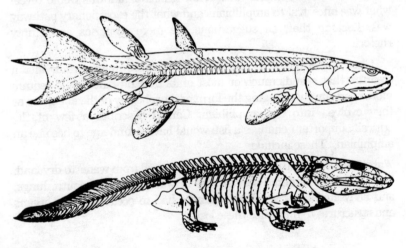

Figure 3. Reconstructions of an ichthyostegid amphibian and his supposed crossopterygian ancestor. From Romer's *Vertebrate Paleontology*, by permission of the University of Chicago Press.

for locomotion on land. In contradiction to predictions of some evolutionists, deep-sea photography from a submersible vessel revealed the fact that the coelacanth *Latimeria* does not even walk on the bottom of the ocean, even in spite of the fact it could use buoyancy in water. It will also be noted that during the hypothetical evolutionary conversion of the fish into an amphibian, somehow, for some reason, it also surrendered its two dorsal and anal fins. Evolutionists point to the presence of the fish-like tail fin as evidence that *Ichthyostega* is a descendant of rhipidistian fish, but as Forey points out, such ideas are flawed because fish-like tails are characteristic of the general group of vertebrates with jaws (Gnathostomata).

Carroll states:

> The most conspicuous differences between rhipidistines and amphibians are in the appendicular skeleton. . . . In the early amphibians, the structure of the limb joints and the distal portion of the limb are considerably remodeled.[8]

Carroll points out that the function of the thick, lobate-paired fins of the rhipidistians was very different from the function of the feet and legs of the amphibians. In the rhipidistian fish the humerus (of the front paired fins) and the femur (of the rear paired fins) were held close to the body, which restricted lateral or rotational movement. Thus their fins point in a posterior direction. In the "primitive" tetrapods, however, the limbs are extended forward and away from the trunk during locomotion. The mode of locomotion of amphibians, including the "earliest" or most "primitive" amphibians, was thus drastically different from that of any fish.

Paleontologists point to the fact that there are bones in the pectoral fins of crossopterygian fish that are similar to, or homologous with, the humerus, radius, and ulna of the forelimb of amphibians. But there the similarity of either the pectoral or pelvic fins of these fishes to the forelimbs and hind limbs of amphibians ceases. There is nothing in any of these fish to equate to or homologize with hand and feet of amphibians.

Carroll states:

---

[8] *Ibid.*, pp. 161, 162.

More distally, there are no large endoskeletal supports for the fin and one must suppose that the metacarpals and phalanges of tetrapods developed as almost, if not entirely, new structures.[9]

Ahlberg and Milner state:

The proximal [upper] elements of tetrapod limbs thus correspond closely to those of sarcoptergian fins. However, the process then "switches sides" to produce the digits as a series of postaxial branches (figure 5e–g). No process resembling this is known to occur or to have occurred in lobe-finned fishes. It appears that hand and feet are "new" structures, produced by a major developmental change affecting the distal parts of the paired appendages.[10]

(The article by Ahlberg and Milner is a review article that describes the most recent ideas, as of this writing, of evolutionists concerning the origin and early diversification of tetrapods.)

The chapter of Hans-Peter Schultze in the recent book on the origins of the higher groups of tetrapods[11] is appropriately entitled "Controversial Hypotheses on the Origin of Tetrapods." In his conclusion, Schultze states:

Four different phylogenetic arrangements derived from the analyses of the same features have been discussed. Each author interpreted the characters such that they favored his or her preferred relationship of tetrapods. Jarvik emphasized a distinction between eutetrapods and urodeles and the similarities between urodeles and porolepiforms. Rosen *et al.* downplayed the significance of similarities between osteolepiforms and tetrapods and then interpreted the features of dipnoans in tetrapod fashion. Chang held to the view that all sarcopterygian fishes, including dipnoans, lack a choana. Thus, in her opinion, the history of tetrapods

---

[9] *Ibid.*, p. 145.

[10] Per A. Ahlberg and Andrew R. Milner, *Nature* 368:509 (1994).

[11] Hans-Peter Schultze and Linda Trueb, eds., *Origins of the Higher Groups of Tetrapods* (Ithaca, New York: Comstock Publishing Associated, 1991).

is separate from that of all other sarcopterygians. Vorobyeva and Schultze argued that the internal opening of the palate of osteolepiforms and panderichthyids is a true choana, and that only in osteolepiforms is the internal structure of the fins comparable to tetrapods . . . the entire question of relationships turns on an evaluation of similarities and dissimilarities of features in order to assess their homologies accurately. . . . Rosen et al. (1981) argued that an analysis of relationships must be based first on extant forms, with fossils being introduced in the analysis secondarily. The incompleteness of the fossil record is a given. As a result the fossils contribute nothing to the resolution of the phylogenetic scheme.[12]

Schultze and others have described the immense amount of finagling with the data that each author must perform in order to account for the many contradictions and difficulties each scheme generates. As noted above, Schultze states: "the entire question of relationship turns on an evaluation of similarities and dissimilarities of features. . . ." But in numerous examples, according to evolutionists, similarities prove nothing about ancestral-descendant relationship, because similar structures in different animals do not exist because they were inherited from a common ancestor, but were acquired independently. Thus, evolutionists invoke what they call **Parallel Evolution** when they assume that a feature evolved independently in closely related species. According to evolutionists, this is a common occurrence in evolution. Another common phenomenon in evolution according to evolutionists is what they call **Convergent Evolution**. In these cases, it is assumed that distantly related species have independently evolved similar structures or features. A frequently cited example are the eyes of vertebrates and the eyes of the invertebrate cephalopods (squid) which are very similar, but an assumed common ancestor of these two types of creatures would have existed hundreds of millions of years ago, long before the eyes of either the cephalopods or those of vertebrates had evolved. Futuyma states:

In many instances convergent evolution results in such similar features that we would be hard put to say whether

---

[12] *Ibid.*, p. 59-62.

they had the same genetic bases if we did not know that they had evolved independently in unrelated groups.[13]

Thus, similarities in different animals may serve as evidence of evolution from a common ancestor, but then again they may not, having arisen independently by parallel or convergent evolution. Another common feature in evolutionary theory which further complicates and confuses evolutionary schemes, but which can be invoked to save these schemes, is the so-called reversals. This notion of reversals is hypothesized by evolutionists when a structure in an evolutionary line of descent is lost but then reappears later in supposed descendant species. It was long held that reversals could not occur in evolution. It was maintained that the genetic changes involved in the origin of a complex structure are so numerous and must be acquired in such a complicated sequence that once the structure is eliminated by subsequent evolutionary changes the chances of it being reacquired is essentially nil. In fact, this principle was thought to be so well established that it was raised to the status of a "law," the so-called **Dollo's Law**. Now, however, Dollo's supposed law has been cast into an evolutionary garbage can, as reversals must be repeatedly invoked in modern evolutionary schemes. For example, Schultze states:

> Reversals such as those described above also are necessary to explain many cranial as well as post-cranial features. Among the paired skull roofbones, two reversals are needed to account for the presence of parietals and postparietals in actinopterygians, three for the frontals, parietals, and postparietals in the common ancestor of sarcoptrygians and tetrapods, and two for the parietals and postparietals in actinistians, porolepiforms, and *Diabolepis*. Phylogenetic sequences from two to one to two squamosals and external nasal openings, and from absence to presence to absence of a choana and vertebrae are implied. . . . A sister-group relationship among all sarcopterygian fishes and tetrapods would imply that the common ancestor was more similar to a tetrapod than it was to the derived, fishlike descendants.

---

[13] Douglas J. Futuyma, *Evolutionary Biology* (Sunderland, Massachusetts: Sinauer Associates, Inc., 1979), p. 142.

Such an arrangement would entail numerous character reversals that seem most unlikely.[14]

As noted earlier, Schultze remarked that "each author interpreted the characters such that they favored his or her preferred relationship of tetrapods." In other words, each investigator decides on the basis of an assumed evolutionary pathway which, *a priori*, he or she prefers, and then interprets the evidence accordingly, invoking whatever reversals, parallel evolution, or convergent evolution, as the scheme may require. Such theories are so plastic that they are rendered non-falsifiable even if false, and thus they cannot be called scientific theories. Thus Ahlberg and Milner, in reference to the published ideas of Rosen et al. on the origin of tetrapods,[15] states:

> They stated categorically that evolutionary scenarios, such as those that purported to reconstruct the evolution of tetrapods from osteolepiforms, were unfalsifiable "stories" and not testable science.[16]

Osteolepiforms are those fish within the rhipidistian crossopterygians that are considered by the majority of evolutionists to have been the ancestor of amphibians.

A very recent find of the fossil of an amphibian in Upper Devonian rocks (of the Middle to Upper Famennian formations, judged by evolutionists to be about 365 to 363 million years before the present) in the Catskill Formation of Pennsylvania greatly reinforces the evidence that those creatures believed to be the oldest amphibians were fully developed with no evidence of transitional forms. The report on this amphibian, designated *Hynerpeton bassetti*, appeared in the July 29, 1994, issue of *Science* by Daeschler, Shubin, Thomson, and Amaral.[17] They state,

> Derived features of the shoulder girdle indicate that appendicular mechanisms of support and propulsion were well developed even in the earliest phases of tetrapod history.

---

[14] Schultze, p. 56.

[15] Rosen et al., p. 159-276.

[16] Ahlberg and Milner, p. 507.

[17] E. B. Daeschler et al., *Science* 265:639-642 (1994).

In describing the strata in which the fossil was found, these authors report,

> This stratigraphic position suggests that *H. bassetti* is Middle to Upper Famennian in age (~ 365–363 Ma), which is older than *Ichthyostega, Acanthostega,* and *Tulerpeton,* which are uppermost Famennian. . . . The morphology of the shoulder girdle of *H. bassetti* also suggests that it was capable of powerful protraction, retroaction, and elevation of the forelimb.

What we have here is a creature, believed to be older than the creatures previously thought to be the oldest known amphibians, that is 100% amphibian, with fully developed amphibian limbs and other features believed to be advanced. This further falsifies predictions based on evolutionary theory, but provides powerful additional evidence for creation.

We thus note, first of all, that all of the schemes that try to derive amphibians, and thus the "first" tetrapods, from a fish ancestor are nothing more than scenarios that cannot qualify as scientific theories. Furthermore, **there is a great discontinuity between all fish and all amphibians,** regardless of which evolutionary pathway is imagined between fish and amphibians. All of the fish cited as being the most likely ancestors of amphibians are 100% fish which were required to spend all of their time in the water, while all of the so-called descendant amphibians were 100% amphibians with the basic amphibian limbs, feet, and legs. No one has succeeded in finding a single transitional form with part fins and part feet. If such had been found, it would immediately become clear which of the competing candidates as the ancestor of amphibians was the true ancestor. But the controversies rage on. Transitional forms have not been found because they never existed. Evolution of living organisms did not take place on the earth.

The Great Diversity of Amphibians

Modern amphibians are immensely diverse, with more than 4,000 species. These 4,000 species are included in three orders: the Urodela (salamanders and newts); the Gymnophiona (caecilians, also called apodans, wormlike amphibians with no trace of limbs); and the Anura (frogs and toads). When they first appeared in the fossil record, they were just as they are today, modern in appearance and very diverse in structure. Carroll says:

> When they first appear in the fossil record, both frogs and salamanders appear essentially modern in their skeletal anatomy. The described fossil record of Gymnophiona (caecilians) is limited to isolated vertebrae from the Upper Cretaceous and Paleocene that are very similar to those of modern genera.[18]

These modern amphibian orders are usually placed within the Subclass Lissamphibia because of a few similarities that they share. Many paleontologists are skeptical, however, of grouping such diverse creatures together. Carroll remarks:

> Despite these similarities, frogs, salamanders, and caecilians are very different from one another in skeletal structure and ways of life, both now and throughout their known fossil record . . . we have found no fossil evidence of any possible antecedents that possessed the specialized features common to all three modern orders. . . . In the absence of fossil evidence that frogs, salamanders, and caecilians evolved from a close common ancestor, we must consider the possibility that each of the modern orders evolved from a distinct group of Paleozoic amphibians.[19]

Similarly, Colbert and Morales state:

> Despite these similarities, there is no evidence of any Paleozoic amphibians combining the characteristics that would be expected in a single common ancestor. The oldest known frogs, salamanders, and caecilians are very similar to their living descendants.[20]

Both Carroll[21] and Colbert and Morales[22] do mention the very frog-like *Triadobatrachus* as suggesting a possible link between other,

---

[18] Carroll, *Vertebrate Paleontology and Evolution*, p. 180.

[19] *Ibid.*, pp. 181, 182, 184.

[20] E. H. Colbert and M. Morales, *Evolution of the Vertebrates* (New York: John Wiley and Sons, 1991), p. 99.

supposedly ancient amphibians, and modern frogs. Carroll states that the closest similarity of *Triadobatrachus* to Paleozoic amphibians is to the dissorophid temnospondyl, *Doleserpeton*. There is, however, a fundamental difference between all frogs, and, in fact, all modern amphibians, and the temnospondyls, and all of the supposed earliest amphibians. These alleged most ancient amphibians had complex, arch-type vertebrae, composed of several separate elements linked together to form each vertebra. The various types of fish that have been suggested as possible ancestors of amphibians also had a similar, complex-type vertebrae, and this is one of the characteristics suggestive of a link between these fish and the supposed earliest amphibians. All modern amphibians have a very different type of vertebrae, a spool-like bony cylinder. If something like *Doleserpeton* was ancestral to frogs or any of the other modern amphibians, there had to be a gradual evolution of the complex, arch-type vertebrae of *Doleserpeton* into the simple, spool-type vertebrae. There is absolutely no evidence of this in the fossil record.

Amphibians with the spool-type vertebrae are called lepospondyls. Three diverse orders of lepospondyls are found in rocks of the Mississippian and Pennsylvanian. These include the Aistopoda, snakelike creatures with very long bodies with up to 230 vertebrae and with neither limbs nor limb girdles. Carroll states:

> The skulls of these forms are highly specialized, which implies that each family has a long history separate from the other as well as from any labyrinthodonts or rhipidistians.[23]

Speaking of aistopids, Romer says:

> One would expect that such specialized forms would represent a late development among the older amphibian groups; but material as yet undescribed proves that the aistopods had developed early in the Mississippian and hence are among the oldest of all known amphibians.[24]

---

[21] Carroll, *Vertebrate Paleontology and Evolution*, p. 184.

[22] Colbert and Morales, *Evolution of the Vertebrates*, p. 99.

[23] Carroll, *Vertebrate Paleontology and Evolution*, p. 176.

[24] A. S. Romer, *Vertebrate Paleontology*, 3rd ed. (Chicago: Chicago Univ. Press, 1966), p. 97.

In fact, aistopods recovered from Lower Mississippian rocks are now well-described. These amphibians appear abruptly in the fossil record fully-formed and highly specialized, unlike any previous amphibians. Since they appear fully-formed in Lower (Early) Mississippian rocks, that means that, if they evolved, they had to evolve sometime in the Devonian Period. However, the so-called earliest or most ancient amphibians, the alleged evolutionary offspring of fish, are also found in the Devonian. Thus, if evolutionary scenarios are true, while the immediate ancestors of such amphibians as *Ichthyostega* were busily evolving feet and legs from their fish ancestors, the intermediates between fish and aistopods were just as busy discarding any trace of limbs. What selection pressures would lead to an evolutionary origin of feet and legs in amphibians while ensuring at the same time that other amphibians would end up with no limbs at all?

Furthermore, if the complex, arch-type vertebrae found in such amphibians as *Ichthyostega* are similar to the arch-type vertebrae found in rhipidsitian fish, and thus supports a link between the two, from what did the lepospondyl amphibians, with their simple, spool-type vertebrae, evolve? Where are the transitional forms showing some fish evolving into a limbless aistopod with its snake-like body with up to 230 vertebrae, all of the simple, spool type? It is facts of this kind that emphasize the total bankruptcy of evolutionary theory.

The other two orders of lepospondyl amphibians that appear along with the Aistopoda are the Nectridea and the Microsauria. The nectrideans had long bodies with very small limbs. They were apparently largely aquatic, with laterally compressed tails that served as a swimming organ. The microsaurians had a more normal type of body build, although the limbs were rather small. The name Microsauria, meaning "little reptiles," is quite inappropriate, for, as Romer states, the resemblances to reptiles are mere parallelisms. The microsaurs were the most varied of the lepospondyls, with diverse body proportions. The Aistopoda, Nectridea, and Microsauria are found in Mississippian, Pennsylvanian, and Permian rocks and are referred to as the Paleozoic group of lepospondyls.

There is an immense gap on an evolutionary timescale between the Paleozoic lepospondyls and the modern amphibians, in the Subclass Lissamphibia. Romer states, speaking of the Lissamphibia:

Between them and the Paleozoic group is a broad evolutionary gap not bridged by fossil materials.[25]

Carroll writes:

We have not found any lepospondyl fossils later than the Lower Permian. There is a surprising gap in the record of small amphibians until the appearance of frogs and salamanders with the Jurassic.[26]

It is absolutely clear that the fossil record of amphibians offers no support whatsoever for the notion that tetrapods, and amphibians in particular, have evolved from some fish ancestor. The extremely broad gap between the rhipidistian crossopterygians, or other similar fish, and the ichthyostegids or other "earliest" amphibians; the sudden appearance, in fact, of all Paleozoic amphibian orders with diverse ordinal characteristics complete in the first representatives, and the absence of any transitional forms between these Paleozoic orders and the three living orders, makes it absolutely incredible to believe that these forms arose by an evolutionary process. The facts are, however, completely in accord with predictions based on the creation model.

The Origin of Reptiles

We find the same situation concerning the origin of reptiles that is found with amphibians—the abrupt appearance of each basic type with no transitional forms to provide the expected evolutionary links and to reveal the evolutionary pathways leading to each basic kind.

Reptiles are included with the class Reptilia. Reptiles, birds, and mammals are included in the assemblage, Amniota. The amniotes, unlike amphibians, can lay their eggs in environments free of water or moist surroundings because they produce eggs that are equipped with extraembryonic membranes. The amniotic egg of the reptile is vastly more complex than the egg of an amphibian. The eggs of reptiles contain a membrane, the amnion, which provides a sac within which the developing embryo floats. The allantois provides a reservoir in which waste products accumulate, and there is a yolk sac containing the food supply for the developing embryo. The whole is surrounded by

---

[25] *Ibid.*, p. 98.
[26] Carroll, *Vertebrate Paleontology and Evolution*, p. 180.

a shell strong enough to protect the contents of the egg, but at the same time porous enough to allow the exchange of gases with the environment, the intake of oxygen, and the passage out of carbon dioxide. Evolutionists must imagine that this utterly complex system somehow evolved, step by step, via a series of random, undirected, accidental changes in the genetic system of an amphibian. These changes had to be accompanied by the necessary alterations in the reproductive system of the proto-reptile, also produced by purely accidental changes in the genetic system of the ancestral amphibian. During the transition each intermediate stage had to be fully functional and possess advantages over the preceding stage that enabled it to outcompete and thus replace the preceding stage. Many of the vital structures, such as the amniotic cavity and the amnion, has to be produced *de novo* in the reptile, since there are no homologous structures in the amphibian from which they could have been derived. It is likely that no evolutionist would even try to imagine the evolutionary pathway taken and the intermediate stages involved in the evolutionary origin of the amniotic egg.

Evolutionists believe that there exists in certain amphibians and reptiles a number of characteristics that indicate a link between reptiles and amphibians. For example, Colbert and Morales states:

> The mixture of amphibian and reptilian characters seen in *Seymouria* is indicative of the gradual transition that took place between the two classes during the evolution of the vertebrates.[27]

Any attempt to use *Seymouria* as suggestive of an intermediate between reptiles and amphibians immediately encounters serious contradictions. Those creatures suggested as the earliest known reptiles, *Hylonomus* and *Paleothyris*, are found in Lower Pennsylvanian rocks (about 330–315 million years before present on the evolutionary time scale) and the Middle Pennsylvanian rocks (about 310–315 million years), respectively. Fossils of *Seymouria* are found in Lower Permian rocks, dated at about 280 million years, or at least 25 to 35 million years too late to be ancestral to reptiles.

Furthermore, there are other serious problems in attempts to link *Seymouria* to reptiles. Romer asks the question, "Did *Seymouria* lay

---

[27] Colbert and Morales, *Evolution of the Vertebrates*, p. 102.

its eggs frog fashion, in the water, or produce shelled, land-laid eggs of amniote type?" He goes on to say that the answer must be derived by studying the broad group of creatures included within the order Seymouriamorpha. He cites *Kotlassia*, which

> . . . show in flattened skulls, relatively feeble ossification of the skeletons, and other features, a series of regressive changes associated in typical amphibians with a reversion to permanent water-dwelling existence. Again, there have been discovered in the early Permian of Moravia gill-bearing larvae of *Discosauriscus* similar to the "branchiosaur" larvae of rhachitomes, and indicating that in reproductive features the seymouriamorphs were definitely amphibians.[28]

Diadectes is often cited as being very close to the dividing line between amphibians and reptiles. It is also a most improbable candidate, however. It is about 30 million years too late on the evolutionary time scale to be ancestral to reptiles, and it was a large, clumsy creature, about ten feet in length, in contrast to the "primitive" reptiles, which were very small, with bodies from snout to the base of the tail only about four inches in length.

Although a number of characteristics in *Seymouria* and *Diadectes* are cited as revealing similarities to *Hylonomus*, *Paleothyris*, and other "early" reptiles, there is an unbridged gap between amphibians and reptiles. Here are a few examples that establish that reptiles were reptiles at the start, with no transitional forms linking them to any so-called ancestral amphibians. Carroll states (all quotes are from note 1):

> The earliest known amniotes are immediately recognizable as members of this assemblage because of similarities of their skeleton to those of primitive living lizards (p. 193).

> The most significant feature of the palate in early amniotes is the presence of a transverse flange on the pterygoid. . . . In modern lizards, the transverse flange of the pterygoid serves as the origin of one of the largest of the jaw-closing muscles, the pterygoideus. . . . There is little

---

[28] Romer, *Vertebrate Paleontology*, p. 95.

evidence of the existence of a large pteryoideus muscle in any primitive amphibian (p. 194).

The general structure of the braincase of early amniotes resembles that of modern lizards (p. 195).

The postcranial skeleton of early amniotes generally resemble that of the primitive living reptile *Spenodon* (p. 195).

In contrast [to early labyrinthodont amphibians], the early amniotes closely resemble primitive living lizards in their small body size and proportionately small skull. The structure of the teeth and probable arrangement of the jaw musculature in early amniotes resemble those of living lizards that feed almost exclusively on insects and other small arthropods (p. 198).

The skeletal anatomy of protorothyrids [*Hylonomus* and *Paleothyris* are placed in the family Protorothyridae] remains relatively constant from the Lower Pennsylvanian through the Lower Permian. During this time, a series of other amniote groups appear in the fossil record. Each may have independently evolved from the proterothyrid pattern. None show close relationships with one another (p. 201).

The early amniotes are sufficiently distinct from all Paleozoic amphibians that their specific ancestry has not been established (p. 198).

The last statement just quoted establishes beyond doubt that transitional forms between amphibians and reptiles do not exist. If they had been found, there would be no doubt concerning which amphibian gave rise to reptiles.

Just where transitional forms are most critically needed, as just described above, they are always absent. That will be abundantly illustrated as the origin of distinctly different types of reptiles is documented. These widely divergent groups of reptiles include the flying reptiles, the marine reptiles, the gliding reptiles, the snakes, and the turtles.

Flying Reptiles

The differences between nonflying and flying reptiles were dramatic. In figure 4 is shown a reconstruction of *Saltoposuchus*, the thecodont reptiles that Romer believed gave rise to flying reptiles, dinosaurs, and birds. The vast gulf between this creature and representatives of the two suborders of pterosaurs, shown in figures 5 and 6, is obvious.

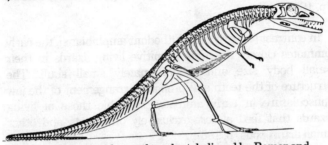

Figure 4. *Saltoposuchus*, a thecodont, believed by Romer and others to be the ancestor of dinosaurs, birds, and flying reptiles. From Romer's *Vertebrate Paleontology*, by permission of The University of Chicago Press.

Almost every structure in *Rhamphorhynchus*, a long-tailed pterosaur (figure 5), was unique to this creature. Especially obvious (as in all pterosaurs) was the enormous length of the fourth finger, in contrast to the other three fingers possessed by this reptile. This fourth finger provided the major support for the wing membrane. It was certainly not a delicate structure, and if the pterosaurs evolved from the thecodonts or some other earthbound reptile, transitional forms should have been found showing a gradual lengthening of this fourth finger. Not even a hint of such a transitional form has ever been discovered, however. The "earliest" pterosaurs are found in Upper Triassic rocks, and are reported to resemble later rhamphorhyncoids very closely.

The skeleton of the earliest pterosaurs was adapted to active flight as much as that found in modern birds, although their structure was very different from birds. It seems apparent that if all of the highly modified structures required for flight that are present in *Rhamphorhynchus* and similar flying creatures had evolved gradually during millions of years from an ordinary land reptile, a considerable

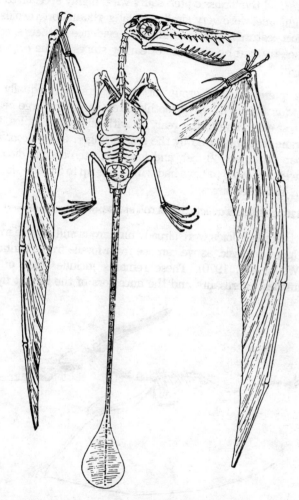

Figure 5. *Rhamphorhynchus*, a long-tailed pterosaur. From Williston's *The Osteology of the Reptiles*, by permission of The Harvard University Press.

number of transitional forms documenting this transition would have been found. **Not one such transitional form has ever been found**. Thus, Carroll states:

> . . . all the Triassic pterosaurs were highly specialized for flight and were very similar to later rhamphorhyncoids in most features. They provide little evidence of their specific ancestry and no evidence of earlier stages in the origin of flight.[29]

The pterodactyloid group of pterosaurs was equally unique. *Pteranodon* (figure 6) was a toothless reptile with a large beak and a bony crest extending to the rear. As with all flying reptiles, the wing membrane was supported by the fourth finger. *Quetzalcoatlus* had a wingspan of almost 40 feet, and fossils of pterodactyls discovered in Texas were reported to have had wingspans up to 54 feet—longer than modern jet-fighter aircraft!

Concerning the pterodactyls, Carroll states:

> Pterodactyloids were already numerous and diverse in the Upper Jurassic, as we can see from fossils from Solnhofen (Wellnhofer, 1970). These remains include some of the smallest pterosaurs and the ancestors of the largest flying

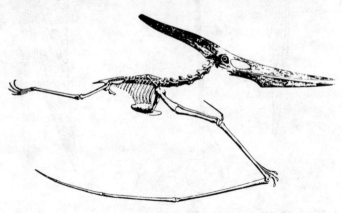

Figure 6. *Pteranodon*, a giant flying reptile with a wingspan of over 50 feet. From Romer's *Vertebrate Paleontology*, by permission of The University of Chicago Press.

reptiles. No forms are known that are intermediate between rhamphorhyncoids and pterodactyloids. . . . The fossil record of pterosaurs extends for approximately 150 million years, and nearly 90 species have been reported from every continent except Antarctica.[30]

It is obvious that if these extremely unique flying creatures, the rhamphorhyncoids and pterodactyloids, had evolved from land reptiles during a period of 150 million years, and their fossils have been discovered essentially throughout the entire world, a great number of transitional forms should have been discovered that would establish beyond doubt that these creatures had evolved from ancestral land reptiles. Precisely the opposite is the case. **The rhamphorhyncoids and pterodactyloids appear fully-formed without a trace of transitional forms.**

The very notion that a land reptile could have gradually been converted into a flying reptile is absurd. The incipient, part-way evolved structures, rather than conferring advantages to the intermediate stages, would have been a great disadvantage. For example, evolutionists suppose that, strange as it may seem, mutations occurred that affected only the fourth fingers a little bit at a time. Of course, other random mutations occurring concurrently, incredible as it may seem, were responsible for the gradual origin of the wing membrane, flight muscles, tendons, nerves, blood vessels, and other structures necessary to form the wings. At some stage, the developing flying reptile would have had about 25% wings. This strange creature would never survive, however. What good are 25% wings? Obviously, the creature could not fly, and he could no longer run, as he would be forced to drag those useless appendages along as, presumably, his hind limbs could still function. he could no longer catch prey nor escape predators. Good bye, Charlie! That such an experiment would have been a complete failure is testified to by the complete failure to find even a trace of an ancestor or transitional form for these totally unique flying reptiles.

---

[29] Carroll, *Vertebrate Paleontology and Evolution*, p. 336.
[30] *Ibid.*, p. 337.

Marine Reptiles

The abrupt appearance of marine reptiles in a fully-formed state is just as dramatic as was the case with flying reptiles. Nevertheless, according to evolutionary theory, the conversion of a land reptile into a marine reptile (or a freshwater reptile) was a gradual process over millions of years, as feet and legs were gradually transformed into paddles, and, with the ichthyosaurs, a land reptile was changed into a reptile very fish-like in its form and function. This is what Colbert and Morales have to say about this incredible process:

> During their long evolutionary history the tetrapods had freed themselves from any dependence on water to become, as reptiles, animals that throughout their entire life history were completely terrestrial. Some of them went back to the water, and all the various adaptations that had made reptiles efficient and independent land-living animals needed to be modified . . . they assumed the old problems with which their fish ancestors had contended many millions of years past—the problem of buoyancy, of propulsion through the water, and of reproduction away from land . . . lungs were not abandoned when reptiles went back to water, but rather were used for breathing, in place of gills that had long since been lost. The reptiles had legs and feet. These were transformed into paddles, similar in function to the fins of fish. The old fish tail had long since disappeared, so that some of the aquatic reptiles evolved substitute tails for propulsion, tails that imitated the fish tail to an astounding degree.
>
> . . . It can thus be seen that among these reptiles there was a reversal in the trend of evolution—from distant aquatic fish ancestors, through intermediate land-living amphibian and reptile ancestors to aquatic reptilian descendants.[31]

What makes such stories or scenarios so incredible is the belief of evolutionists that what ever is needed will be produced by genetic change or mutations, which are totally random with no particular end in view. Thus, as ordinary land reptiles ventured into the water,

---

[31] Colbert and Morales, *Evolution of the Vertebrates*, p. 192.

abandoning their life on land where they had been remarkably successful supposedly for millions of years, they now needed fish-like tails. Obligingly, with no possible knowledge that such was needed, random, accidental mutations altered the incredibly complex genetic apparatus that had produced reptiles in such a way that beautifully designed, marvelously functional fish-like tails were produced on a reptile previously floundering awkwardly around in the water. Likewise, feet and legs were no longer useful for propulsion in water, and so the vast complex of genes that coded for all the structures in feet and legs was somehow, a mutation here, a mutation there, transformed miraculously into the incredible complex of genes required to code for the tendons, blood vessels, nervous system, muscles, bones, and other structures, all arranged in a precise way, to constitute the paddles now highly efficient for propulsion in water. It is evident that, in spite of fervent denials, evolutionists do *believe*, even in miracles.

Just as today when we have some reptiles that are fully aquatic (marine or sea turtles), so it was in the past, but we wish shortly to draw attention to those reptiles that were fully aquatic, especially the plesiosaurs and ichthyosaurs. One of the earliest marine reptiles, according to evolutionists, in fact one of the earliest of known reptiles, was *Mesosaurus*, found in Lower Permian rocks. Surprisingly to evolutionists, it was highly specialized, with a deep tail for swimming and broad paddles in place of feet and legs. Colbert and Morales state:

> On the whole it is most probable that mesosaurs represent a very ancient and independent evolutionary line of reptiles descended from very primitive captorhinomorphs that developed briefly during early Permian times.[32]

This highly specialized aquatic reptile, with its fish-like tail and paddles in place of feet and legs, appeared fully formed with no trace of transitional forms. Thus, the best that Colbert and Morales can suggest is that it evolved so rapidly that there just was not sufficient opportunity to leave fossils of transitional forms—this in spite of the millions of years required for exceedingly rare good mutations of just the right kind to accumulate in a single line of descent to produce such a remarkable creature. Evolutionists believe that this most ancient of

---

[32] *Ibid.*, p. 111.

all aquatic reptiles died out without leaving evolutionary descendants. Carroll states:

> No amniotes other than mesosaurs are known from the Carboniferous or Lower Permian in South America or southern Africa. There is no evidence for the relationship of mesosaurs to any subsequent group of aquatic reptiles.[33]

Please notice another rather incredible situation faced by evolutionists according to their evolutionary time frame. The very first reptiles that appeared in South America or southern Africa were not ordinary land reptiles but were highly specialized aquatic reptiles whose fossils have been found in Lower Permian rocks. Supposedly during the Lower Permian the land mass of the earth constituted a single continent, facilitating the migration of creatures, like reptiles, throughout the world. Why is it then that only aquatic reptiles are found in Lower Permian rocks in South America and southern Africa, creatures whose evolutionary origin from ordinary land reptiles would have required millions of years? Fossils of several of the so-called early reptiles are found in Lower Pennsylvanian and Middle Pennsylvanian rocks in North America and Europe. These creatures supposedly existed millions of years before the Permian and thus would have had plenty of time to migrate from North America to South America and from Europe to southern Africa by the Permian times. Why then are only aquatic reptiles, supposedly derived from some of the early land reptiles, found in South America and in southern Africa in Permian rocks? Why are no other amniotes of any kind, except for these highly specialized aquatic reptiles, found in Pennsylvanian and Permian rocks in South America and southern Africa? The evolutionary scenarios simply do not make sense.

Now let us consider the highly specialized marine reptiles, the plesiosaurs and ichthyosaurs. Fossils of plesiosaurs are found in Jurassic and Cretaceous rocks and were worldwide in extent. Many of the plesiosaurs found in Jurassic rocks were ten to twenty feet in length, and those found in Cretaceous rocks were up to forty feet and more in length, in many of which a very long neck made up much of this length. They had very large paddles, and the placement of powerful muscles allowed the paddles not only to be pulled back with

---

[33] Carroll, *Vertebrate Paleontology and Evolution*, p. 206.

great force but also to pull the paddles forward with great force. Nowhere has anyone found fossils of transitional forms showing the gradual conversion of feet and legs into paddles or the origin of the many other unique features of plesiosaurs.

The nothosaurs were elongated marine reptiles with long, sinuous necks. They had short paddles. It is believed that their tail would have provided the major propulsion force for these aquatic reptiles. The nothosaurs have been suggested as possible ancestors for plesiosaurs. Carroll believes that many skeletal features of nothosaurs indicate that they constitute plausible ancestors for plesiosaurs, but then he says,

> However, such a relationship seems to be contradicted by the structure of the palate and the shoulder girdle. The palate of plesiosaurs is *less* specialized than that of nothosaurs. . . . This configuration suggests that plesiosaurs may have evolved from more primitive diapsids rather than from any of the well-known nothosaurs. . . . The other problem in accepting a nothosaurian origin for plesiosaurs is the great difference in configuration of the shoulder girdle.[34]

If paleontologists had been able to find transitional forms leading up to the plesiosaurs, there would be no difficulty whatsoever in identifying its ancestor and the intermediate stages or evolutionary pathway between ancestor and descendant. Lacking these, evolutionists can only suggest hypothetical evolutionary pathways.

The ichthyosaurs provide a clear and convincing indictment of evolutionary theory. Ichthyosaurs were marine reptiles that differed dramatically from all other reptiles. These creatures, of the genus *Ichthyosaurus* ("fish reptile"), were very fish-like, and were up to ten feet or more in length. Their fossils are found in Jurassic rocks in many places around the world, and not only fossilized bones have been found, but the outline of the body has sometimes been preserved. Here we have, then, an ideal test case of creation versus evolution—an incredibly unique creature which supposedly arose over millions of years by the gradual modification, via random mutations, from a vastly different kind of a reptile. Thus, the long series of transitional forms created during this hypothetical transition would give clear and evident proof that the transition actually did take place. Just a few of

---

[34] *Ibid.*, pp. 245, 25, 46.

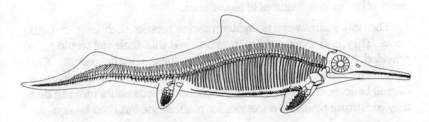

Figure 7. Restoration of an ichthyosaur.

the transitional forms, scattered through time would be sufficient to establish the truth of the alleged evolutionary origin of ichthyosaurs. Fossils of the ichthyosaurs have been found all around the world, so any claims as to scarcity of fossils or appeals to local or regional geological conditions or events that might account for absence of transitional forms have absolutely no validity. In any case, it would be incredible to believe that somehow only the terminal forms remain as fossils while all of the transitional forms scattered through millions of years either escaped fossilization or were subsequently destroyed. On the other hand, if *Ichthyosaurus* appeared abruptly in the fossil record, fully-formed, with no trace of transitional forms, this would provide powerful, positive evidence for creation. What is the truth in this case?

Colbert and Morales state:

> The ichthyosaurs, in many respects the most highly specialized of the marine reptiles, appeared in early Triassic times. Their advent into the geologic history of the reptiles was sudden and dramatic; there are no clues in pre-Triassic sediments as to the possible ancestors of the ichthyosaurs. It is only through an interpretation of the anatomical structures of these highly specialized reptiles that we are able to make some estimations as to their origin, which probably was from some early diapsid ancestor. The basic problem of ichthyosaur relationships is that no conclusive evidence can be found for linking these reptiles with any other reptilian order.[35]

Romer, after acknowledging that at their earliest appearance ichthyosaurs were very highly specialized forms, says:

> No earlier forms are known. The peculiarities of ichthyosaur structure would seemingly require a long time for their development and hence a very early origin for the group, but there are no known Permian reptiles antecedent to them.[36]

While acknowledging that the earliest ichthyosaurs were highly adapted to an aquatic way of life and suggesting that these individuals were in some features more "primitive" than their later counterparts, Carroll says:

> However, not even the most primitive features link them to any particular group of terrestrial or aquatic reptiles. . . .[37]

Thus, the conclusions are unanimous. The ichthyosaurs, the most highly specialized of any reptiles that ever existed on the earth, extremely fish-like in form and locomotion, living in the sea and giving birth to young alive, appeared abruptly in the fossil record, fully-formed, without a trace of ancestors or transitional forms. Furthermore, as Colbert and Morales acknowledge, there is no actual evidence to link the ichthyosaurs to any other reptiles. There is an undoubted vast unbridged gulf between the ichthyosaurs and all other reptilian orders. Here we do not find the endless arguments of evolutionists, based on this or that similarity, which reptilian order is alleged to be closest to ichthyosaurs; yet it is here that the transitional forms, if they ever existed, would be the most obvious, as supposedly some terrestrial or aquatic reptile was gradually changed into the very fish-like *Ichthyosaurus*. Natural history museums should have on display these obvious transitional forms for all to see. Here would be undoubted proof of evolution. **What we have is undoubted proof of special creation, if ever such proof is possible.** What greater evidence for creation could the rocks provide?

---

[35] Colbert and Morales, *Evolution of the Vertebrates*, p. 193.
[36] Romer, *Vertebrate Paleontology*, p. 120.
[37] Carroll, *Vertebrate Paleontology and Evolution*, p. 253.

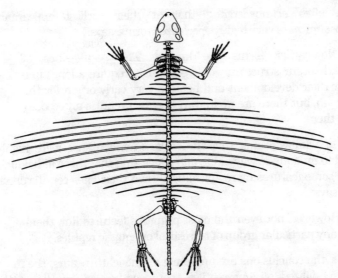

Figure 8. *Coelurosaurus*, a gliding reptile found in Permian
rocks in Madagascar. From *Vertebrate Paleontology and
Evolution* by Carroll. Copyright 1994 by W. H. Freeman and
Company. Used by permission.

The Gliding Reptiles

These gliding reptiles were highly specialized reptiles, which
possessed greatly elongated ribs supporting a membrane that enabled
them to glide considerable distances. The modern reptile of the genus
Draco is a living representative of gliding reptiles, which can glide
nearly 100 feet from tree to tree. *Coelurosauravus* was a gliding reptile
with numerous elongated ribs, whose fossils are found in Upper
Permian rocks. *Kuehneosaurus*, whose fossils have been found in
Upper Jurassic rocks, was another of these highly specialized gliding
reptiles. No paleontologist suggests that any of the gliding reptiles are
related in any way. Concerning the enormous horizontal elongation of
the ribs to support a gliding membrane, Carroll says, "this
specialization evolved separately in each of these groups."[38] Neither
Carroll nor Colbert and Morales even hints at the total lack of

---

[38] *Ibid.*, p. 230. Here Carroll illustrates the gliding reptiles *Coelurosauravus*, *Kuehneosaurus*, and *Draco*.

transitional forms showing an ordinary lizard or reptile being transformed into gliding reptiles. Each gliding lizard appears in the fossil record complete in its first representatives, with no transitional forms of any kind. This evidence is directly contradictory to predictions based on evolutionary theory, but exactly as expected based on creation.

Snakes

Snakes and lizards are placed in the order Squamata, with lizards included in the suborder Lacertilia, or Sauria, while snakes are placed in the suborder Ophidia, or Serpentes. Evolutionists assume that snakes evolved from lizards. Snakes are highly specialized reptiles, vastly different in many way from lizards, their hypothetical evolutionary ancestors. The trunk of snakes is enormously elongated, with up to several hundred vertebrae in some snakes, the number of precaudal vertebrae varying from 120 to 454. There is no trace of forelimbs or pectoral girdles in any snake, although some snakes have a small pelvic girdle and hind limbs. These are not vestigial structures as evolutionists believe, but have important functions. The pelvic bones serve as anchors for certain muscles, and the hind limbs are used during mating and also possibly serve to grasp the surface during locomotion. The palate and structures of the upper and lower jaw are modified in such a way that the mouth can be opened wide so that large prey can be swallowed whole. The brain must be protected during ingestion of prey. Thus, the frontals and parietals are enlarged in such a way that the brain is completely protected. The vertebrae are also modified to permit the sinuous movement of the snake's body.

On the basis of evolutionary theory, one would expect to find a series of transitional forms between lizards and snakes documenting the gradual multiplication of vertebrae, loss of limbs, modification of the skull, and other significant changes as a lizard was transformed into a snake. Also, the question must be answered, why would an enormously successful lizard, via any selection process, undergo gradual changes resulting in losing its limbs, exchanging its efficient mode of locomotion for stages intermediate between lizards and snakes that certainly would be very inefficient? What can be said about fossil evidence documenting the evolution of lizards into snakes? The oldest fossil of a snake in which sufficient remains of the skull have been recovered is *Dinilysia* from the Upper Cretaceous of South America. Carroll reports that *Dinilysia* "shows a fairly advanced stage of evolution of these features" [the specialized features of the skull of snakes.][39] Colbert and Morales state:

> Unfortunately, the fossil history of the snakes is very fragmentary, so that it is necessary to infer much of their evolution from the comparative anatomy of modern forms.[40]

Romer, after commenting that snakes are poorly known as fossils, states:

> The snakes are certainly derived from lizards, and while there is no certainty as to the point of origin, a relationship to the varanoids is quite probable. . . .[41]

If snakes really did evolved from varanoid lizards, as some believe, there certainly should be an adequate fossil record documenting the gradual change of a lizard into a snake. We do have many thousands of fossils of the alleged lizard ancestors and many thousands of fossil snakes. If just a few fossils of the intermediate stages between lizards and snakes could be found, that would be sufficient to trace the origin of snakes back to the ancestral lizard, or whatever reptile proved to be the ancestor. Since transitional forms have not been found, as Colbert and Morales confess, much of the supposed evolutionary "history" must be hypothesized from the comparative anatomy of living forms.

Turtles

Turtles are some of the most highly specialized reptiles that have ever existed. Not only do they have the bony protective cover, or carapace, that is unique to turtles, but the positions of the ribs and the pectoral and pelvic girdles are completely reversed, with the ribs outside, or dorsal, to the girdles, which lie inside, or ventral, to the ribs. Here again, because of the amazingly unique structure of turtles, if they evolved from ordinary reptiles of some kind, it should be a rather easy task to find the transitional forms that would trace the evolutionary pathway from ancestral reptile to turtles. The changes

---

[39] *Ibid.*, p. 235.
[40] Colbert and Morales, *Evolution of the Vertebrates*, p. 223.
[41] Romer, *Vertebrate Paleontology*, p. 134.

required would not be subtle, but obvious, even to one with no training in anatomy or paleontology. There should be no argument among evolutionists concerning which reptile was the true ancestor and which fossilized creatures constituted the intermediate stages. On the other hand, creationists predict that at their first appearance in the fossil record, turtles would be instantly recognized as turtles, with carapace and other unique features fully-formed at the start. Which model of origins, creation or evolution, does the fossil record of turtles support?

Romer says:

> But little light is shed on the ultimate origin of the turtles from a study of fossil members of the order. Some early Triassic forms, such as *Proganochelys*, show a structure slightly more primitive than that of most later turtles. But even at that time the armor was almost perfectly developed; we are dealing, definitely, with a true turtle and not with a transitional form.[42]

Colbert and Morales state:

> The first true turtles made their appearance by the late part of the Triassic period, by which time they were far advanced along the lines of adaptive radiation typical of modern turtles. In *Proganochelys*, a characteristic Triassic genus, the bones of the skull had been reduced in number, teeth were absent from the margins of the jaws, and the body was protected by a heavy shell. These are the basic turtle adaptations, and evolution among turtles since Triassic times has been mainly a matter of refining the characteristics that were established in *Proganochelys*.[43]

Carroll reports:

> The earliest turtles are found in Upper Triassic sediments in Germany. They are immediately recognizable from the pattern of the shell, which is closely comparable to that of modern genera. No trace of earlier or more primitive turtles

---

[42] *Ibid.*, p. 116.
[43] Colbert and Morales, *Evolution of the Vertebrates*, p. 216.

has been described, although turtle shells are readily fossilizable and even small pieces are easily recognized.

In relation to the evolution of the shell, the postcranial skeleton of even the earliest turtles is so altered from that of primitive amniotes that it gives few clues of their specific relationships. The skulls of late Triassic turtles are also highly specialized. There is no evidence for the prior existence of temporal openings, which precludes their close relationship to early synapsids or diapsids. The presence of large postemporal fossae and the absence of the ectoterygoid bone in the palate are features that are shared with members of the Family Captorhinidae, but the skull is otherwise so much altered that we cannot establish with assurance that turtles evolved from that family rather than from some other, as yet unrecognized, lineage of early anapsids.[44]

It is abundantly clear that turtles are highly specialized reptiles whose transitional forms, if they ever existed, would be readily recognizable and abundant. Yet, **not one transitional form has ever been discovered.**

Recently, Michael S. Y. Lee published an article entitled "The Origin of the Turtle Body Plan: Bridging a Famous Morphological Gap."[45] From the title, one would be led to expect a real breakthrough by the discovery of the fossilized remains of some as yet unreported transitional form bearing incipient stages of unique characteristics of turtles, such as the skull or inversion of rib cage and girdles. What Lee's paper incorporates, however, is nothing more than a restudy of pareiasaurs. According to Lee, his study of the characteristics of pareiasaurs and turtles shows sufficient similarities that pareiasaurs should be judged the closest relatives of turtles among primitive reptiles. What were pareiasaurs? They were large, clumsy reptiles, almost ten feet in length. The limbs were stocky and supported a massive trunk. Carroll terms them "elephantine animals." Of course, one glance at their fossils would immediately label them as the most

---

[44] Carroll, *Vertebrate Paleontology and Evolution*, p. 207.

[45] M. S. Y. Lee, *Science* 261:1716-1720 (1993); see also M. S. Y. Lee, *Natural History* (June 1994), pp. 63-65.

unlikely ancestors of turtles, far, far removed from anything that bears even the faintest resemblance to turtles. Lee's attempt to ally pareiasaurs to turtles is added proof of the vast, unbridged gap between turtles and any possible ancestor among other reptiles.

We see, then, that a careful examination of the fossil record of those highly specialized and unique creatures among reptiles—flying reptiles, marine reptiles, gliding reptiles, snakes, and turtles—reveals a systematic absence of transitional forms between these highly specialized reptiles and all other reptilian orders. Just where transitional forms are most needed and where transitional forms would be most easily recognized, they are totally absent. These facts provide powerful, positive evidence for special creation.

Dinosaurs—A Powerful Testimony for Creation

Of all creatures that have ever lived, the dinosaurs are of greatest fascination to man, particularly to children. This is perhaps because of their spectacular size in many cases (dinosaurs ranged in size from that comparable to a rooster to the *Brachiosaurus*, weighing up to eighty tons and standing as high as a five-story building), and because they possessed so many unusual anatomical features. The fossil record of dinosaurs speaks out as clearly for creation as would be possible for creatures now extinct.

The first fossil of a dinosaur was discovered in England over 150 years ago. A large tooth was discovered in 1822 by the wife of Dr. Gideon Mantell, a physician who was also an amateur paleontologist. Dr. Mantell searched for additional fossils and found several more teeth and some bones. He sent the fossils to Baron Cuvier, a famous French scientist. Having never seen anything comparable to these fossils before, this time the great French scientist was wrong. He identified the teeth as being those of an ancient rhinoceros and the bones as those derived from an extinct hippopotamus.

Later, a friend of Dr. Mantell informed him that the teeth were similar in structure, although much larger, to those of the iguana, a lizard found in Mexico and South America. Dr. Mantell decided that he had found the remains of an amazing new kind of creature. He gave it the name *Iguanodon* ("Iguana-toothed"). Not long afterward the fossilized bones and teeth of a huge carnivorous lizard-like animal were discovered and given the name *Megalosaurus*. It was soon realized the *Iguanodon* and *Megalosaurus* were members of a heretofore unknown extinct type of creature. The great British anatomist and paleontologist, Sir Richard Owen, gave them the name Dinosaur ("terrible lizard").

A sharp beak-like bone had been found with the remains of *Iguanodon* and was thought to be a beak. In 1877, however, a spectacular discovery was made in a Belgian coal mine which revealed the true nature of the "beak." Miners found the fossilized skeletons of about two dozen *Iguanodons* deep in the coal mine. How to account for this amazing fossil graveyard of *Iguanodons* deep in a coal mine has posed a formidable challenge to evolutionary geologists. Some have suggested that at one time there was a deep fissure in the earth into which these *Iguanodons* tumbled to their death. It seems strange, however, how all other animals managed to elude this trap. Only a few lonely voices have suggested that these creatures and the coalified plant material in which they were entombed had been swept there and buried by a vast aqueous catastrophe.

A study of the fossils revealed that the "beak" actually corresponded to a thumb. It is impossible to know for sure just how *Iguanodon* used its "thumb." It may be possible that it used it in stripping plant material. Some have suggested that it may have been used in defense.

The dinosaurs (Orders Saurischia and Ornithischia), the crocodiles (Order Crocodilia) and the flying reptiles (Order Pterosauria) and various other reptiles (Order Thecodontia) have been grouped together in the sub-class Archosauria ("rutling reptiles"), although there are few diagnostic features possessed by all of these creatures, and, therefore, little to link them together. The distinguishing feature that sharply divides the saurischian dinosaurs from ornithischian dinosaurs is the fact that saurischian dinosaurs possessed a "reptile-like" pelvic structure or hip while the ornithischian dinosaurs possessed a "bird-like" hip (see p. 65 of *Dinosaurs by Design*, D. T. Gish, Master Books, Colorado Springs, CO, 1992, for a description of these two pelvic structures), and the ornithischian dinosauria possessed a predentary bone not found in saurischians. The thecodonts, and more particularly, the Pseudosuchia, a suborder of the Thecodontia, are thought by many to be the reptile ancestral to the crocodiles, dinosaurs, flying reptiles, and birds.

That this supposed ancestry is highly contrived seems to be immediately apparent by a reading of evolutionary literature. Speaking of *Saltoposuchus*, a pseudosuchian thecodont (see figure 4), Romer says:

> It is obvious that it was forms of this sort from which arose the pterosaurs, birds, and dinosaurs. There are no known thecodonts which show positive indications leading toward the first two groups mentioned, nor toward one of the two dinosaurian orders, the Ornithischia.[46]

How can it be obvious that something like *Saltoposuchus* was ancestral to flying reptiles, birds, and ornithischian dinosaurs if these creatures reveal no "positive indications leading toward" flying reptiles, birds, and ornithischian dinosaurs? It seems apparent that Romer has simply adopted the thecodont reptiles as ancestors for birds, flying reptiles, bird-hipped dinosaurs, and crocodiles (mentioned by Romer elsewhere) for lack of a better candidate, because the fossil record fails to produce any actual ancestors and the necessary transitional forms.

Earlier in his discussion of the archosaurs (thecodonts, crocodiles, flying reptiles, and dinosaurs) Romer says:

> Many similarities in structural features among end forms of different archosaurian lines have not been inherited as such from a common ancestor but have been independently acquired by members of the different groups. This, however, does not debar such characters from consideration as indications of relationship. Study of fossil forms increasingly indicates that there has been an enormous amount of parallelism in evolution; but this study also appears to demonstrate that close parallelism occurs only in closely related forms.[47]

What Romer is admitting here is that these groups of creatures have been linked together because of many similarities, but that in

---

[46] Romer, *Vertebrate Paleontology*, p. 140.
[47] *Ibid.*, p. 136.

each case many of the structural features that were shared in common by the supposed evolutionary end products were not inherited from the assumed common ancestor since the assumed common ancestor did not possess those structural features. Evolutionists assume in cases like these that after the evolutionary ancestral population split into separately evolving lines, each evolving line independently acquired the same structure or structures ("parallel evolution"). It is obvious that when two or more creatures possess a structural feature in common, and it is known that the assumed common ancestor did not possess that structural feature, then the possession of that feature by these creatures does not in any way indicate common ancestry.

Romer tells us that crocodiles, flying reptiles, thecodonts, and dinosaurs have been grouped together in the Archosauria because of similarities. Then he goes on to say that many of these similarities have not been inherited from a common ancestor. Nevertheless, they serve as a basis for the assumption of common ancestry. He attempts to justify this evolutionary story-telling by the assumption that close parallelism occurs only in closely related forms. But if the similarities that are being used to establish relatedness have been independently acquired, how then can we know that the creatures in question are really related? This obviously involves a great leap of faith.

In an article entitled "Mysteries of Early Dinosaur Evolution," Cox states, "Although many pages have been written discussing the mystery of the extinction of the dinosaurs, almost as much uncertainty surrounds their origin—or origins."[48]

As pointed out earlier, it is assumed that dinosaurs evolved from pseudosuchians. One problem with this notion is that the assumed pseudosuchian ancestors were still present after the dinosaurs had presumably evolved. Thus, Cox says: "Throughout the Late Triassic, at least, a variety of pseudosuchians therefore coexisted with a variety of their presumed descendants, the dinosaurs." Speaking of the ornithischian and the saurischian dinosaurs, Cox states:

> If one now attempts to relate these two types of dinosaur
> to the Triassic pseudosuchians, there appears to be a
> puzzling overlap in time between the two groups, although

---

[48] Barry Cox, *Nature* 264:314 (1976).

possible evolutionary links between them obstinately refuse to appear.

As described earlier, Romer admits that there is no way to connect the ornithischian dinosaurs to their presumed thecodont ancestors. He does believe, however, that some saurischian dinosaurs were sufficiently similar to thecodonts that one could presume that saurischian dinosaurs had evolved from thecodont reptiles, even though, as Cox relates, the presumed pseudosuchian thecodont ancestors and their dinosaur offspring coexisted in the Late Triassic and no evolutionary links between them have been found.

When considering the credibility of each model of origins, creation and evolution, with reference to the specific origin of dinosaurs, the most definitive approach is not whether or not it is possible to imagine a link between some generalized form of a dinosaur and a thecodont reptile, but to look for possible evolutionary transitional forms that would document the evolutionary origin of dinosaurs with unique structures. If evolution were true, we should easily find a series of transitional forms showing these unusual structures gradually coming into being. If creation were true, the dinosaurs bearing these unique structures should appear all at once, fully-formed from the start. Here, creation wins hands down. In not a single case can the required transitional forms be found.

The unique feature of horned dinosaurs (suborder Ceratopsia) was, of course, the horns, from one to several in number. The bony horn cores of these ornithischian dinosaurs were similar in appearance to those of a modern bison. *Triceratops* weighed about eight to ten tons and varied from sixteen to twenty feet in length. It had three large horns, one above each eye and a central horn in the nasal region. *Triceratops* had a large bony frill, several inches thick, formed by an extension of the parietal and squamosal bones of the skull. This shield offered considerable protection to the neck region. *Centrosaurus*, which also was equipped with a bony shield, had a single horn in the nasal region.

Protoceratops was the name given to a dinosaur found in the Upper Cretaceous of Mongolia. A variety of similar dinosaurs, placed in the family Protoceratopsidae, have been found in Mongolia and North America. As Romer has pointed out, *Protoceratops* has been

Triceratops

Stegosaurus

Centrosaurus

Protoceratops

Trachodon

Lambeosaurus

Corythosaurus

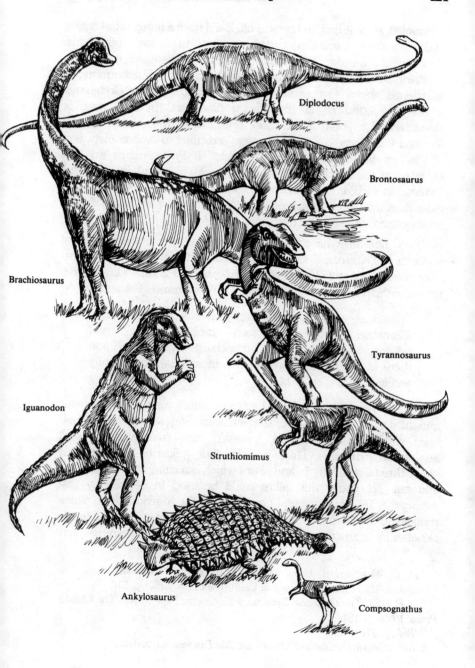

Diplodocus

Brontosaurus

Brachiosaurus

Tyrannosaurus

Iguanodon

Struthiomimus

Ankylosaurus

Compsognathus

misnamed, since it had no horns at all. It did have a horny nasal region and rugosities (wrinkles) were present in some individuals. Evolutionists imagine that horns could have developed on such a creature, but no transitional forms have been found. Furthermore, as mentioned above, *Protoceratops* is found in the Upper Cretaceous where are found all of the horned dinosaurs. In fact, what is characterized as one of the most primitive of the protoceratopsid dinosaurs, *Leptoceratops gracilis*, was, according to evolutionists, one of the last dinosaurs in North America.[49] If *Protoceratops* was the ancestor of the horned dinosaurs, it should be found in geological formations such as the Middle or Lower Cretaceous, presumed to be older than the Upper Cretaceous. *Protoceratops* thus fails miserably as an ancestor for the horned dinosaurs.

Two dinosaurs have been mentioned as possible evolutionary variants of *Triceratops*. One, *Sterrholophus*, is now believed to have been an immature *Triceratops*,[50] and *Diceratops* is now said to have been a pathological form of *Triceratops*.[51] Weishampel et al. state:

> There is a sharp discontinuity in size and correlative allometric features between protoceratopsids and ceratopsids [ceratopsids are true horned dinosaurs], and there is never confusion between members of one family and members of the other.[52]

Unlike *Triceratops*, whose head and shield was equal to about one-third of the total length of that dinosaur, *Stegosaurus* had a small head with no horns. It did, however, have some very unusual anatomical structures. These included four spikes on the tail, each about three feet in length, and plates which ran along the neck, trunk, and tail. No doubt the spikes could be used in defense by this twenty-foot long quadrupedal dinosaur, but the function of the plates remains in doubt. Some have suggested that the plates, fastened to the skeleton by ligaments, could have served as armor. The arrangement

---

[49] D. B. Weishampel, Peter Dodson and Halszka Osmolska, eds., *The Dinosauria* (Berkeley: University of California Press, 1990), p. 610.

[50] D. F. Glut, *The Dinosaur Dictionary* (Secaucus, New Jersey: The Citadel Press, 1972), p. 181.

[51] *Ibid.*, p. 57.

[52] Weishampel, Dodson and Osmolska, *The Dinosauria*, p. 610.

in a double alternating row and the configuration of these plates suggest, however, that they served as heat exchangers. In any case, we do not find a series of transitional forms showing the gradual evolutionary origin of the spikes and plates. *Stegosaurus*, numerous fossils of which have been found, appears fully-formed, contrary to what would be expected on the basis of evolution, but precisely as predicted on the basis of creation.

Another very unusual type of dinosaur was the duck-billed dinosaur, or hadrosaur. Numerous fossils of these bipedal creatures have been found in rocks of the Upper Cretaceous. They were almost worldwide in distribution. Although these dinosaurs were equipped with duck-bills, they had many teeth crowded towards the back of the duck-bill. In fact, *Trachodon* had perhaps as many as two thousand teeth. Many of these duck-billed dinosaurs had odd-shaped bony crests. These included *Parasaurolophuys*, *Saurolophus*, *Lambeosaurus*, and *Corythosaurus*. They apparently spent considerable time in the water, since they had webbed feet which had hooves but no claws. The length of the body averaged about thirty feet.

If these dinosaurs had evolved from a thecodont reptile or from an ordinary dinosaur, then surely we would be able to find numerous transitional forms in the fossil record showing, for example, duck-bills gradually evolving from ordinary jaws and teeth. Not a single such transitional form has ever been found. All of the duck-billed dinosaurs appeared fully-formed, offering positive evidence for creation.

Dinosaurs of the sub-order *Ankylosauria* were very heavily armored, the "reptilian tanks" among dinosaurs. The head, back, and tail of these low, broad quadrupeds were covered with bony knobs, and long spikes extended outward from the shoulder region. In some the tail bore long, bony spikes. *Ankylosaurus* had, in addition, a large bony knob near the end of its powerful tail, providing a very effective war club. If a carnivorous dinosaur chose to have *Ankylosaurus* for dinner, he might end up with broken teeth and a broken leg! No transitional forms have been found for these armored dinosaurs.

The Iguanodons, duck-billed dinosaurs, stegosaurians, horned dinosaurs, and ankylosaurians were all ornithischian, or bird-hipped dinosaurs. Among the saurischian, or reptile-hipped dinosaurs, we find some of the largest and fiercest as well as some of the smallest of dinosaurs. Within the infraorder Coelurosauria are found the small dinosaurs, varying from three to six feet in length, including the tail. The coelurosaurians were slender-built bipeds. *Coelophysis* was about six feet in length, *Podokesaurus* was about three feet long, and *Compsognathus* was about as large as a chicken. *Struthiomimus* ("Ostrich mimic") was somewhat like an ostrich in its general proportions, with a small head, a long neck, and a long, slim body. Lest one should suggest that *Struthiomimus* was ancestral to the birds, we are reminded that *Struthiomimus* did not have even a suggestion of a feather, it had reptile-hips instead of bird-hips, and it had no teeth (*Archaeopteryx* had teeth). All of the specializations found in *Struthiomimus* appear in that creature complete all at once, with no transitional forms, as is also the case with all other coelurosaurians.

In contrast to the small coelurosaurians, the carnosaurian dinosaurs of the infraorder Carnosauria were very large carnivorous bipeds. *Allosaurus* was about thirty to thirty-five feet long, with powerful jaws equipped with large, sharp teeth. *Tyrannosaurus* was the largest known carnivorous dinosaur, standing nearly twenty feet high and nearly fifty feet in length. Its jaws were about six feet long, with teeth nearly six inches long. Once again, the fossil record fails to produce the transitional forms required by evolutionary theory.

Some of the largest and most spectacular of all dinosaurs were the huge quadrupedal herbivorous dinosaurs of the suborder Sauropodomorpha. These included *Diplodocus* ("double-beamed") with a long neck and long tail, giving a total length of nearly 100 feet. *Brontosaurus* ("thunder-lizard"—now redesignated *Apatosaurus*) was about eighty feet long and weighed about forty tons. Recently a fossil of *Brachiosaurus* has been found that may have weighed nearly eighty tons and which stood as high as a five-story building. The nostrils of *Brachiosaurus* were not on the end of the snout but were located in a bony dome on the top of the head! No one knows why *Brachiosaurus* had this unusual arrangement, but we do know that not a single transitional form has been found showing the nostrils migrating from the snout into the bony dome on top of the head.

Supposedly some earlier bipedal creature or creatures had reverted to a quadrupedal mode of locomotion and then evolved into these herbivorous dinosaurs. No transitional forms can be found, however, to document the origin of these monstrous creatures from some little fellows. *Diplodocus* is *Diploducus*, *Brontosaurus* is *Brontosaurus*, and *Brachiosaurus* is *Brachiosaurus* right from the start.

A startling development and a challenge to evolutionary scenarios has been the discovery of fossils of dinosaurs not far from the North and South Poles. Michael Thomson, who headed a six-week expedition, a geological research cruise around the north and east of James Ross Island in British Antarctic Territory, reported they had found the fossil remains of an ornithischian (bird-hipped) dinosaur, fossils of which had also been found in Australia, North America, Europe, and North Africa. It was about ten feet long and bipedal. They also found fossilized shells, leaves from conifers and broad-leaved trees, tree trunks, and ferns. He reported that several years earlier they had found fossils of a plesiosaur, a marine reptile.[53] It was reported that the age of the ornithischian dinosaur was about seventy million years, thus Late Cretaceous.

Hammer and Hickerson report the discovery of fossils of four different kinds of dinosaurs, including a large crested carnivorous theropod, *Cryolophosaurus ellioti*, in Antarctica. The unusual cranial feature of this dinosaur shows that it was rather widely divergent from other dinosaurs. Also recovered from this site at an elevation of about 13,000 feet on Mount Kirkpatrick, about 400 miles from the South Pole, were the fossils of a humerus of a pterosaur, or flying reptile, the molar tooth from a tritylodont, a mammal-like reptile, and fossilized tree trunks of conifers, revealing that the area had been forested when these creatures existed.[54] Thus, fossils of dinosaurs, marine reptiles, flying reptiles, and mammal-like reptiles have been found very near the South Pole, where today the temperature is extremely cold much of the year, and there are months of darkness.

Several reports describe the discovery of fossils of dinosaurs and other creatures along the Colville River north of Umiat on the North Slope of Alaska, which is at about 70°N, thus above the Arctic Circle. Evolutionary geologists believe that Alaska was even farther north when these dinosaurs existed, possibly as far north as 85°N (The North Pole is at 90°N). The formation in which these fossils have been found is said to be of Late Cretaceous in age. Davies reports the

---

[53] Associated Press Report, *San Diego Union*, 5 March 1989, p. A-33.
[54] W. R. Hammer and W. J. Hickerson, *Science* 264:828-830 (1994).

discovery of the fossils of a duck-billed dinosaur.[55] He describes the quality of preservation as remarkable with little permineralization (petrification). Most of the bones were from small individuals, but some bones indicate the presence of some individuals nearly thirty feet long. Davies suggests that the presence of both large and small duck-billed dinosaurs that far north is evidence for an equable, or uniform, climate extending nearly to the poles. Brouwers et al. describe the discovery of fossils of lambeosaurine duck-billed dinosaurs (the "hatchet-head" dinosaurs), dinosaurs similar to *Tyrannosaurus rex*, and *Troodon* (a dinosaur with a bony dome similar to *Corythosaurus*).[56] There was very little permineralization of the fossil bones. In fact, in a newspaper article describing some of the fossils found at the same site, one of the scientists, Bill Clemens, professor of paleontology at the University of California, Berkeley, in reference to the lack of permineralization of the fossils, remarked that "It looks much more like Ice Age deposits rather than something 60–70 million years old."[57] Perhaps thousands of years rather than 60–70 million years for the ages of these creatures is closer to the truth. Brouwers et al. also reported the finding of fossils of herbaceous vegetation, conifers, and broad-leaved trees. They maintain the evidence indicates that these animals did not migrate preceding winter, but remained there the year round.

Parrish et al. describe the recovery of fossils of horned dinosaurs and of a turtle in the Colville River region.[58] This is the first report of a fossil turtle from the North Slope of Alaska. Thus, this one area of a far north region of Alaska has produced fossils of duck-billed dinosaurs, tyrannosaurid dinosaurs, a troodontid dinosaur, horned dinosaurs, a turtle, herbaceous vegetation, conifers, and broad-leaved trees. High on a mountain, just a few hundred miles from the South Pole, there has been found fossils of four different kinds of dinosaurs, a flying reptile, and a mammal-like reptile. Near James Ross Island of Antarctica were found the fossil of an ornithischihan dinosaur, and fossils of ferns, conifers, and broad-leaved trees. A fossil of a marine reptile, a

---

[55] K. L. Davies, *Journal of Paleontology* 61(1): 198-200 (1987).

[56] Elisabeth M. Brouwers et al., *Science* 237:1608-1610 (1987).

[57] Sam Bishop, "North Slope Dinosaurs," *Northland News*, Fairbanks, Alaska, March 1989.

[58] J. M. Parrish et al., *Palois* 2:377-389 (1987).

plesiosaur, was also found in Antarctica. Fossils of a considerable variety of other animals have been found in Antarctica.

How could animals, such as dinosaurs, marine reptiles, flying reptiles, mammal-like reptiles, and turtles survive in regions which today have long periods of intense cold and months of darkness? How could ferns, conifers, and broad-leaved trees survive in areas with very low temperatures and months of darkness? This is a serious challenge to evolutionary scenarios. According to the creationist view of the history of the earth, there was a time before a catastrophic worldwide flood when the atmosphere of the earth contained much more water vapor than the present atmosphere. Of the three gases in the present atmosphere responsible for absorbing and retaining the heat from the sun, carbon dioxide, ozone, and water vapor, water vapor is by far the most important. Thus, if a pre-flood atmosphere contained much more water vapor than the present atmosphere does today, it would absorb and retain much more solar heat, resulting in what is commonly referred to as a "greenhouse" effect. This would have given the earth a worldwide mild climate and would account for the fact that the animals and plants described above could thrive practically in the vacinity of the North and South Poles, with abundant vegetation. These conditions would have been drastically altered after the flood, with a greatly reduced amount of water vapor now in the post-flood atmosphere. The worldwide mild climate with a worldwide cover of lush vegetation and forested areas was replaced with the present day Arctic and Antarctic, temperate, and tropical climatic zones. Greenland, which once had a sub-tropical climate similar to the Caribbean, now is covered perpetually with ice and snow. The reason dinosaurs and many other creatures, vegetation, conifers, and broad-leaved trees could thrive at or near the North and South Poles was because of the worldwide mild climate resulting from the above "greenhouse" effect due to the greater atmospheric content of water vapor under pre-flood conditions.

Many theories have been suggested to explain the extinction of dinosaurs. The most popular theory today is the idea that an asteroid struck the earth, raising a vast cloud of dust and gas which enveloped the earth, resulting in a drop in temperature sufficiently catastrophic to wipe out the dinosaurs. Rather than this "deep freeze" theory, other scientists suggest that the impact of the asteroid would have covered the earth with burning embers, igniting vast grass and forest fires sufficiently intense and worldwide to have wiped out all of the dinosaurs. This might be called the "fiery furnace" theory. These notions have a fatal flaw, however. Whatever caused the extinction of the dinosaurs had to be a worldwide catastrophe sufficiently catastrophic to kill every dinosaur on the face of the earth—big ones, little ones, plant eaters, meat eaters, bipedal, quadrupedal, armored, horned, duck-billed—not one survived. If such a horrendous worldwide catastrophe blasted the earth, then why did it not kill all the delicate, fluttery, little birds? How could birds survive such a vast, worldwide catastrophe? How could the little thin-skinned mammals survive? Why did other reptiles, such as snakes, lizards, turtles, and crocodiles survive such a catastrophe that destroyed all of the dinosaurs, flying reptiles, and marine reptiles? The notion that all the dinosaurs, flying reptiles, and marine reptiles (and many other creatures) were totally destroyed by a catastrophe that left birds, mammals, crocodiles, turtles, snakes, and lizards untouched is totally unrealistic. On the other hand, the struggle to repopulate a drastically restructured earth with a totally different climate following a worldwide flood would have have resulted in failure for many creatures, while others succeeded. The dinosaurs apparently were among the losers.

Evolutionists believe the dinosaurs were on the earth from before 230 million years before the present up to 65 million years before the present. Thus, supposedly dinosaurs were flourishing and evolving into all kinds of unique creatures for about 165 million years. Untold billions of dinosaurs would have lived and died during that alleged 165 million years. If evolution is true, our natural history museums should have numerous fossils of undoubted transitional forms revealing a gradual evolutionary origin of horns, duck-bills, spikes, plates, crests, bony domes and many other unique features of the dinosaurs. **Not one such transitional form has ever been found**. The fossil record of dinosaurs is a tremendous, positive testimony to the truth of special creation.

Molecular Data

One might suggest that molecular data would be of great help where the fossil record has failed to produce the transitional forms necessary to link the various tetrapods in a plausible phylogenetic tree.

The molecular data, however, muddies the water as badly as do the fossils. For example, Weishampel, Dodson, and Osmolska state:

> Molecular data on tetrapod phylogeny are equivocal regarding the relationship of birds and crocodiles. Some analyses pair these two groups . . . but many tend to link birds and mammals more closely. . . . However, other protein sequence analyses give every other imaginable pairing of tetrapod groups, and their significance is debatable. . . .[59]

It seems obvious that if protein sequence analyses give every imaginable pairing of tetrapod groups, such data are useless in determining the relationships of these groups. Creationists maintain that this is true because these tetrapod groups are not related genetically but have had entirely separate origins.

The Origin of Birds

It has long been maintained by evolutionists that birds have evolved from reptiles. As noted earlier, Romer believed that birds (also crocodiles, flying reptiles, and dinosaurs) had evolved from a creature similar to *Saltoposuchus*, a pseudosuchian thecodont reptile.[60] Today there are those who would agree with Romer, while a more popular notion in recent times is that birds evolved from dinosaurs, and others believe that birds are most closely related to crocodiles. An International *Archaeopteryx* Conference was held in Eichstatt, Bavaria, September 11–15, 1984, during which advocates of the above ideas put forth their arguments.[61] Especially interesting was the fact that those attending the conference felt it necessary to adopt a communiqué "expressing the unanimous belief of all participants in the evolutionary origin and significance of *Archaeopteryx* in order to forestall possible misuse by creationists of apparent discord among scientists."[62] In other words, these evolutionists unanimously agree that evolution is a fact even though they cannot agree on the ancestry of birds, and more particularly on the origin of *Archaeopteryx*. Why be

---

[59] Weishampel, Dodson and Osmolska, *The Dinosauria*, p. 12.

[60] Romer, *Vertebrate Paleontology*, p. 140.

[61] Peter Dodson, *Journal of Vertebrate Paleontology* 5(2): 177-179 1985).

[62] *Ibid.*, p. 179.

bothered with troublesome facts when minds have already been made up that evolution is a fact? And, by all means, don't miss an opportunity to put down the creationists!

The reason that there is so much confusion and discord among evolutionists concerning the origin of birds, of course, is the lack of transitional forms linking birds to a reptilian ancestor. If just a few transitional forms scattered through time could be found documenting the evolution of a reptile into a bird, the opinion of evolutionists concerning the reptilian ancestor and evolutionary pathway from reptile to bird would be unanimous.

A. D. Walker has suggested that birds evolved from an early crocodilian.[63] Based on their study of the ear region of birds, crocodiles, and fossil reptiles and dinosaurs, Whetstone and Martin reject a dinosaurian ancestry for birds. They state:

> These advanced features in the ear region support a common ancestry for crocodiles and birds, independent of both saurischian and ornithischian dinosaurs.[64]

John H. Ostrom has been most instrumental in advancing the theory that birds had evolved from a small coelurosaurian dinosaur similar to *Compsognathus*.[65] Today the notion that birds evolved from dinosaurs is so widely accepted that some have suggested that birds, rather than being placed in the Class Aves, should be relegated to a position within the Dinosauria. In fact, it is being commonly maintained that dinosaurs still survive today in the form of birds, their feathered offspring. For the skeptic, it is a bit difficult when one sees a hummingbird or a robin to visualize these feathered creatures as the evolutionary offspring of a dinosaur, let alone the descendants of a crocodile. Ostrom pointed out what he believed to be important similarities between the coelurosaurian dinosaurs and *Archaeopteryx*, a fossil bird that evolutionists maintain exhibits both avian and

---

[63] A. D. Walker, in *Problems in Vertebrate Evolution*, ed. S. M. Andrews, R. S. Miles and A. D. Walker (New York: Academic Press, 1977), pp. 319-358.

[64] K. N. Whetstone and L. D. Martin, *Nature* 279:236 (1979).

[65] Dodson, *Journal of Vertebrate Paleontology* 5(2): 177-179 (1985); J. H. Ostrom, *Nature* 242:136 (1973); see also J. H. Ostrom, *Quarterly Review of Biology* 49:27-47 (1974); and J. H. Ostrom, *Biological Journal of the Linnean Society, London* 8:91-182 (1976).

Figure 9. *Archaeopteryx* (Restoration by Heilmann).

reptilian features, thus constituting an intermediate between reptiles and birds.

The fossils of *Archaeopteryx* were found in the Solnhofen Plattenkalk of Franconia, Bavaria. The first fossil was found in the Solnhofen limestone. The sixth specimen was found, or recognized as such, in a private collection in Solnhofen in November 1987.[66] the skeleton is nearly complete and well preserved, with clear impressions of the feather shafts of the left wing. The seventh specimen from Solnhofen was reported in April, 1993.[67] This seventh specimen is remarkable in that it includes a bony sternum. No evidence of a bony sternum had been found in any of the previous specimens. This led paleontologists to declare that *Archaeopteryx* did not possess a bony sternum, a structure of modern flying birds to which powerful flight muscles are attached. This had induced many to believe that *Archaeopteryx* either could not fly or was a poor flyer. In spite of the failure earlier to find a bony sternum in *Archaeopteryx*, it had been pointed out that *Archaeopteryx* had feathers identical to those of modern flying birds.[68] Rayner states:

> The most striking feature of *Archaeopteryx* is its well-developed feathered wings. These wings are not significantly different in size and shape from those of modern birds such as magpies or coucals, and they give every indication that *Archaeopteryx* was a flying bird. The feathers also appear to be strong evidence of flight ability. . . . In *Archaeopteryx* the feathers are remarkably similar to those of modern birds. They have a stiffened central shaft to transmit aerodynamic forces generated over the feather vanes to the body, and this would not be expected if the feathers had no mechanical function. More significantly, the feather shaft is set asymmetrically against the vanes of the feather. This permits the feather to distort optimally to compensate for bending in flight due to aerodynamic

[66] Peter Wellnhofer, *Science* 240:1790–1792 (1988); Pat Shipman, *Discover*, January 1989, p. 63.

[67] Kathy Svitil, *Discover*, January 1994, p. 52.

[68] Alan Feduccia and H. B. Tordoff, *Science* 203:1021 (1979); J. M. V. Rayner, in *Biomechanics in Evolution*, ed. J. M. V. Rayner and R. J. Wooten (Cambridge: Cambridge University Press, 1991).

loads, and is important in both gliding and flapping flight. . . . vane asymmetry is characteristic of modern flying birds, but the feathers of most modern flightless birds are symmetrical.[69]

Olson and Feduccia had also argued that, even in the absence of a bony sternum, there was nothing in the anatomy of *Archaeopteryx* that would have prevented it from being a powered flyer.[70] Now the discovery of a bony sternum in this last specimen to be discovered should settle the matter conclusively. There is no doubt that *Archaeopteryx* was as capable of powered flight as modern flying birds.

It has been asserted that *Archaeopteryx* shares twenty-one specialized characteristics with coelurosaurian dinosaurs, indicating that birds had evolved from these, or very similar, dinosaurs.[71] In spite of these similarities, there are two facts that would exclude *Compsognathus* as an ancestor of birds. *Compsognathus* and *Archaeopteryx* were contemporaries, both of which occur as fossils in the Solnhofen limestone, said to be Upper Jurassic, or about 150 million years in age. How can a parent be as young as its offspring? Furthermore, *Compsognathus* and coelurosaurian dinosaurs were saurishian, or lizard-hipped, dinosaurs. A proper reptilian or dinosaurian ancestor of birds should have had bird-hips. Coelurosaurian dinosaurs cannot be the ancestor of birds.

Research on various anatomical features of *Archaeopteryx* in the last ten years of so has shown, in every case, that the characteristic in question is bird-like, not reptile-like. When the cranium of the London specimen was removed from the limestone and studied, it was shown to be bird-like, not reptile-like.[72] Benton has stated that "details of the brain case and associated bones at the back of the skull seem to suggest that *Archaeopteryx* is not the ancestral bird, but an offshoot from the early avian stem."[73] In this same paper, Benton states that the quadrate (the bone in the jaw that articulates with the squamosal of the skull) in *Archaeopteryx* was single-headed, as in reptiles. Using a

---

[69] Rayner, *Biomechanics in Evolution*, p. 194.

[70] S. L. Olson and Alan Feduccia, *Nature* 278:247 (1979).

[71] A. J. Charig, *A New Look at Dinosaurs* (London: Heinemann, 1979), p. 139.

[72] K. N. Whetstone, *Journal of Vertebrate Paleontology* 2(4): 439 (1983).

[73] M. J. Benton, *Nature* 305:99 (1983).

newly devised technique, called computed tomography, Haubitz et al. established that the quadrate of the Eichstätt specimen of *Archaeopteryx* was double-headed, and thus similar to the condition of modern birds,[74] rather than single-headed, as stated by Benton.

L. D. Martin and co-workers have established that neither the teeth nor the ankle of *Archaeopteryx* could have been derived from theropod (coelurosaurian) dinosaurs—the teeth being those typical of other (presumably later) toothed birds, and the ankle bones showing no homology with those of dinosaurs.[75] John Ostrom, a strong advocate of a dinosaurian ancestry for birds, had claimed that the pubis of *Archaeopteryx* pointed downward—an intermediate position between that of coelurosaurian dinosaurs, which points forward, and that of birds, which points backward. A. D. Walker, in more recent studies, asserts that Ostrom's interpretation is wrong, and that the pubis of *Archaeopteryx* was oriented in a bird-like position.[76] Further, Tarsitano and Hecht criticize various aspects of Ostrom's hypothesis of a dinosaurian origin of birds, arguing that Ostrom had misinterpreted the homologies of the limbs of *Archaeopteryx* and theropod dinosaurs.[77]

A. D. Walker has presented an analysis of the ear region of Archaeopteryx that shows, contrary to previous studies, this region is very similar to the otic region of modern birds.[78] J. R. Hinchliffe, utilizing modern isotopic techniques on chick embryos, claims to have established that the "hand" of birds consists of digits II, III, and IV, while the digits of the "hand" of theropod dinosaurs consist of digits I, II, and III.[79]

Ostrom and others have claimed that birds had evolved via feathered ground-dwelling (cursorial) predators that had arisen from

---

[74] B. Haubnitz et al., *Paleiobiology* 14(2): 206 (1988).

[75] L. D. Martin, J. D. Stewart and K. N. Whetstone, *The Auk* 97:86 (1980). See Martin, in *Origins of the Higher Groups of Tetrapods* (Ithaca, New York: Comstock Publishing Association, 1991), pp. 485-540.

[76] A. D. Walker, *Geological Magazine* 117:595 (1980).

[77] S. Tarsitano and M. K. Hecht, *Zoological Journal of the Linnaean Society* 69:149 (1980).

[78] A. D. Walker, as described by Dodson, *Journal of Vertebrate Paleontology* 5(2): 178 (1985).

[79] J. R. Hinchliffe, as described by Dodson, *Journal of Vertebrate Paleontology* 5(2) 178 (1985).

coelurosaurian dinosaurs. The claim was made that *Archaeopteryx* had claws similar to those of ground-dwelling birds rather than similar to those of perching, tree-dwelling birds. D. W. Yalden, however, demonstrated that the claws of the manus (forelimb) of *Archaeopteryx* were nearly identical to those of tree climbers.[80] Alan Feduccia compared the claw geometry of *Archaeopteryx* to that of modern ground-dwelling birds, tree-dwelling birds, and trunk-climbing birds. The arc of the claws of tree-dwelling and trunk-climbing birds exceeds considerably that of ground-dwelling birds. He established that the arc of the claws of *Archaeopteryx* was comparable to that of tree-dwelling (perching) birds. His analysis established that *Archaeopteryx* was not a cursorial predator but was a perching bird. Feduccia's conclusion was that:

> *Archaeopteryx* probably cannot tell us much about the early origins of feathers and flight in true protobirds because *Archaeopteryx* was, in a modern sense, a bird.[81]

Larry D. Martin, an ornithologist and professor of systematics and ecology at the University of Kansas and head of the vertebrate paleontology division in the university's Museum of Natural History, accepts a modified version of the pseudosuchian ancestry of birds that makes birds a sister group to crocodilians. In a newspaper article originally published in *Newsday* he states:

> The theory linking dinosaurs to birds is a pleasant fantasy that some scientists like because it provides a direct entry into a past we otherwise can only guess about. But unless more convincing evidence is uncovered, we must reject it and move on to the next better idea.[82]

Scales are flat horny plates; feathers are very complex in structure, consisting of a central shaft from which radiate barbs and barbules. Barbules are equipped with tiny hooks which lock onto the barbs and bind the feather surface into a flat, strong, flexible vane. Feathers and scales arise from different layers of the skin. Furthermore, the

[80] D. W. Yalden, as described by Dodson, *Journal of Vertebrate Paleontology* 5(2): 178 (1985).

[81] Allan Feduccia, *Science* 259:790-793 (1993).

[82] Larry D. Martin, "The Barosaurus Is no Five-Story-Tall Canary," *Sunday World-Herald*, Omaha, Nebraska, 19 January 1992, p. B-17.

development of a feather is extremely complex, and fundamentally different from that of a scale. Feathers, as do hairs but unlike scales, develop from follicles. A hair, however, is a much simpler structure than a feather. The developing feather is protected by a horny sheath and forms around a bloody, conical, inductive dermal core. Not only is the developing feather sandwiched between the sheath and dermal core, it is complex in structure. Development of the cells that will become the mature feather involves complex processes. Cells migrate and split apart in highly specific patterns to form the complex arrangement of barbs and barbules.[83]

Philip Regal attempts to imagine how feathers may have developed from scales.[84] Regal presents a series of hypothetical events whereby the elongation of body scales on reptiles, as an adaptive response to excessive solar heat, eventually produced feathers. What we are left to believe is that a series of genetic mistakes, or mutations, just happened somehow to result in a sequence of incredible events that not only converted a simple horny plate into the tremendously complex and marvelously engineered structure of a feather, but completely reorganized the simple method of development of a scale into the highly complex process necessary to produce a feather. What an incredible faith in the blind forces of evolution! Regal's paper simply adds another "Just-so" story to evolutionary scenarios, completely devoid of empirical support.

P. F. A. Maderson has also suggested a scenario for the origin of feathers from reptilian scales. He is frank enough to admit, however, that:

> I emphasize that this model only attempts to explain how an archosaurian scale might have given rise to a proto-feather. The end product as shown in figure 1d resembles a feather in the usual sense of the word only in that it is a highly specialized keratinous integumentary appendage. We cannot as yet offer any plausible explanation for the origin of the unique shaft, barbs, and barbules without which modern feathers would have neither aerodynamic nor insulatory function.[85]

---

[83] A. M. Lucas and P. R. Slettenhein, *Avian Anatomy: Integument* (Washington, DC: GPO, 1972).

[84] P. J. Regal, *The Quarterly Review of Biology* 50:35 (1975).

Thus, no evolutionist can come even close to providing an evolutionary explanation of how feathers could have evolved from scales. The scenario of how a scale could evolve into a proto-feather, as limited as that may be, is nothing more than empty rhetoric without a shred of empirical content.

Recent events cast even further doubt on *Archaeopteryx* as a transitional form. If the claims of Sankar Chatterjee prove to be valid, then certainly *Archaeopteryx* could not be the ancestral bird, and dinosaurs could not be ancestral to birds. Chatterjee and his co-workers at Texas Tech University claim to have found two crow-sized fossils of a bird near Post, Texas, in rocks supposedly 225 million years old—thus allegedly 75 million years older than *Archaeopteryx* and as old as the first dinosaurs.[86]

If Chatterjee is right, his fossil bird is as old as the oldest fossil dinosaur. How could dinosaurs then be ancestral to birds? Chatterjee claims that the forelimbs, shoulder, hip girdles, and skull are definitely bird-like. His reconstruction also shows portals extending from the rear of the skull to the eye socket—a characteristic of modern birds not seen in any dinosaur—as well as a flexible neck, binocular vision, and a large brain, which are features of modern birds. In fact, Chatterjee claims that his fossil bird, which he has named *Protoavis*, is more bird-like than *Archaeopteryx*, since it has a substantial keel-like breastbone, or sternum, and hollow bones. If Chatterjee's analysis is correct, then obviously neither dinosaurs nor *Archaeopteryx* could be ancestral to birds. Furthermore, if birds really did evolve from reptiles of some sort, then a bird 75 million years older than *Archaeopteryx*, or 225 million years old, should be extremely reptilian. Chatterjee's *Protoavis*, according to Chatterjee, is just the opposite, even more bird-like than *Archaeopteryx*. Chatterjee finally published a scientific paper on *Protoavis*, but he included a description of the skull only.[87] This publication, including his bold claim that *Protoavis* was a bird in the full sense of the word, has generated intense controversy. This controversy has been described in detail.[88]

---

[85] P. F. A. Maderson, *The American Naturalist* 146:427 (1972).

[86] Tim Beardsley, *Nature* 322:677 (1986); Richard Monastersky, *Science News* 140:104-105 (1991); Alan Anderson, *Science* 253:35 (1991).

[87] Sankar Chatterjee, *Philosophical Transactions of the Royal Society*, London B., 332:277-349 (1991).

Some evolutionists insist that since *Archaeopteryx* had characteristics of both reptiles and birds, it does represent an intermediate between reptiles and birds, but whatever features it had were complete, not part-way or transitional. Furthermore, since creatures within each family, order, or class are so highly variable, it would be predictable on the basis of the creation model that animals in different orders and classes would have some characteristics in common. Even humans share characteristics in common with reptiles. For example, we share in common the vertebrate eye. Among other characteristics, evolutionists emphasize that *Archaeopteryx* had teeth, a long tail, and claws on the wings, which, it is claimed, are reptilian characteristics, inherited from a reptilian ancestor. As already described, *Archaeopteryx* did not have reptile-like teeth, but teeth that were uniquely bird-like, similar to teeth found in a number of other fossil birds. As pointed out by Martin, Stewart, and Whetstone, *Archaeopteryx* and other toothed birds had unserrated teeth with constricted bases and expanded roots, while theropod dinosaurs, its alleged ancestors, had serrated teeth with straight roots.[89] Furthermore, it should not be surprising that some birds had teeth, since this is true of all other vertebrates. Some fish have teeth; some do not. Some amphibians have teeth; some do not. Some reptiles have teeth; some do not. Most mammals have teeth, but some do not.

Archaeopteryx did have a long tail, while modern birds have a short tail, with a half dozen vertebrae terminating in a solid bone called the pygostyle. The long tail is supposed to be a reptilian feature, but, of course, some reptiles have short tails, while many have long tails. *Archaeopteryx* had three wing claws, and evolutionists point to this characteristic as being definitely reptilian. A number of modern birds have claws on their wings, however. These include, for example, the young of the touraco (*Touraco corythaix*), an African bird which has claws on its wings. The hoatzin (*Opisthocomus hoazin*), a South American bird, possesses two claws on its wings in the juvenile stage. It has a very small keel and is a poor flyer. Surprisingly, it has recently been discovered that the hoatzin is a ruminant. It is the only bird known to digest food (95% of its diet is leaves) in the same way as cows, sheep and other ruminants, using bacteria to digest fibrous plant

---

[88] Carl Zimmer, "Ruffled Feathers," *Discover*, May 1992, pp. 44-54.
[89] Martin, Stewart, and Whetstone, *The Auk*, p. 86.

material in a special foregut chamber above its stomach. Evolutionists must assume that this process evolved in hoatzins totally independent of other ruminants.[90] It is so unusual that some ornithologists find it hard to believe. The little hoatzin is unusual in many other respects. The ostrich has three claws on its wings, which would be characterized as even more reptile-like than those on *Archaeopteryx*. Swans and ibis also have wing claws. No one would ever suggest any of these birds are transitional between reptiles and birds, since they are modern-day birds.

The duck-billed platypus is a strange mosaic, a definite mammal also possessing both reptilian and bird-like characteristics. As such it could not possibly be the ancestor or descendant of any other creature. The duck-billed platypus is a creature which evolutionists wish never existed.

It is interesting to note the comment of Stephen Jay Gould of Harvard University and Niles Eldredge of the American Museum of Natural History, both ardent anti-creationists. With reference to *Archaeopteryx*, they state that:

> At the higher level of evolutionary transition between morphological designs, gradualism has always been in trouble, though it remains the "official" position of most western evolutionists. Smooth intermediates between *Baupläne* are almost impossible to construct, even in thought experiments; there is certainly no evidence for them in the fossil record (curious mosaics like *Archaeopteryx* do not count).[91]

There are several important aspects of this statement, each of which seriously damages the credibility of evolutionary theory. We first need to explain that *Baupläne* is a German word meaning basic morphological designs or basically different types of creatures. Note that Gould and Eldredge state that it is at this taxonomic level, that is, at the level of higher categories, such as orders, classes, and phyla (which possess different basic morphological designs), that the evidence for gradual change has always been lacking. Not only is it

---

[90] A. Grajal et al., *Science* 245:1236–1238 (1989).
[91] S. J. Gould and N. Eldredge, *Paleobiology* 3:147 (1977).

impossible at this level to find a smooth series of intermediates in the fossil record, it is even impossible to *imagine* what such intermediates may have looked like (for example, try to imagine an emergent *Pteranodon* with half a jaw and half a wing!). Finally, note that Gould and Eldredge specifically exclude *Archaeopteryx* as a transitional form, terming it, as is the duck-billed platypus, a strange mosaic that does not count. So much for *Archaeopteryx* as an intermediate!

Concerning the status of *Archaeopteryx*, it is interesting to note what some evolutionists have had to say in the past. Lecomte du Nouy states:

> Unfortunately, the greater part of the fundamental types in the animal realm are disconnected from a paleontological point of view. In spite of the fact that it is undeniably related to the two classes of reptiles and birds (a relation which the anatomy and physiology of actually living specimens demonstrates), we are not even authorized to consider the exceptional case of the *Archaeopteryx* as a true link. By link, we mean a necessary stage of transition between classes such as reptiles and birds, or between smaller groups. An animal displaying characters belonging to two different groups cannot be treated as a true link as long as the intermediary stages have not been found, and as long as the mechanisms of transition remain unkown.[92]

Swinton, an evolutionist and an expert on birds, states:

> The origin of birds is largely a matter of deduction. There is no fossil evidence of the stages through which the remarkable change from reptile to bird was achieved.[93]

Romer has said that:

> This Jurassic bird (*Archaeopteryx*) stands in splendid isolation; we know no more of its presumed thecodont ancestry nor of its relation to later "proper" birds than before.[94]

---

[92] L. du Nouy, *Human Destiny* (New York: The New American Library, 1947), p. 58.

[93] W. E. Swinton, in *Biology and Comparative Physiology of Birds*, ed. A. J. Marshall (New York: Academic Press, 1960) vol 1, p. 1.

In reference to *Archaeopteryx*, *Ichthyornis*, and *Hesperornis*, Beddard stated: "So emphatically were all these creatures birds that the actual origin of Aves is barely hinted at in the structure of these remarkable remains."[95] During the nearly 100 years since the publication of Beddard's book, no better candidate as an intermediate between reptiles and birds than *Archaeopteryx* has appeared. Not a single intermediate with part-way wings or part-way feathers has been discovered. Perhaps this is why, with the passage of time, *Archaeopteryx*, in the eyes of some evolutionists, has become more and more "reptile like"! In contrast to Beddard's assessment of *Archaeopteryx*, some evolutionists today not only assert that this bird is undoubtedly linked to reptiles, but that if clear impressions of feathers had not been found, *Archaeopteryx* would have been classified as a reptile. This is a gross misstatement, since no reptile has avian wings and the many other bird-like features possessed by *Archaeopteryx*.

It is only because of their desperate lack of transitional forms that evolutionists have trumpeted so loudly about *Archaeopteryx*. *Archaeopteryx* appears abruptly in the fossil record, a powered flyer with wings of the basic pattern and proportions of the modern avian wing, and feathers identical to those of modern flying birds, an undoubted true bird without a single structure in a transitional state. The statement by du Nouy that "we are not even authorized to consider the exceptional case of the *Archaeopteryx* as a true link" is even more valid today than it was when published nearly fifty years ago. *Archaeopteryx* was a "curious mosaic that doesn't count." Reptiles and birds are thus separated by a large gap, just as predicted on the basis of creation.

A very significant aspect of the fossil record of birds is the absence of transitional forms leading up to each of the specialized types of birds. It is here that transitional forms would be most easily recognized and where they must be found if evolution is true. The origin of a generalized type of bird from a generalized type of reptile would be much more difficult to trace than the origin of highly specialized birds.

---

[94] A. S. Romer, *Notes and Commentary on Vertebrate Paleontology* (Chicago: University of Chicago press, 1968), p. 144.

[95] F. E. Beddard, *The Structure and Classification of Birds* (London: Longmans, Green and Co., 1898), p. 160.

It is thus instructive to examine carefully what paleontologists have to say about the origin of these specialized birds. For example, let us see what Carroll has to say about the origin of these birds. All references are to his book (footnote 1). Concerning penguins, Carroll says:

> Penguins are among the most highly specialized birds in the total loss of aerial flight and the high degree of specialization for subaqueous locomotion. . . . They have retained the basic structure and functions of flying birds, but their flight occurs underwater rather than in air. . . . Even the earliest known fossils from the Upper Eocene of Seymour Island, Antarctica, are highly specialized for underwater flight and provide no evidence of their origin from primitive flying ancestors (pp. 356-357).

Carroll mentions that *Ogygoptynx* is the oldest known fossil owl, and he mentions that it "appears to belong to a group that could include the ancestry of both living owl families," but he says nothing about the ancestry of *Ogygoptynx* (would even an expert on owls know how to pronounce *Ogygoptynx*?) or of owls in general (p. 351). Speaking of kiwis, flightless birds now found only in New Zealand, Carroll states: "Their fossil record, which is limited to the Pleistocene, casts no light on their origin" (p. 349). With reference to ostriches, Carroll says: "The ostriches are the only group of ratites [flightless birds] in which the fossil record contributes significantly to establishing their prior history" (p. 349). In other words, the fossil record not only tells us nothing about the origin of any of the flightless birds—rheas, elephantbirds, moas, cassowaries, emus, kiwis, and ostriches—but also tells us nothing even about the history of any of these birds, except for the ostriches. The living genus of ostriches is *Struthio*, and fossil ostriches of several species found in Europe, Asia, and Africa in Upper Miocene, Pliocene, and Pleistocene rocks are included in the genus *Struthio*. Ostriches are unique among modern birds in having only two toes. Only vague suggestions, based on the gradual reduction of the lateral digit among large crane-like birds, can be offered as a possible affiliation of ostriches to other birds. That is the most that evolutionists can offer for the ancestry of the array of highly specialized flightless birds included with the ratites.

Concerning the most numerous type of modern birds (the small or medium sized perching songbirds), the passerines, Carroll says:

> Passerine birds include over 5000 species and are dominant elements of the avian fauna on all continents except Antarctica. However, their fossil record is still very sketchy (p. 352).

Carroll says that "the earliest-known passerines come from deposits in France that are latest Oligocene in age" (p. 352), but nowhere does he have anything to say about the origin of passerines. Concerning the Rails (including coots), which include a great number of flightless species, Carroll states:

> Some species include both flying and flightless races, which suggests that the loss of flight may occur very rapidly. Unfortunately the fossil record tells us little about the history of the family (p. 353).

Concerning the Pelecaniformes, Carroll states:

> Among the living families, the frigatebirds (Frigatidae) have the earliest fossil record, which goes back to the Lower Eocene. The boobies and gannets (Sulidae) and cormorants (Phalacrocoracidae) first appear in the early Oligocene. We find pelicans (Pelecanidae) and anhingas (Anhingidae) in the Lower Miocene. Although they are primitive in some respects, even the earliest members of these groups are readily recognized as characteristic of their respective families (p. 355).

What can Carroll say about the origin of parrots? Nothing. He states:

> Parrots (order Psittaciformes) are known from the Lower Miocene. They are specialized in the evolution of a zygodactylous foot structure but are otherwise similar in some respects to pigeons and may share a common ancestry with them (p. 350).

Mention has been made earlier concerning Richard Goldschmidt and his rejection of the orthodox slow and gradual Darwinian evolution in favor of his macromutation, or "hopeful monster," mechanism of evolution (p. 3). One of the challenges that Goldschmidt gave to his fellow evolutionists who follow the party line of present-day Darwinism ("neo-Darwinism") was the hummingbird. He demanded that they explain a gradual evolutionary origin of a hummingbird from, say, a grain-eating bird. Goldschmidt pointed out that the hummingbird could not function or survive until all of its special characteristics—high metabolic rate with overnight hibernation, special bill for sucking nectar, ability to hover, etc.—were complete and functioning. What does Carroll have to say about the origin of hummingbirds? All he says is that ". . . Caprimulgiformes in turn may have given rise to the Apodidae (swifts) and the hummingbirds" (p. 351). What are the Caprimulgiformes? Carroll says,

> The Caprimulgiformes encompass a diverse group of families including the echo-locating oil bird, frogmouths, nightjars, and goat suckers, all of which are mainly nocturnal and have gaping mouths for catching insects (p. 351).

We are left with no explanation whatever as to why Carroll imagines the little hummingbirds could have evolved from birds that are nocturnal and have big gaping mouths. Hummingbirds are not nocturnal, nor do they have big gaping mouths. He offers not one shred of evidence to support his conjecture that hummingbirds, some of which are the smallest terrestrial vertebrates, had evolved from a caprimulgiformes.

Woodpeckers are some of the most highly specialized birds, with special claws for gripping a tree trunk, stiff tail feathers to act as braces, a sharp, strong beak, shock absorbers surrounding the brain to prevent damage, a very long tongue anchored in the right nostril, and glands which secrete a sticky substance to coat the tongue for entrapping insects. One would think that if such an unusual creature had evolved, evolutionists would have a number of transitional forms to document the transition and a logical explanation for the evolutionary origin of each intermediate stage in their origin. Woodpeckers and toucans and various other tropical birds are placed in the Order Piciformes. All that Carroll has to say about the origin of woodpeckers is: "True woodpeckers, Picidae, which are specifically adapted for tree trunk foraging, appear in the Middle Miocene" (p. 352). In other words, he has absolutely nothing to say about their origin. All that Romer has to say about woodpeckers is:

> *Order Piciformes*—This includes the woodpeckers and the toucans and various tropical birds. The Piciformes are all stout billed and have the peculiar zygodactylous type of foot noted above for the parrots and cuckoos.[96]

In other words, Romer says absolutely nothing about an evolutionary origin of woodpeckers. Colbert and Morales say nothing about woodpeckers, and they say little about birds in their book, devoting only a few pages to that subject.[97] No mention of woodpeckers appears in the book edited by Schultze and Trueb.[98]

Thus, in every case of the origin of distinct types of birds where transitional forms should be relatively numerous and easily recognizable, we find almost complete silence in the evolutionary literature. If there were such transitional forms, we can be certain they would be extensively documented and illustrated in scientific articles and books by evolutionists. What evolutionists do not say speaks loud and clear. The required transitional forms have never been found, the gaps are large and systematic, and the evidence demanded by evolutionary theory is non-existent.

The transitional forms have not been found because they never existed. These facts provide powerful positive evidence for special creation.

---

[96] Romer, *Vertebrate Paleontology*, p. 172.

[97] Colbert and Morales, *Evolution of the Vertebrates*, pp. 182-190.

[98] Hans-Peter Schultze and Linda Trueb, eds., *Origins of the Higher Groups of Tetrapods* (Ithaca, New York: Comstock Publishing Associated, 1991).

Chapter VI

The Fossil Record—The Origin of Mammals

The Mammal-Like Reptiles

Introduction

The "mammal-like" reptiles were a highly varied, widely distributed group of reptiles that had a number of characteristics that are found in mammals. Assuming that evolution is a fact and that mammals must have arisen from reptiles, evolutionists thus quite logically assume that the presence of these mammal-like characteristics provide support for the theory that mammals arose from one or more groups of creatures within these mammal-like reptiles.

Creationists do not accept these assumptions, of course. They point out that the vertebrates are extremely varied. Some weigh less than an ounce, while others weigh several hundred tons. Some are restricted to the land, with considerable differences in mode of locomotion. Others are skillful fliers, while others live exclusively in the sea. Evolution or no, it would be surprising indeed if vertebrates from different classes did not share many characteristics in common.

Looking at the problem with a broad overview, we would have to say that the evidence is all in favor of the creationist view, since there is not a shred of evidence in the fossil record to link the vertebrates to any supposed ancestor among the invertebrates. Even though this transition is supposed to have taken 100 million years, not a single intermediate has ever been discovered. If vertebrates themselves have not evolved, as seems certain, evolution theory is dead, and it is foolish to speculate about evolution of groups within the vertebrates, or within any other division. If we look at the problem with a more limited perspective, if we confine our attention to the reptiles, mammal-like reptiles, and mammals, then there is evidence which supports each viewpoint.

The Evolutionary View of the Evidence

Let us first examine the evidence which supports the assumption that mammals have evolved from reptiles. In doing so, we will look at the geological column and time spans through the eyes of evolutionists, as must be done if the evidence is to be evaluated within the assumptions of the evolution model. "Primitive" mammal-like reptiles appear simultaneously in the fossil record with the "reptile-like" reptiles in the late Pennsylvanian Period. From the start these creatures possessed certain characteristics which are now associated with mammals, but other mammal-like characteristics, such as a secondary palate and a double occipital condyle, were lacking. Later, in the Permian and then in the Triassic, "advanced" mammal-like reptiles appeared that possessed these and other mammalian characteristics, including highly differentiated teeth and an enlargement of the dentary bone of the lower jaw and a reduction in size of the other bones of the lower jaw. Finally, at about the Triassic-Jurassic boundary, or approximately 180 million years ago on the evolutionary geological time scale, a creature existed, it is maintained, which possessed most of these mammal-like characteristics and which, though it still retained a fully-functional reptilian type (quadrate-articular) jaw-joint, also possessed, side-by-side with this reptile jaw-joint, a mammalian type (squamosal-dentary) jaw-joint. We then had a creature which evolutionists designate as the first mammal. Although published thirteen years ago, the extensive review of mammal-like reptiles by Tom Kemp[1] is still an excellent

---

[1] T. S. Kemp, *Mammal-like Reptiles and the Origin of Mammals* (New York: Academic Press, 1982).

source for the evolutionist view of the evidence. This is the main source used throughout our evaluation of the evidence.

A Creationist View of the Evidence

When evolutionists wish to cite evidence for evolution, they almost always point to the alleged reptile-to-mammal transition, *Archaeopteryx* (a supposed intermediate between reptile and bird), and the horse series. As we have already noted, Gould and Eldredge exclude *Archaeopteryx* as a transitional form,[2] and Eldredge, although he does believe that horses have evolved, states that there are no transitional forms between the different types of fossils horses.[3] Thus, there seems to be pitifully little evidence for evolution, if indeed millions of species have gradually evolved through hundreds of millions of years. If this has happened, our museums should be overflowing with vast numbers of unquestionable transitional forms. There should be no room for question, no possibility of doubt, no opportunity for debate, no rationale whatsoever for the existence of the Institute for Creation Research. Instead of these vast numbers of undoubted transitional forms that should exist, however, the case for evolution rests on a very few doubtful examples, one of which is the alleged reptile to mammal transition.

In their attempts to establish an evolutionary tree or phylogeny for the mammal-like reptiles and the mammals, evolutionists rely almost entirely on similarities to link these creatures in an evolutionary scenario. They are forced to do this because of the lack of transitional forms required for their hypothetical evolutionary ladder. We have noted this previously throughout all earlier reviews of the evidence relative to alleged transitions. Does the possession by a creature of some characteristics which are possessed by a second class of creatures necessarily indicate that it is transitional between these two classes? To answer that question in the negative, we can cite numerous examples. *Seymouria* was a creature that possessed some characteristics found in amphibians and some characteristics found in reptiles. It should therefore constitute a "perfect transitional form" between amphibians and reptiles. It could not possibly have been such

---

[2] S. J. Gould and Niles Eldredge, *Paleobiology* 3:147(1977).

[3] Niles Eldredge, as quoted by Boyce Rensberger (New York Times Service), *Houston Chronicle*, 5 November 1980, sec 4, p. 15.

an intermediate, however, since it first appeared at about the beginning of the Middle Permian, which is at least 20 million years too late on the evolutionary time scale to be the ancestor of the reptiles, which had already made their appearance in the preceding Pennsylvanian Period.

Another example is the living duck-billed platypus. This creature is a mammal, and yet it has a duck-bill, webbed feet, and lays eggs, in addition to possessing other characteristics that might be called reptilian. It has characteristics of mammals, reptiles, and birds, and perhaps could be called a "primitive" mammal. It could not possibly be ancestral to mammals, however, because it appeared much too late to be the ancestor of mammals! In fact, this unique combination of structural features renders it impossible to suggest that it arose from any particular class of vertebrates or that it could have been an intermediate between any two classes. Many similar examples could be cited. Thus the existence in a single creature of characteristics possessed by animals of two different types does not necessarily indicate that this creature is an intermediate between these two types or that they are genetically related.

Since the mammal-like reptiles have supposedly progressed from early, very reptile-like forms to very mammal-like forms and finally to mammals, one would assume that the changes resulted in a more or less steady progression from reptile to mammal. Actually, the mammal-like reptiles possessed a mosaic pattern of features found in reptiles and mammals. For example, Colbert has remarked that:

> It is not easy to determine the precise line of mammalian ancestors among the theriodont reptiles. Some theriodonts were far advanced toward the mammals in certain characters, but comparatively primitive in others; and among all the theriodonts the mixtures of advanced and conservative characters are so varied that it is not possible to point to any one particular group and define it as progressing most positively in the direction of mammals.[4]

In other words, while one of these so-called mammal-like reptiles might possess certain characteristics said to be mammalian, such as,

---

[4] E. H. Colbert, *Evolution of the Vertebrates*, 3rd ed. (New York: John Wiley and Sons, 1980), p. 246.

for example, a secondary palate and differentiated teeth, it might also possess characteristics judged to be primitively reptilian. According to Colbert this mixture of "advanced" and "primitive" features was so universally characteristic of theriodonts ("advanced" mammal-like reptiles) that it is impossible to select any one as the actual ancestor of the line that led to mammals.

Furthermore, not only were the mammal-like reptiles mosaics which included characteristics generally associated with both reptiles and mammals, but many possessed structures that are found in no living tetrapod, either mammalian or reptilian. Thus, Kemp has stated,

> The fossil structure is unlikely to resemble the living structure in any great detail, and yet the very differences may relate to important functional differences. Indeed in many cases concerning the mammal-like reptiles, structures are present which simply have no reasonable analogy amongst living tetrapods.[5]

Obviously, all such creatures would be too highly specialized to be the ancestor of mammals (or of any other living creature, for that matter).

In fact, the gaps in the supposed evolutionary line leading from reptile to mammal are so systematic that no creature can be considered to be the direct ancestor to another.

All mammal-like reptiles have been placed in the sub-class Synapsida. Evolutionists assume that these creatures are a natural grouping, all having shared ultimately a common ancestor, the common ancestor having originated very early in the history of the reptiles. They are actually a diverse group of creatures. The only diagnostic feature common to all members was the presence of a single lateral opening in the temporal region, a condition found only in this group. The mammal-like reptiles have been further divided into two orders, the Pelycosauria, constituting what is considered to be the earlier members of the mammal-like reptiles, and the Therapsida, considered by evolutionists to constitute more advanced types. The pelycosaurians are found abundantly only in the Texas redbeds (Lower Permian), although a few have been found in Europe. The therapsids have been found mainly in South America, Russia, and the Karoo Supergroup of South Africa. Romer terms this arrangement into these

---

[5] Kemp, *Mammal-like Reptiles*, p. 9.

two orders illogical but convenient.[6] Within these two orders families, genera, and species have been arranged in a sequence believed to represent, at least generally, the order in which these reptiles arose.

Does this general order represent a true time-sequence of the origin of these creatures or has the sequence been arranged to fit preconceived notions about evolution? There seems to be at least some basis for suspicion that many of these creatures were placed in the sequence according to demands of evolutionary theory. The sequence is then offered as proof of the theory!

A few citations from the literature may be quoted to document the suspicion mentioned above. Kemp has stated that,

> The record is also geographically patchy, no locality yielding more than a relatively short segment of the history of the mammal-like reptiles, and in many cases a region contains fossils of a single age. Similarly, no single taxonomic group of synapsid occurs worldwide even though there is little doubt that at least some of them had a very extensive distribution in life.[7]

It seems rather obvious that since no locality yields more than a short segment of the so-called history of the mammal-like reptiles, various segments must be juxtaposed according to an imagined evolutionary sequence, or at least according to some scheme determined by assumptions based on indirect evidence.

Especially suggestive is the statement by Kemp that "synapsids are also of some use to geologists as stratigraphic indicators of the relative ages of the continental rocks in which they are found. . . ."[8] In other words, fossils, in this case fossils of mammal-like reptiles, are used to date the rocks. But how do we know the relative ages of the mammal-like reptiles if we use them to date the rocks? By their order in the evolutionary scheme adopted by evolutionists, of course!

Equally revealing is the statement by Romer:

---

[6] A. S. Romer, *Vertebrate Paleontology*, 3rd ed. (Chicago: University of Chicago Press, 1966), p. 173.

[7] Kemp, *Mammal-like Reptiles*, p. 3.

[8] *Ibid.*, p. 4.

Although correlation with marine stages is impossible in most cases, the general evolutionary story of therapsids and other contained forms suggests that the pelycosaur-bearing beds should be regarded as early Permian, the Tapinocephalus Zone of the Beaufort and the early Russian horizons as Middle Permian, the Endothiodon and Cistecephalus Zones of the Beaufort and their equivalents as late Permian. Olson has proposed that any middle term be eliminated, and that the whole sweep of Russian and African beds (and his Double Mountain or Pease River American finds) be called late Permian. This appears to me to be a most uneven dichotomy, and the customary early-middle-late Permian terminology more in accord with a broad view of the Permian evolutionary picture.[9]

It thus appears that Romer's arrangement of these various beds in a supposed time-sequence was determined by "the general evolutionary story of therapsids" and by "a broad view of the Permian evolutionary picture." It is no wonder, then, that what is presented in the literature, and especially textbooks, as a time-sequence for the mammal-like reptiles does generally accord with evolutionary expectations. It was constructed to do just that.

It is often suggested, however, that radiometric dating methods are used to date fossils, a method entirely independent of any supposed stratigraphic correlation or evolutionary stories. Derek Ager, Professor of Geology at University College, Swansea, Wales, has reacted angrily to such claims. He says,

My frustrations as a geologist were brought to boiling point by David Challinor's article on natural history museums (*New Scientist*, 29 September, 1983, p. 959) and in particular by his remark that "Originally, paleontologists dated fossils by identifying the geological strata in which they were found. Today the age of a fossil is determined by measuring the decay of radioactive carbon or by means of the decay of their radioactive potassium into argon" . . . . Ever since William Smith at the beginning of the 19th century, fossils have been and still are the best and most

[9]A.S. Romer, *Bulletin of the Indian Geological Association* 2(1-2): 17 (1969).

accurate method of dating and correlating the rocks in
which they occur. . . . As for having all the credit passed to
the physicists and the measurement of isotopic decay, the
blood boils! Certainly such studies give dates in terms of
millions of years, with huge margins of errors. . . . I can
think of no cases of radioactive decay being used to date
fossils.[10]

Thus it seems that fossils are used to date rocks, not radiometric
dating methods. That seems to bring us back into a circle, for how do
we date fossils? In the final analysis, all appears to rest on an assumed
evolutionary sequence.

The remainder of this chapter is devoted to an evaluation of the
enormous physiological and morphological differences between reptiles
and mammals, followed by a critical examination of the fossil record of
mammal-like reptiles and mammals in order to answer the question,
"Which model of origins, creation or evolution, do the data fit best?"

Physical and Physiological Differences Between Reptiles and Mammals

The changes in the physiology and the concomitant morphological
changes required to convert a reptile into a mammal are profound. The
English creation scientist, Douglas Dewar, listed 21 major differences
between reptiles and mammals, a list he declared was by no means
complete.[11] Kemp presents and discusses a list of hypothetical
intermediates between reptiles and mammals and the difficulty,
because of lack of transitional forms, of knowing whether the
evolutionary changes were gradual or by quantum jumps. He then
says:

Overall, however, the evolution of each system can be
described as gradual at the particular phylogenetic
resolution presently available. It follows that there is an
apparent correlation between the evolution of the separate
systems, changes in one tending to be accompanied by
changes in the others. . . . There are other mammalian

---

[10] D. Ager, *New Scientist* 100:425 (1983).

[11] Douglas Dewar, *The Transformist Illusion* (Murfreesboro, Tennessee: Dehoff Publications, 1957), pp. 223-225.

characteristics which are not represented at all in the fossil forms, or at best only by highly tentative associations with skeletal characters. Such things as the structure of the heart, and double circulation, the kidney and its specialized physiology, hair, lactation and temperature physiology are of fundamental importance in understanding the nature of the origin of mammals. By analogy with the osteological features, it is likely that these soft structures also evolved gradually through the mammal-like reptiles and early mammals, but in order to investigate such a hypothesis further, the way in which all the various characters relate functionally to one another and to the environment must be considered.[12]

Kemp lists three major problems facing an animal living on land and discusses each in the context of the origin of mammal-ness. These major problems are temperature control, chemical control, and spatial control. The physiology of mammals must permit the maintenance of a constant, relatively high body temperature. This characteristic, termed endothermy, is accomplished by heat production through a cellular metabolic rate that is about seven times that of a cold-blooded (ectothermic) reptile. Endothermy requires a finely adjusted, highly complex biological organization that is found in mammals but not in reptiles. In describing what had to evolve as a reptile was converted into a mammal, Kemp says:

> ... the fine control mechanisms of temperature regulation are necessary, so that neither alterations in the rate of metabolic heat output during differing levels of activity, nor variations in ambient temperature are allowed to cause a change in body temperature. Thus hair, sweat glands, and specialized skin blood vessels must evolve. More indirectly, but equally important in the functioning of endothermy, are several other aspects of the biology of mammals. The locomotory apparatus must become capable of carrying the animal about in search of its some tenfold increase in food requirements. The feeding apparatus has to ingest at this greater rate and also assist in the breakdown of the food, a process which would be far too slow if left solely to the

---

[12] Kemp, *Mammal-like Reptiles*, p. 306.

intestinal processes. The diaphragm is needed for the greater rate of external gas exchange that occurs. The potential increase in water loss that would result from the higher temperature and greater breathing rate must be combated by the kidney, and finally the sense organs and central nervous system must be designed to organize and control these activities.[13]

Insulation of the mammalian body requires hair. The vast differences between reptilian scales and feathers and their mode of development have previously been discussed. Hairs, as do feathers, develop from follicles, and thus have a mode of development completely different from that of scales. Evolutionists must believe that somehow, via random, accidental genetic mistakes, reptiles "solved" the problem of converting reptilian scales into mammalian hair.

Kemp discusses the evolution of chemical control, which he states is "the second great terrestrial problem solved by mammals." In using such terms as "solved" in the evolutionary process, evolutionists speak as if there were intelligence, planning, and experimentation involved in the blind processes of evolution. The problem that must be overcome by mammals, as with all tetrapods, is the tendency to lose water. The main organ involved in overcoming this problem is the kidney, which Kemp states is more elaborate in the mammal than in any other vertebrate. In describing the complexity of the mammalian kidney, Kemp says:

> The blood pressure in the renal artery supplying the kidneys is high and the number of kidney tubules is large. The first point about the mammalian kidney, therefore, is that there is a very high ultrafiltration rate of the blood. The second point is the very long loop of Henle, which is associated with the production of a concentrated, hypertonic urine, the main means of water conservation. The third point of importance is that by producing hypertonic urine, sufficient water is conserved that the animal can afford to excrete liquid. There is therefore a flow of aqueous solution passing out of the body which gives the opportunity for very fine regulation of the plasma levels of ions and other soluble

---

[13] *Ibid.*, p. 309.

substances. By appropriate rates of secretion into or reabsorption from the fluid flowing through the kidney tubules, the level of each ion or molecule can be maintained constant in the blood.[14]

Kemp mentions the multitude of enzyme-controlled reactions that must be integrated by a finely tuned hemostatic system. He then goes on to say:

> The heart and circulatory system must be designed to produce the high blood pressure needed by the kidney. There must also be a complex endocrine system in order to detect the level of each of the substances controlled and to initiate appropriate rates of secretion and reabsorption in the kidney tubules.[15]

In his discussion of the spatial control by mammals, that is, the matter of locomotion over a great variety of land surfaces, Kemp says:

> Mammalian limbs have a wide range of amplitudes and angles through which they can be moved, and they can cope therefore with very irregular ground, surmounting or circumventing obstacles. The limbs are long but slender, giving a potentially rapid locomotion, and the feet are placed on the ground close to the animal's midline, which makes the animal highly maneuverable or agile. As well as these geometrical properties of the locomotory system, mammals have muscles capable of sustained aerobic activity at a high rate. Thus, although they are noticeably faster or more efficient at moving, they can maintain rapid movement for much longer periods than equivalent-sized reptiles.
>
> . . . As well as the obvious changes in the limbs, the locomotory system requires an increased food and oxygen supply, a complex sensory and central nervous system for control, and possibly a higher metabolic rate for the sustained efforts.[16]

---

[14] *Ibid.*
[15] *Ibid.*, p. 310
[16] *Ibid.*

Kemp then discusses the concept of homeostasis, that is, the ability of mammals to withstand external fluctuations of the environment by means of regulation of the animal's internal environment. In a figure on page 312, Kemp illustrates the integration of twenty-seven structures and processes of mammals that are involved in the maintenance of homeostasis. He emphasizes that no one of the components of homeostasis can function independently, and what exists is a single, integrated homeostatic mechanism.

Finally, he says:

> To conclude, the essence of mammalian biology is the very high degree of complexity and internal integration of the various structures and functional processes.[17]

Earlier, Kemp emphasized the fact that since all features of mammals are highly complex and intimately integrated, especially those structures and processes that are involved in maintaining homeostasis, their evolutionary origin would have involved very gradual change. None of these could have arisen independently of any other.[18] He reemphasizes this in a later chapter, stating:

> It was noted that the fossil record supports the view that evolution towards mammalian levels of homeostasis involved practically all aspects of the organism simultaneously. No single structure or function could evolve very far without being accompanied by appropriate changes in all the other features.[19]

Kemp then goes on to explain that just as the internal changes required to maintain homeostasis during the conversion of a reptile into a mammal must be gradual and intimately correlated, so also must the morphological changes be carefully correlated and thus gradual. He says:

> To take as an example dicynodonts, their herbivorous specialization requires the replacement of the teeth by horny tooth plates, reorientation of the jaw musculature, changes in the form of the jaw hinge, and an extensive

---

[17] *Ibid.*, p. 313.

[18] *Ibid.*, p. 310.

[19] *Ibid.*, p. 331.

remodeling of the shape of the skull and lower jaws. Also suitable locomotion and central nervous programming and behavior are needed. No one of these features has much adaptive value unless accompanied by the others, and therefore the evolution of the dicynodont type of organism must have followed a correlated progression, each feature evolving gradually and in association with changes in all the other features.[20]

The Fossil Record of Mammal-Like Reptiles

Kemp rightly maintains that the large number of internal changes in the physiology and the large number of external changes in morphology required to convert a reptile into a mammal must of necessity have occurred gradually. The fossil record must thus document a gradual origin of each species, genus, family, and order, if evolution is true.

In a great number of cases we should be able to trace, via transitional forms, the origin of each distinct kind, as the many different types of mammal-like reptiles evolved, until we arrive at the final stage, a creature no longer merely mammal-like, but 100% mammal. We should then be able to trace, via fossilized transitional forms, the gradual origin of each of the thirty-two orders of mammals—rodents, odd-toed ungulates (perissodactyls), even-toed ungulates (artiodactyls), whales, bats, primates, etc.—from this primitive mammal.

The fossil record produces neither the evidence of gradual change nor the transitional forms predicted on the basis of evolution. Very early in his book, after asserting that the reptile to mammal transition is the one example known where the evolution of one class of vertebrates from another class is well documented by the fossil record, Kemp immediately admits:

> Of course there are many gaps in the synapsid fossil record, with intermediate forms between the various known groups almost invariably unknown. However, the known groups have enough features in common that it is possible to reconstruct hypothetical intermediate stage.[21]

---

[20] Ibid.

Kemp asserts that the reptile to mammal transition is the best documented case for evolution, but then must admit that hypothetical transitional forms must be constructed because intermediate forms between known groups are almost invariably unknown! The first mammal-like reptiles appear in the rocks of the Upper Pennsylvanian, allegedly about 350 million years ago, and supposedly became extinct at the end of the Triassic. Thus, evolutionists believe the mammal-like reptiles spent almost 200 million years evolving before reaching mammalian status. Countless billions of transitional forms would have lived and died during that vast stretch of time. Our museums should have many thousands of actual transitional forms on their shelves. Resorting to hypothetical intermediates would certainly not be necessary if these creatures had actually evolved.

The absence of transitional forms occurs at all taxonomic levels—species, genera, families, and orders. Kemp states:

> Gaps at a lower taxonomic level, species and genera, are practically universal in the fossil record of the mammal-like reptiles. In no single adequately documented case is it possible to trace a transition, species by species, from one genus to another.[22]

Kemp attributes the absence of transitional forms between species and the absence of transitional forms between genera to the notion that at the species level evolution occurs rapidly in small populations. He accepts the punctuated equilibrium theory of evolution suggested by Niles Eldredge and Stephen Jay Gould. This idea will be discussed in a later chapter. The theory of punctuated equilibrium is supposed to account for the absence of transitional forms between species but has nothing to say about the absence of transitional forms between genera, families, orders, classes, and phyla. Any resort to that unproven (and unprovable) hypothesis to explain the absence of transitional forms between basically different kinds, such as families, orders, and higher taxa, is totally without merit.

Kemp admits that the absence of transitional forms is evident at all levels. Thus, he says:

---

[21] *Ibid.*, p. 3.
[22] *Ibid*, p. 319.

The sudden appearance of new higher taxa, families and even orders, immediately after a mass extinction, with all the features more or less developed, implies a very rapid evolution. This is invariably followed by a much slower rate of morphological change of the lineage, usually no more than generic, or at most sub-family level. It is possible that this observation is an artifact, and that the new taxa had long histories before they appeared in the fossil record, during which they gradually acquired their characteristic features. However, in no case is such a long history known by even a single specimen, and therefore it is much more reasonable to accept that very high rates of morphological evolution characteristically occur following a mass extinction.[23]

Note that Kemp is forced to admit that, just as is the case with species and genera, representatives of mammal-like reptiles at the level of families and orders also appear fully-formed, with all features more or less completely developed. He says that these facts imply a very rapid evolution, that it is reasonable to believe that high rates of morphological evolution characteristically occur following a mass extinction.

What Kemp believes is that the fossil record shows an abrupt appearance of mammal-like reptiles representing various stages of the transition of reptiles into mammals, each stage showing an increase in mammal-like characteristics. The fossilized remains of each of these stages appear fully-formed, with no transitional forms documenting the gradual transition of one stage into the next, and very little, if any, further change occurs until this stage or level is abruptly replaced by the next.

To account for this very non-Darwinian evolution, Kemp suggests that there was a very rapid radiation at each level of development of mammal-like reptiles, which later was followed by a mass extinction. Each mass extinction was followed by a radiation, beginning with a single surviving lineage which radiated into the next stage, which eventually also suffered a mass extinction. Thus a series of radiations and mass extinctions, with each radiation resulting in more

---

[23] *Ibid.*, p. 327.

progressive, mammal-like creatures, finally culminated in the origin of mammals. He states that:

> The new lineages are more or less fully developed at their first appearance in the fossil record, and thereafter they remain relatively conservative.[24]

Kemp tells us that this evolutionary development occurred in three phases. The first phase resulted in the appearance of pelycosaurs in the Upper Pennsylvanian and Lower Permian. Kemp states:

> The structural similarity between all the pelycosaurs is so great that there is no doubt that they all shared a common ancestor which had already evolved the essential features of the group.[25]

Note that the claim that pelycosaurs had evolved from a common ancestor is based solely on the assumption that possession of certain similarities indicates common ancestry. The actual evidence is contrary to that notion because the assumed common ancestor, at its first appearance, already possessed all the essential features of the group. No transitional forms, not even one, can be found in the fossil record that documents an evolutionary origin of the hypothetical common ancestor, or of the evolution of this hypothetical common ancestor into the various different types of pelycosaurs.

A taxon of vague affinities, Cotylosauria, is commonly used with reference to a wide range of so-called primitive reptilian tetrapods. Thus cotylosaurs are, by definition, stem reptiles. Since this is the case, evolutionists must assume that pelycosaurs evolved from a cotylosaur. Romer and Price thus state: "That pelycosaurs are descended from Cotylosaurs seems certain."[26] Just a bit later they state, however, that "an attempt to sort out pelycosaur ancestors from among the cotylosaur assemblage is, however, more difficult." By a process of elimination they conclude that among the cotylosaurs, the captorhinomorphs must by definition include the ancestors of the pelycosaurs, but they confess that "Most attempts to find traits distinctively pelycosaurian are disappointing."

[24] *Ibid.*, p. 321.

[25] *Ibid.*, p. 27.

[26] A. S. Romer and L. W. Price, *Geological Society of America Special Papers* 28:178 (1940).

Thus reptiles with distinctive pelycosaurian features appear abruptly in the fossil record fully-formed. No presumed ancestors with any of these unique features among the cotylosaurs have been found, so evolutionists simply assume that pelycosaurs evolved from cotylosaurs because they have nothing better to suggest.

Romer and Price, in their extensive review of the Pelycosauria, argue strenuously that the ancestors of the Therapsida, the next stage in the evolutionary origin of the mammals, are to be found in the Pelycosauria.[27] They describe what they believe to be numerous similarities between pelycosaurs and therapsids, and suggest that more particularly, those pelycosaurs included within the Sphenacodontidae were ancestral to therapsids. Concerning the similarities between the appendicular skeletons of the sphenacodontids and therapsids, the most that Romer and Price can say is that the appendicular skeleton of the sphenacodontids "in at least a few details show the beginning of therapsid features."[28] Concerning the axial skeleton they say, "The axial skeleton presents no strong argument for a particularly close genetic connection between the groups but on the other hand offers no obstacles." Thus, there are no real similarities in the appendicular and axial skeletons to link sphenacodontids to therapsids. Romer and Price, however, believe that "In the cranial structure the resemblances are numerous and significant,"[29] but even these similarities, they state, could be due to similarity in habits and/or parallelisms. Lacking better candidates, Romer and Price conclude that "the mammal-like reptiles have in all probability descended from the sphenacodontid pelycosaurs." They immediately state, however, that:

> The pelycosaurs are very primitive in most skeletal features and hence could be considered in most regards as morphologically antecedent to later reptiles of almost any type.[30]

The notion that pelycosaurian sphenacodontids gave rise to therapsids is also supported by Hopson[31] and by Kemp.

---

[27] Ibid., pp. 178-195.

[28] Ibid., p. 193.

[29] Ibid.

[30] Ibid., p. 194.

[31] James A. Hopson, "Systematics of the Nonmammalian Synapsids," in Origins of the Higher Groups of the Tetrapods, ed. Hans-Peter Schultz and

Dimetrodon, which had hugely elongated neural spines, creating a large sail-like structure, believed possibly to have functioned as a heat-exchanger, was one of the most numerous of the sphenacodontids (fig. 10). There are no fossils whatsoever of any transitional forms showing a gradual evolutionary origin of these enormous spines. Sphenacodon was a more conservative member of the sphenacodontids (fig. 11). No suggestion is made concerning which creature is the specific ancestor of the therapsids.

It is apparent that the argument for linking pelycosaurs to the therapsids is extremely weak and is based solely on certain similarities. There are no transitional forms that would provide actual evolutionary links between pelycosaurs and therapsids.

According to Kemp's idea, a mass-extinction of the pelycosaurs (except for one or very few lineages) was followed by a very rapid radiation into non-cynodont therapsids in the Late Permian, which made an abrupt appearance as a series of totally different mammal-like reptiles.[32] Referring to fossils found in Russia, South Africa, and North America, Kemp states:

> All the more advanced, non-pelycosaur mammal-like reptiles of these three continents are members of the Therapsida. Even at their earliest appearance, they had diversified into several distinct types, but the similarities that they all share, in terms of characters evolved from the pelycosaur condition, indicate that the Therapsida form a

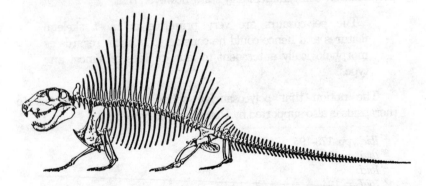

Figure 10. Skeletal restoration of *Dimetrodon milleri* (from Romer and Price, p. 337).

Figure 11. Skeletal restoration of *Sphenacodon* (from Romer and Price, p. 324).

monophyletic group, having descended from a single hypothetical pelycosaur ancestor.[33]

It must be emphasized that the non-cynodont therapsids appeared abruptly, that is, with all their basic characteristics complete; at their earliest appearance they already constituted several distinctly different types; and a hypothetical pelycosaur must be suggested as the common ancestor. There are no transitional forms, no intermediates, that link these several distinct types to one another or to some hypothetical pelycosaur ancestor. This evidence is precisely what would be expected if these creatures had each been separately created but is unquestionably contradictory to predictions based on evolutionary theory.

The non-cynodont therapsids were very diverse in size, morphology, and feeding habits. Some were carnivores, some were herbivores. Some were quite large, some were very small. The gorgonopsids, termed the "saber-toothed" reptiles because of their very large canine teeth, appeared with a full suite of gorgonopsid characteristics with no hint of transitional forms.[34] The therocephalian *Euchambersia* apparently had a poison gland associated with a snake-like fang for administering a venomous bite.[35] Some whaitsiid therocephalians like *Theriognathus* had no postcanine teeth at all (fig. 12).[36]

Linda Trueb (Ithaca, New York: Comstock Publishing Associates, 1991), p. 646.

[32] Kemp, *Mammal-like Reptiles*, pp. 69, 320.

[33] *Ibid.*, p. 70.

[34] *Ibid.*, pp. 105-108.

[35] *Ibid.*, p. 165.

[36] A. S. Brink, *Paleontol. afr.* 4:97-115 (1956).

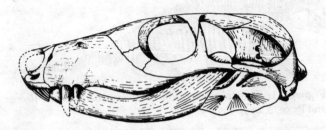

Figure 12. The Whaitsiid therocephalian *Theriognathus.* (From Brink, *Paleontological africanus* 4:97-115, 1956).

Members of the Therocephalia have all their distinctive characters present at their first appearance in the fossil record, and concerning them Kemp states:

> Derived characters shared with any of the individual kinds of therapsids so far discussed have not been discovered and therefore the relationships to these other groups are obscure.[37]

Since the therocephalians appear with all of their distinctive characteristics complete in the very first representatives, and none of these distinctive characteristics are found in any other of the therapsid mammal-like reptiles, it is absolutely clear that none of the evolutionary links required by evolutionary theory exist and these creatures stand completely isolated from all other mammal-like reptiles. This is the evidence predicted on the basis of creation but is directly contradictory to evolutionary theory.

After a sudden mass extinction of the non-cynodont level of mammal-like reptiles, according to Kemp's scenario, a third and final phase of the evolution of mammal-like reptiles resulted from a very rapid radiation that gave rise to the cynodonts, which are found at the earliest levels in rocks of the Late Permian. Cynodonts are cynodonts from their first appearance, for Kemp says:

> Although these earliest forms are in several respects more primitive than Triassic cynodonts, they are nevertheless unmistakably at the cynodont level of evolution.[38]

---

[37] Kemp, *Mammal-like Reptiles*, p. 161.

It is believed that one of the "advanced" cynodonts finally gave rise to mammals, but just which one was closest to the actual ancestor of mammals is a matter of dispute.

The two mammal-like reptiles *Morganucodon* (also called *Eozostrodon*) and *Kuehneotherium* supposedly represent the most definitive transitional forms between the reptiles and mammals. Thousands of fragments, representing many different individuals, of *Morganucodon* have been found. The material consists of teeth, jaws, and fragments of skull and postcranial skeleton from Wales, a complete skull and jaws from the Lufeng Red Beds of China, as well as material from two similar genera found in the Red Beds of the Karoo Supergroup of South Africa.[39] Only isolated teeth and jaw fragments of *Kuehneotherium* from Wales have been recovered. These creatures were very small, with a length of about four inches. All of this material is placed in the Upper Triassic of the geological column.[40]

These are the creatures that, it is claimed, possessed the mammal-type jaw-joint side by side with the reptile-type jaw-joint. In mammals there is a single bone in each half of the lower jaw, called the dentary, since it bears the teeth, and this bone articulates directly with the squamosal area of the skull. Reptiles have six bones in each half of the lower jaw. Articulation of the jaw with the skull is indirect, with the articular (one of the bones of the jaw) articulating with the quadrate bone, a bone not found in mammals. Another fundamental difference between reptiles and mammals is the fact that all reptiles, living or fossil, have a single bone in the ear, a rod-like bone known as the columella. Mammals possess three bones in the ear, the stapes, malleus, and incus. Evolutionists maintain that the stapes corresponds to the columella and that the quadrate and articular bones of the reptile somehow moved into the ear to become, respectively, the incus and malleus bones of the mammalian ear. No explanation is given how the intermediates managed to hear while this was going on.

Another difficulty with the above notion is the fact that while thousands of fossil reptiles have been found which possess a single ear bone and multiple jaw bones, and thousands of fossil mammals have been found which possess three ear bones and a single bone in the jaw,

---

[38] *Ibid.*, p. 180.
[39] *Ibid.*, p. 255.
[40] *Ibid.*, p. 263.

not a single fossil creature has ever been found which represents an intermediate stage, such as one possessing three bones in the jaw and two bones in the ear.

Morganucodon[41] and *Kuehneotherium*[42] each possessed a full complement of the reptilian bones in its lower jaw. Furthermore, there was no reduction in the functional importance of the reptilian (quadrate-articular) jaw-joint, even though these creatures are supposed to be intermediates between reptiles and mammals, allegedly possessing a mammalian (squamosal-dentary) jaw-joint in addition to the reptilian jaw-joint. Kermack et al. state:

> The most striking characteristic of the accessory jaw bones of *Morganucodon* is their cynodont character. Compared with such a typical advanced cynodont as *Cynognathus*, the accessory bones present show no reduction, either in size or complexity of structure. In particular, the actual reptilian jaw-joint itself was relatively as powerful in the mammal, *Morganucodon*, as it was in the reptile *Cynognathus*. This was quite unexpected.[43]

These authors relate that it has long been generally held by evolutionists that there was a progressive weakening of the jaw joint in passing from early to late cynodonts, and this weakening continued into the first mammals (the cynodonts were "advanced" mammal-like reptiles). This is what one would predict if mammals evolved from reptiles and there was thus a gradual evolutionary replacement of the reptilian jaw-joint by the mammalian jaw-joint. Kermack and his co-workers now reject this idea, since the reptilian jaw-joint of *Cynognathus* was extremely powerful and the lower jaw of *Morganucodon* closely resembled that of *Cynognathus*.

There is no doubt whatsoever, therefore, that *Morganucodon* had a powerful standard reptilian type jaw-joint. Although almost all of the available material related to *Morganucodon* consists of disarticulated bones (the individual bones consist of fragments), a fragment of a jaw

---

[41] K. A. Kermack, F. Mussett and H. W. Rigney, *Zool. J. Linn. Soc.* 53(2): 157 (1973).

[42] D. M. Kermack, K. A. Kermack and F. Mussett, *Zool. J. Linn. Soc.* 47(312): 418 (1968).

[43] Kermack, Mussett and Rigney, *Zool. J. Linn. Soc.* 53(2): 157 (1973).

was recovered with the quadrate bone still in contact with the articular bone, leaving no doubt about the existence of a reptilian jaw-joint in this creature. But did *Morganucodon* and *Kuehneotherium* have, in addition to this reptilian jaw-joint, a point of contact between the dentary and squamosal and, if so, does this indicate the incipient formation of a mammalian type jaw-joint?

Kermack and his colleagues certainly believe that this has been established for *Morganucodon* and *Kuehneotherium* (it is also said to have been accomplished in several other groups of mammal-like reptiles).[44] What is the basis for this belief? Regardless of how strongly this belief is held, it rests on inference. The evidence is extremely fragmentary and no fossils are available showing the dentary in actual contact with the squamosal of the skull. In fact, not even a single intact lower jaw is available, all such specimens being reconstructed from fragments.

What is the evidence for a squamosal-dentary joint in these creatures? This evidence consists of an alleged condyle on the dentary. A condyle is a rounded process at the end of a bone forming a ball and socket joint with the hollow part (termed the fossa) of another bone. In mammals there is a very prominent condyle on the posterior end of the dentary which articulates to the squamosal bone of the skull. The squamosal contains a fossa for the reception of the condyle and the contact forms the jaw joint. With *Morganucodon* and *Kuehneotherium*, the dentary extends sufficiently posteriorly to encourage the belief that it made contact with the squamosal and the alleged point of contact on the dentary is called the condyle.

Whether the dentary bone of these creatures actually made contact with the squamosal can only be inferred. But if there had been a real contact between the dentary and squamosal, could it be said that this constituted a mammalian jaw-joint which existed alongside the reptilian jaw-joint? We must remember that these creatures had a fully-developed, powerful reptilian jaw-joint. The anatomy required for such a jaw-joint, including the arrangement and mode of attachment of musculature, the arrangement and location of blood vessels and nerves, etc., must be quite different from that required for a

---

[44] A. W. Crompton and F. A. Jenkins, Jr., "Origin of *Mammals*" in *Mesozoic Mammals*, ed. J. A. Lillegraven, Z. Kielan-Jaworowska and W. A. Clemens (Berkeley: University of California Press, 1979), p. 62.

mammalian jaw-joint. How then could a powerful, fully functional reptilian jaw-joint be accommodated along with a mammalian jaw-joint?

It is significant that similar claims concerning a double jaw-joint in *Probainognathus* and *Diarthrognathus* have been questioned. *Probainognathus* and *Diarthrognathus* are represented as being very close to the hypothetical direct ancestors of mammals. Concerning *Probainognathus* Kemp states:

> A second much quoted feature of *Probainognathus* that relates it to mammals is the secondary contact between the dentary and the squamosal. In fact, there is some doubt whether there is actual contact between these bones (Crompton and Jenkins, 1979). . . .[45]

With reference to *Diarthrognathus*, Gow states:

> The ictidosaur, *Diarthrognathus*, from the Clarens Formation (Cave Sandstone) (Crompton, 1958) is generally held to exhibit the expected morphological grade intermediate between cynodonts and mammals; more specifically, it is thought to have both reptilian and mammalian jaw-joint. However, several of Crompton's interpretations of the morphology of the lower jaw and its articulation with the skull were wrong; some, but not all of these he has conceded in print (Crompton, 1972).[46]

Thus we see that the notion that there was both a mammalian and a reptilian jaw-joint in these two creatures has been challenged from within evolutionary circles. These creatures are all extinct—all that remains is extremely fragmentary fossil material. The manner in which these creatures are reconstructed and their function is visualized is often critically affected by preconceived notions of what should be expected. Evolutionists feel certain that reptiles evolved into mammals. This would have required the replacement of the reptilian jaw-joint with a mammalian jaw-joint. With extremely fragmentary and incomplete material available, it is thus possible that what is being "seen" is what one expected to see rather than what was really there.

---

[45] Kemp, *Mammal-like Reptiles*, p. 271.
[46] C. E. Gow, *Paleontologia Africana* 24:15 (1981).

Finally, and this is conclusive, not a single intermediate between an animal with a powerful, fully functional reptilian jaw-joint and a powerful, fully functional mammalian jaw-joint has been found. All reptiles, whether *Morganucodon, Kuehneotherium,* or whatever, had a full complement of reptilian bones in the jaw and all mammals, fossil or living, have a single bone on each side of the lower jaw. No intermediates have been found.

The Reptilian vs. the Mammalian Ear

Furthermore, we cannot divorce the evidence related to the jaw-joint from that related to the auditory apparatus. As mentioned earlier, evolutionists believe that as the bones in the reptilian jaw, except for the dentary, gradually became relieved of their function in the jaw they were now free either to evolve out of existence or to assume some new function. Thus, the quadrate and articular bones became free (they were, by the way, firmly attached to the dentary in *Morganucodon*) and somehow worked their way into the middle ear to eventually become the incus and malleus, respectively. This would have required that the stapes (columella) of the reptile become free from its attachment to the tympanum (ear drum), and the retroarticular process of the articular gain an attachment to the tympanum (since the articular bone of the reptile supposedly became the malleus of the mammal, which is attached to the tympanum). Somehow while all of this was going on, the quadrate bone of the reptilian ancestor must gain its freedom, move into the middle ear, and insert itself between the stapes and malleus. While all of this maneuvering was going on, all of these bones must somehow have been refashioned and reengineered in a most miraculous manner so that they could function in an entirely new auditory apparatus.

There is absolutely no fossil evidence whatsoever to support such an incredible scenario. *Kuehneotheruim* is supposed to be in the direct line leading to therian mammals (marsupial and placental mammals), but it did not possess ear ossicles. Kemp states:

> The exact stage at which the therian ossicles evolved is unknown. Kuehneotheruim, the earliest and most primitive therian, must have lacked them, for a groove to house the post-dentary bones is still present on the inner face of the dentary.[47]

It does seem strange that this most critical stage in the evolutionary conversion of a reptile into a mammal, the alleged movement of the articular and quadrate bones of the reptilian jaw into the ear of the incipient mammal and their reshaping into the incus and malleus of the mammalian ear, is completely devoid of any documentation whatsoever in the fossil record. Certainly an adequate fossil record should have been produced during the millions of years required for random genetic errors and natural selection to engineer such a miraculous apparatus.

The anatomical problems associated with such a postulated process are vastly greater than merely imagining how two bones precisely shaped to perform in a powerfully effective jaw-joint could detach themselves, force their way into the middle ear, reshape themselves into the malleus and incus, which are precisely engineered to function with a remodeled stapes in a vastly different auditory apparatus, while all at the same time the creature continues to chew and to hear! As insuperable as this problem appears to be, it pales into relative insignificance when we consider the fact that the essential organ of hearing in the mammal is the organ of Corti, an organ not possessed by a single reptile, nor is there any evidence that would provide even a hint of where this organ came from.

The organ of Corti is an extremely complicated organ. It is suggested that the reader consult one of the standard texts on anatomy for a description. One cannot help but marvel at this complex and wondrously designed organ. It has no homologue in reptiles. There is no possible structure in the reptile from which it could have been derived. It would have had to have been created *de novo*, since it was entirely new and novel.

According to evolution theory, all evolutionary changes occur as the result of mistakes during the reproduction of genes. Each change brought about by such mutations which survived must have been superior to preceding forms. Thus, if evolution is true, we must believe that a series of thousands of mistakes in a marvelously coordinated fashion gradually created the organ of Corti to function in an ear which at the same time had to be reengineered accordingly while dragging in two bones from the jaw which had to be redesigned. Furthermore, each intermediate stage not only had to be fully

---

[47] Kemp, *Mammal-like Reptiles*, p. 293.

functional but actually must have been superior to the preceding stage. And after all this was accomplished, we still have reptiles and birds today with the same old-fashioned reptilian and avian auditory apparatus which are just as efficient as the corresponding mammalian apparatus.

Other Required Changes

Furthermore, while all of the above miraculous changes were occurring, these creatures also invented (by genetic mistakes) many other marvelous new physiological and anatomical organs and processes, including a new mode of reproduction, mammary glands, temperature regulation, hair, and a new way of breathing.

The structure of the thoracic girdle of the mammal differs fundamentally from that of the reptile. In the reptile it articulates with the breastbone by means of the coracoid bones and forms part of the thorax. This is not the case with mammals. In reptiles the fore part of the thorax is rigid and incapable of expansion. In mammals the thorax is expansible. In mammals the thoracic and abdominal cavities are partitioned by the diaphragm, a fibro-muscular organ. Since reptiles have no diaphragm, their thorax is not a closed box. As a consequence of the above, reptiles cannot breathe as mammals do. They cannot alternately expand and contract the thorax as is the case with mammals. They must breathe buccally (by mouth).

There is no structure in a reptile that is in any way similar or homologous to the mammalian diaphragm. There is no structure found in a reptile from which it could have been derived. Again, a complicated structure had to be created *de novo* (and by a series of mistakes!) to perform a function that was already being very satisfactorily performed in a different manner in the assumed reptilian ancestor.

The Great Hiatus in Mammalian Evolution

Mammal-like reptiles appeared supposedly right at the start of the reptiles, gradually became more mammal-like through the Permian and Triassic, and finally culminated in the appearance of the first real mammals at the end of the Triassic. At this time the mammal-like reptiles essentially became extinct, even though earlier they had been amongst the most numerous of all reptiles, worldwide in distribution. Since evolution is supposed to have involved natural selection, in which the more highly adapted creatures reproduce in larger numbers and thus gradually replace the less fit, we would now expect the mammals, triumphant at last, to flourish in vast numbers and to dominate the world. A very strange thing happened, however. For all practical purposes, the mammals disappeared from the scene for the next 120 million years! During this supposed vast stretch of time, the "reptile-like" reptiles, including dinosaurs and many other land-dwelling creatures, the marine reptiles, and the flying reptiles, swarmed over the earth. As far as the mammals were concerned, however, the "fittest" that replaced the mammal-like reptiles, they were almost nowhere to be found. Most of the fossil remains of mammals recovered to date from the Jurassic and Cretaceous Periods, allegedly covering more than 120 million years, could be contained in two cupped hands. Most such mammals are represented by a few teeth. If evolution is supposed to involve survival of the fittest, and the fittest are defined as those that reproduce in larger numbers, the origin of mammals represents something very strange, indeed. Since they survived in very few numbers, evolution apparently occurred by survival of the unfit!

Evolutionists would have us believe that mammalian evolution stood still for about 120 million years. For 120 million years, according to evolutionary theory, mammals, apparently existing for that vast, vast stretch of time in extremely few numbers, remained evolutionarily dormant as rather small, generalized forms. Then, in the blink of an eye of geologic time, most reptiles, including the dinosaurs, disappeared, and appearing abruptly, fully-formed were the thirty-two orders of mammals, all highly specialized so that they could immediately be classified as primates, whales, bats, rodents, odd-toed ungulates, even-toed ungulates, etc.

In case it is suspected that we have overstated the case because of creationist bias, let us consider comments on the matter from George Gaylord Simpson, one of the world's leading evolutionists. He has said that:

> The most puzzling event in the history of life on earth is the change from the Mesozoic, the Age of Reptiles, to the Age of Mammals. It is as if the curtain were rung down

suddenly on the stage where all the leading roles were taken by reptiles, especially dinosaurs, in great numbers and bewildering variety, and rose again immediately to reveal the same setting but an entirely new cast, a cast in which the dinosaurs do not appear at all, other reptiles are supernumeraries, and all the leading parts are played by mammals of sorts barely hinted at in the preceding acts.[48]

And, we might emphasize again, the preceding acts covered 120 million years on the evolutionary time scale. Lest any evolutionist pretend that there is really no serious problem here, let him be reminded that Simpson has said that this is the most puzzling event in earth history. The problem disappears, of course, if the assumption of evolution is discarded and the creation model of origins is accepted. Furthermore, we might recall the fact that while Simpson calls this problem "the most puzzling event in the history of life," he also termed the abrupt appearance in a fully-formed state of the complex invertebrates in the Cambrian rocks "the major mystery of the history of life." Evolutionists actually are required to view many events in the history of life as shocking and mysteriously unexplainable.

A 100-Million-Year Shock to Evolutionists

A recent discovery has provided an additional shocking surprise to evolutionists. Evolutionists have always assumed that mammal-like reptiles became extinct in what they term the Middle Jurassic, which they believe followed the Late Triassic, by which time mammals had supposedly evolved. They had assumed that since mammal-like reptiles allegedly culminated in the mammals, and paleontologists had failed to find, or at least had failed to identify, fossils of mammal-like reptiles in rocks they think to be younger than Middle Jurassic rocks, the mammal-like reptiles had become extinct about 160 million years ago. Many evolutionary paleontologists and biologists thus find it difficult to accept the claims of Fox, Youzwyshyn, and Krause that they had identified a fossil of a mammal-like reptile in Late Paleocene rocks of Alberta, Canada, which they date at about 60 million years.[49] The

---

[48] G. G. Simpson, quoted in *Life Before Man* (New York: Time-Life Books, 1972), p. 42.

[49] R. C. Fox, G. P. Youzuryshun, and D. W. Krause, *Nature*, 358:233-235 (1992); Jeff Hecht, *New Scientist* 135:18 (1992).

time span from Middle Jurassic to Late Paleocene thus supposedly embraces 100 million years. They named this mammal-like reptile *Chronoperates paradoxus* (chronos, time; perates, wanderer; paradoxus, contrary to expectations). Fox and his collaborators present convincing evidence that identifies their fossil as a mammal-like reptile. Neil Shubin of the University of Pennsylvania is quoted as saying "that if the fossil had been found in the Triassic, he would have no problem calling *Chronoperates* a mammal-like reptile."[50]

These facts immediately generate several embarrassing questions for evolutionists. If mammals evolved from mammal-like reptiles, supposedly replacing them by natural selection, how could mammal-like reptiles survive for another 100 million years side by side with mammals? If *Chronoperates* (or its mammal-like reptilian ancestors) existed for the assumed 100 million years between the Middle Jurassic and Late Paleocene, why are their fossils so incredibly rare that to this date only a single fossil has ever been found? If only one million of these mammal-like reptiles had lived and died each year for 100 million years, 100 trillion would have lived and died during that vast stretch of time, and yet until now only one has been found in the fossil record. This is reminiscent of the coelacanth fish that supposedly had become extinct 70 million years ago until found still thriving in deep waters off the African coast. Something seems to be seriously wrong with the evolutionary scenario. These facts cast considerable suspicion on evolutionary time scales and theoretical processes.

The Great Diversity of Mammals

As is the case with most other major divisions of animal and plant life, mammals have always constituted a diverse lot. Today approximately 4,300 different species of mammals are recognized, and thousands of other species have become extinct. Several recent exciting discoveries will no doubt greatly expand our knowledge of mammals. One of the most exciting and doubtless productive discoveries has taken place in the Gobi Desert by a team of American and Russian scientists.[51] There in the Flaming Cliffs area, famous for its production of dinosaur fossils, a rich lode of mammalian fossils has been uncovered by the team. They have discovered so far the "exquisitely

---

[50] Hecht, *New Scientist* 135:18 (1992).
[51] Daniel Pendick, *Earth* 4(2): 20-23 (1995).

preserved" remains of 187 individual mammals, among which are many complete skeletons. Michael Novacek, one of the leaders of the American team, a senior scientist at the American Museum of Natural History, reports that the material found so far exceeds all the mammal fossils brought back from the Gobi Desert since 1922, when the first findings there were made. Researchers who got a view of the material at a recent meeting were "amazed at how pristine and complete the fossils were." These fossils were recovered from Cretaceous rocks, and evolutionists believe the mammals represented by the fossils existed about fifteen million years before the extinction of the dinosaurs, thus supposedly about eighty million years ago.

It is reported that this discovery may force evolutionists to rethink the way they portray mammals, since this find reveals that mammals were much more extensive and diverse before dinosaurs became extinct and thus, Novacek says, were not direct competitors of dinosaurs. There have been found in the Gobi Desert area fossils of dinosaurs, mammals, lizards, crocodiles, and turtles, so the emerging picture of ancient life is looking more and more as visualized by creationists.

Especially exciting is the discovery of mammalian fossil skulls with intact middle-ear ossicles and other important cranial features. Creationists expect that whatever is found there, each kind will be complete with no evidence of transitional features and thus are eagerly awaiting publication of the findings in a scientific journal. Only brief oral reports are available so far. Here, if evolution is true, we ought to find many evolutionary transitional forms showing generalized mammalian forms evolving to produce the "breathtaking evolutionary expansion" of mammals that appears in early Tertiary rocks, to quote evolutionists.

Another remarkable find of mammalian fossils occurred at a mining pit at Messel, 12 miles from Frankfurt, Germany, which in 1986 was declared a natural preserve by the State of Hesse. So far it has yielded specimens of more than forty mammalian species of fourteen of the approximately thirty-two orders of mammals.[52] These fossils have been assigned to the Eocene Epoch, or about 50–35 million years ago on the current evolutionary time scale. They are remarkably preserved, many being reconstructed on the basis of soft-body outlines.

---

[52] Gerhard Storch, *Scientific American* 266:64-69 (1992).

Many had stomach contents intact, the gut of a bat, for example, holding moths which flew at twilight or night, attesting to the fact that this bat fed at night and thus had the echolocation apparatus found in many modern bats. The fossils included those of odd-toed and even-toed hoofed animals, lemur-like prosimians (a primate), hedgehog-like insectivores, rodents, and opossum-like marsupials. Also found was a fossil of an anteater, *Eurotamandua joresi* of the order Edentata which, although supposedly 50 million years old, already had all the highly complex diagnostic features of the modern genera of anteaters. A fossil of *Eomanis waldi*, the oldest known pangolin, was also found. Pangolins are anteaters with a covering of broad, overlapping scales. Again, although supposedly 50 million years old, *E. waldi* resembled modern species of pangolins.

In his report on this remarkable fossil graveyard,[53] Gerhard Storch is forced to suggest that all of the mammals whose fossils have been found there had migrated into Europe from some other continent because they all appear fully-formed with no evolutionary history. Storch favors Africa, although this conclusion is by inference only because there is no fossil evidence in Africa to support such a scenario. Evolutionists frequently appeal to the notion of migration to explain the abrupt appearance, fully-formed, of creatures in a particular area. Of course the supposed source area cannot produce the required ancestors either.

The Major Divisions of Mammals

There is some confusion and consequent divisions of opinion among taxonomists concerning the major divisions of mammals. Some place modern mammals in two major groups. The living mammals of the Class Mammalia are divided into two major groups or subclasses, the Prototheria, which includes the monotremes, and the Theria, which some further subdivide into two infraclasses, the Metatheria or the marsupials, and the Eutheria, or true placental mammals. The modern monotremes, Order Monotremata, include the duck-billed platypus, *Ornithorhyncus*, and the spiny anteater or ecidna, *Tachyglossus* of Australia and the spiny anteater, *Zaglossus* of New Guinea. These creatures are considered to be both very primitive and highly specialized. They are mammals, since they have mammary

---

[53] *Ibid.*

glands for suckling the young, are warm blooded, have hair and other characteristics of mammals. On the other hand, the platypus has a duckbill, webbed feet, and lays eggs, commonly associated with birds, but it also has a reptilian shoulder girdle, and the postcranial skeleton includes a few other reptilian characteristics. The skulls of the echidna and platypus are highly specialized in a way that diverges from all other mammals, fossil or living. Romer describes them as among the most bizarre and paradoxical of living vertebrates. These are creatures that evolutionists wish never existed. Incorporating characteristics of mammals, birds, and reptiles (none in a transitional state), they could not be the offspring nor the ancestor of any of these three classes of vertebrates. The phylogeny of the monotremes is a matter of dispute among evolutionists. The fossil record of these creatures is extremely scanty and restricted to Australia. It is suggested that they diverged from the remainder of the mammals at a very early stage, but there are no transitional forms whatsoever to document an evolutionary origin of these strange creatures.

When the marsupials (Order Marsupialia) are considered, Australia immediately comes to mind because of the variety of marsupials that now inhabit that subcontinent. However, in times past marsupials were much more common in both North and South America and even Europe, than in Australia. Those that are supposed to be the earliest members of this group are found in late Cretaceous rocks (dated at about eighty million years) of North America. These creatures were very similar to the living opossums. Almost all, but not all, marsupials have a pouch where the young, born at a very immature stage, find refuge while they develop, fastened to the teats.

In what is believed to be the Tertiary Period, marsupials flourished in South America. Most were carnivores, ranging in size from that of an opossum to that of a bear. One of these carnivorous marsupials was *Thylacosmilus*, which had large tusks similar to those of the saber-toothed tiger, and similar to the jaguar in size. A fossil of the marsupial *Antarctodolops* has been found in Antarctica, bolstering the claim that marsupials may have found their way into Australia via Antarctica when these land masses were supposedly joined together.

Today a variety of marsupials occupy Australia. These include, in addition to the familiar kangaroos, the bandicoots, the Tasmanian "wolf," the Tasmanian devil, koalas, wombats (a burrowing animals, whose pouch opens backward to prevent soil from entering the pouch), and marsupial "mice," "moles," "cats," and "squirrels." A number of large extinct marsupials are known from Australian Pleistocene deposits, including *Diprotodont*, the largest marsupial known, about the size of a large rhinoceros, and *Thylacoleo*, about the size of a lion.

It has long been held by evolutionists that marsupial evolutionary ancestor or ancestors of this great variety of Australian marsupials entered Australia, probably via Antarctica, without a concurrent invasion of placental mammals, even though placental mammals existed alongside the marsupials at that time in South America. Free of competition with placental mammals, the marsupials supposedly were able to diversify to occupy the niches occupied by placentals in other areas. This is, however, a most unlikely scenario. First, as stated above, placentals existed side by side with marsupials in South America when it is supposed that marsupials found their way into Australia via Antarctica. If marsupials could find their way into Australia there would be no reason why placentals could not do likewise, perhaps even leading the way. As a matter of fact, placentals did apparently reach Australia at the same time as did the marsupials, if a recent report is correct. Godhelp et al. in a 1992 paper, report the discovery of a fossil non-volant (non-flying) placental mammal in freshwater clays near Murgon, southeastern Queensland, Australia.[54] They claim that these rocks are Early Tertiary, allegedly dated at nearly 55 million years. They state that:

> The presence of non-volant placentals in the Early Tertiary of Australia challenges a common presumption that marsupials dominated Australia's therian assemblages because of failure of such placentals to reach Australia before the Late Tertiary.

Later they state:

> *Tingamarra porterorum* is the earliest non-volant placental mammal known from Australia. Its presence in the Tingamarra Local Fauna demonstrates that Cainozoic dominance of Australia by marsupials should not be attributed to the failure of such placentals to reach this continent in the Early Tertiary. As is the case with South

---

[54] H. Godhelp et al., *Nature* 356:514-515 (1992).

America and probably Antarctica, both placentals and marsupials were present at the beginning of the Cainozoic but, for whatever serendipitous reasons, early placentals failed to survive in Australia.

The age claimed for these fossils is double of that suggested for earlier finds of Australian marsupial fossils, which were placed in the late Oligocene Epoch, supposedly about 25 million years ago. By that time evolutionists assume that most major groups had already differentiated, since the members of each of these groups appear fully-formed with no record of transitional forms.

Carroll states in his book, published in 1988 and thus before the report of Godhelp et al. had appeared, that:

> The fossil record of marsupials in the Australian region begins in the late Oligocene. . . . By this time most of the major groups had already differentiated. There is no direct evidence to document when marsupials first entered Australia.
>
> The place of origin and direction of dispersal of marsupials in the southern continents is subject to continuing debate . . . Marshall emphasizes that there is still no definite evidence.[55]

The Origin of Marsupials

Creationists and evolutionists agree that marsupials reached Australia by migration over connections or land bridges, possibly from South America via Antarctica, although this must remain highly speculative. There the agreement ends, however. Evolutionists believe that the marsupials found in Australia largely differentiated or evolved after migrant marsupial ancestors of these creatures reached Australia. Creation scientists, on the other hand, believe that each of these major kinds were separately created and existed as such before migrating into Australia. The actual fossil record definitely favors the creationist view. In Australia among the living and fossil marsupials are found marsupials of all sizes, shapes, and description. Some were

[55] R. L. Carroll, *Vertebrate Paleontology and Evolution* (New York: W. H. Freeman and Co., 1988), p. 431.

as small as mice. Some were larger than a rhinoceros. There were marsupials that resembled mice, martens, wolves, moles, cats, and squirrels. There were unique marsupials, including koalas, bandicoots, wombats, and kangaroos. If these creatures had evolved from one or a few common ancestors in Australia, the fossil record of what is alleged to embrace the past fifty to sixty million years should surely produce enough transitional forms to document the evolutionary origin of this great array of unique creatures from their common ancestor(s). We should have the ancestral and transitional forms documenting the evolutionary origin of kangaroos, bandicoots, wombats, the Tasmanian wolf, the Tasmanian devil, the philangers, the huge *Diprotodont*, koalas, and the marsupial "cats," "moles," and "mice." We do have fossils, although not many, and most of them are essentially the same as the modern families. What we do not have are transitional forms documenting an evolutionary origin of a single one of these creatures. As far as the scientific evidence is concerned, koalas have always been koalas, kangaroos have always been kangaroos, wombats were wombats when first seen, etc. Evolutionists now believe that neither placentals or marsupials are older than the other and that marsupials are in no way more primitive in physiology and morphology than placentals.[56] Here, as throughout the fossil record, **the rocks yield powerful positive evidence for creation.**

The Amazing Similarities of Placental and Marsupial Mammals

According to theory all of evolution is ultimately due to random genetic errors, or mutations. It is thus commonly maintained, as earlier pointed out, that it is virtually impossible for a complex structure or an organism to evolve independently more than once. It is difficult enough to imagine how a complex organ or an organism could have evolved once by a combination of thousands of hypothetical randomly generated "good" mutations, let alone imagining how it could have happened twice.

Evolutionists believe that placental and marsupial mammals have followed independent evolutionary pathways, splitting off from some mammal-like or primitive mammalian common ancestor. Since that

---

[56] J. A. W. Kirsch, *American Scientist* 65:276-288 (May-June 1977).

time, evolutionists believe, the specialized placental and marsupial mammals have evolved independently. It should therefore be incredibly difficult, if not impossible, for the evolutionary process to produce a pair of creatures, one a placental and the other a marsupial, that are very similar. The evolution of each of these creatures would have occurred in different parts of the world under very different ecological conditions and circumstances, such as availability of prey and predation by predators. Yet, both in the fossil record and living today, there are a variety of placentals that are mimicked by marsupials.

In lower Miocene rocks of South America has been found the fossil of *Necrolestes*, a marsupial so similar to placental insectivores it was for a long time mistaken as a placental insectivore.[57] The Tasmanian "wolf" is very similar to placental wolves. Carroll states, concerning *Thylacinus*, the Tasmanian "wolf," that:

> The general body form as well as details of the dentition provide a strikingly close parallel with the placental canids.[58]

There is the numbat or Australian anteater, *Myrmecobius*, which had a long snout similar to placental anteaters. Then, of course, there are the mouse-like, cat-like, and mole-like Australian marsupials.

Evolutionists imagine that placental and marsupial mammals split off from a common ancestor sometime in the late Cretaceous, supposedly about seventy to eighty million years ago. At that time neither the placental nor the marsupial ancestor of the placental wolf and the Tasmanian or marsupial wolf had any of the specialties that would relate it to a wolf. Then, in different parts of the world, random genetic errors in concert with the ecological, biological, and geological conditions that must have differed very significantly if not drastically, two very similar creatures, similar even in their dentitions, were created by a blind, evolutionary process. And similar events happened not once, but in numerous cases. What an incredible faith!

---

[57] Romer, *Vertebrate Paleontology*, p. 204.
[58] Carroll, *Vertebrate Paleontology and Evolution*, p. 435.

The Origin of Specialized Placental Mammals

It is one thing to attempt to trace the transformation of some sort of generalized creature into another which shares some features in common with the first, but it is another thing, and very much more definitive, to attempt to document the origin of creatures designed for a unique way of life and thus endowed with highly specialized features. Such specialized features include, for example, the wings of flying insects, flying reptiles, and flying mammals; the feathers of birds; duckbills on birds, dinosaurs, and the platypus; the echolocation apparatus of bats; the ear ossicles of mammals; the cranial features required for whales to dive to great depths; the many unique features of various dinosaurs, already discussed, and many, many others. **THIS IS WHERE TRANSITIONAL FORMS WOULD BE THE MOST OBVIOUS AND EASY TO IDENTIFY. THIS IS WHERE THE REQUIRED TRANSITIONAL FORMS ARE MOST CRITICALLY NEEDED. THIS IS WHERE EVOLUTION THEORY INVARIABLY FAILS.**

The Origin of Flight in Mammals

The bats, Order Chiroptera, are the only flying mammals and are the most specialized of all mammals. They have been classified into two suborders. The Megachiroptera are the large fruit-eating bats, or "flying foxes," found today in the Old World tropical areas and the Pacific Region. The Microchiroptera are the generally small bats which are worldwide in distribution. Most are insectivorous, feeding on insects at night, which they can detect and catch in total darkness.

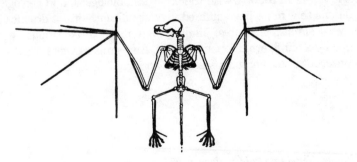

Figure 13. Skeleton of a fossil bat, *Palaeochiropteryx*. From Romer, *Vertebrate Paleontology*, by permission of The University of Chicago Press.

They have this capability because they are equipped with an incredibly complex echolocation system, not found in fruit-eating bats. The bats emit a stream of high-pitched sounds which bounce off of objects. The echo returns to the bat and is received by the very sensitive auditory apparatus of the bat. As a consequence, millions of electronic impulses are transmitted to the brain each second, and the brain converts these electronic messages into an image. Why isn't a bat confused by the sounds emitted by other bats, sometimes in the thousands while in a pitch-dark cave? Incredibly, each bat is capable of recognizing its own signal, apparently all others being filtered out by the bat's auditory system. What an ingenious system! Some microchiropterans are designed to feed on fish, while others, the "vampire" bats, feed by sucking blood from large animals, such as cattle.

Here we have an ideal test case for creation versus evolution—a very highly specialized mammal that supposedly evolved the power of flight, starting from a non-flying mammal, presumably an insectivore. This evolutionary process would have involved a time span of million of years and would have required a large number of exceedingly rare "good" mutations produced randomly among an ocean of bad mutations. Each slightly modified "good" mutant would have to compete against a highly competent competitor (if it were not highly competent it would not have evolved), many generations thus being required to replace the original. Each intermediate must not only be viable but superior to the preceding stage. This process must somehow have gradually converted the forelimbs of the ancestral land-dwelling mammal into wings, as four fingers of each hand (the thumb remaining essentially unaffected) gradually increased in length. The wing membrane had to be gradually generated by a series of other rare "good" mutations. Sometime during this process, other "good" mutations had to produce, step by step, flight muscles and the numerous unique arrangements of tendons, nerves, and blood vessels required for the specialized features of the bat. Skulls and teeth had to be modified in the proper fashion and, in the microcheropterans, somehow, by a series of random genetic errors, a precise series of alterations in existing structures and/or the generation of new structures had to be accomplished by a series of other incredibly rare "good" genetic errors in just the right sequence to create the sonar or echolocation system of these bats, being careful at

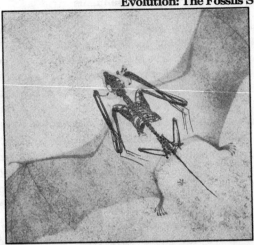

Figure 14. Photo of the oldest fossil bat superimposed on its reconstruction, by J. L. Jepsen. From the cover page of *Science,* December 9, 1966. Copyright 1966 by the American Association for the Advancement of Science.

the same time to provide the necessary filtration system that enables each bat to screen out all signals except those he alone has emitted.

Thus, if evolution is true, the fossil record should produce a series of transitional forms documenting at least some of the intermediate stages, revealing, for example, the gradual conversion of forelimbs into wings, as the fingers became longer and longer, and intermediate stages in the modification of the skull and auditory apparatus to generate the echolocation system of the Microcheroptera. If creation is true, however, what is believed to be the oldest fossil bat should be 100% bat. No evidence of transitional forms linking bats to ancestral land-dwelling mammals would be found. Which model, creation or evolution, do the data fit best? There is simply no contest—creation wins hands down. The following statement by Carroll says it all:

> Bats are among the most specialized of modern mammals. All are accomplished flyers, and the insectivorous microcheropterans have a highly developed sonar that enables them to hunt insects in the dark. Like the pterosaurs, the flight structure of bats was already highly evolved when they first appeared in the fossil record. The

oldest skeleton of a bat, *Icaronycteris*, from the early
Eocene, appears almost indistinguishable from living bats.[59]

No one could say it better, but only repeat it for emphasis.
According to Glenn Jepson, nothing related to a bat has ever been
found in the fossil record that is any older than *Icaronycteris* and it is
essentially identical to a modern bat.[60]

Recent research has revealed that *Icaronycteris* had the sonar
system found in modern microchiropterans.[61] Thus bats appear in the
fossil record fully-formed without a trace of ancestors or transitional
forms, and they have remained essentially unchanged for the supposed
50 million years since they first appeared in the fossil record. This
evidence is absolutely contradictory to evolutionary theory but is
precisely what is predicted on the basis of creation. The paucity of the
fossil record of bats cannot be used as an excuse by evolutionists, since
we do have many fossils of bats. The fossils of bats recovered at Messel
were the most numerous of fossil creatures discovered at that site.[62]
Today the bats, except for rodents, are the most prolific of all
mammals.

ARE MEGACHIROPTERANS MORE CLOSELY RELATED TO HUMANS THAN THEY ARE TO MICROCHEROPTERANS?

As incredible as it may seem, John Pettigrew of Queensland
University in Brisbane, Australia, is suggesting that the
megachiropterans are more closely related to primates than they are to
their fellow bats, the microcheropterans.[63] Since humans are primates,
evolutionists who share Pettigrew's opinion would thus believe that
the fruit-eating bats are as closely related or more so to humans than
to the insectivorous bats. According to Pettigrew, the complex visual
system of the megabats, the way visual stimuli are transmitted to the
brain, is similar to primates but different from that for the microbats.
Pettigrew seriously doubts that the neural characteristics employed in
common by megabats and primates could have evolved independently
in these two different kinds of creatures.

---

[59] *Ibid.*, p. 463.

[60] G. L. Jepson, *Science* 154:1333-1339 (1966).

[61] M. J. Novacek, *Nature* 315:140-151 (1985).

[62] Storch, *Scientific American* 266:64-69 (1992).

[63] J. D. Pettigrew, *Science* 231:1304-1306 (1981); *Systematic Zoology*
40:199-216 (1991).

Critics of Pettigrew's views believe that it is more difficult to imagine two different independently evolving creatures ending up with the same type of bat wings found to exist in common in the megabats and microbats than to imagine the independent evolutionary origin of the visual neural systems found in these two types of bats.[64] Creation scientists hasten to point out that just one or two transitional forms would be sufficient to settle the controversy.

Rodents Provide Positive Evidence for Creation

The order Rodentia should provide evolutionists with a group of animals ideal for evolutionary studies. In number of species and genera, the rodents exceed all other mammalian orders combined. They flourish under almost all conditions. Surely, if any group of animals could supply transitional forms, this group could.

As to their origin, Romer has said:

> The origin of the rodents is obscure. When they first appear, in the late Paleocene, in the genus *Paramys*, we are already dealing with a typical, if rather primitive, true rodent, with the definitive ordinal characters well developed. Presumably, of course, they had arisen from some basal, insectivorous, placental stock, but no transitional forms are known.[65]

Furthermore, transitional forms between the basic rodent types are not found in the fossil record. For example, Romer says,

> . . . the beavers are presumably derived from some primitive sciuromorph stock, but there are no annectant types between such forms and the oldest Oligocene castoroids to prove direct relationship.[66]

Speaking of the Hystricidae, the Old World porcupines, Romer says:

---

[64] J. G. M. Thewissen and S. K. Babcock, *Bioscience* 42(5):340-345 (1992).

[65] Romer, *Vertebrate Paleontology*, p. 303.

[66] *Ibid.*, p. 308.

There are a few fossil forms, back to the Miocene and possibly late Oligocene, but these give no indication of relationship of hystricids to other rodent types.[67]

Commenting on the "rock rat," *Petromus*, Romer says, "almost nothing is known of the ancestry of *Petromus*."[68] Of the superfamily Theridomyoidea, Romer says, "At present we know nothing of their ancestry or possible descendants."[69] Of the lagomorphs (hares and rabbits), once placed in a suborder of the rodents, but now placed in a separate order, Lagomorpha, Romer must admit that "The lagomorphs show no close approach to other placental groups, and the ordinal characters are well developed in even the oldest known forms."[70]

Thus we see that the order Rodentia, which should supply an excellent case for evolution, if evolution really did occur, offers powerful evidence for creation.

The Famous Horse Series

Horses comprise one of the most interesting mammalian groups as far as the question of origins is concerned. Almost all students are familiar with the story of horse "evolution," beginning with *Hyracotherium* (*Eohippus*), a dog-sized "horse" with four toes on the front feet, passing via straight-line evolution through three-toed varieties, and ending with the modern one-toed *Equus*. But while subscribing to the evolution of the horse in general, Birdsell proclaims that "Much of this story is incorrect. . . ."[71] Others hold the same view. George Gaylord Simpson, for example, has declared that several generations of students have been misinformed about the real meaning of the evolution of the horse.[72] These authors believe that the

---

[67] *Ibid.*, p. 309.

[68] *Ibid.*

[69] *Ibid.*

[70] *Ibid.*, p. 310.

[71] J. B. Birdsell, *Human Evolution* (Rand McNally College Pub. Co., 1975), p. 169.

[72] G. G. Simpson, *The Major Features of Evolution* (New York: Columbia University Press, 1953), p. 259.

evolution of the horse is much more complicated than usually portrayed, and is more like a series of bushes, perhaps, than like a tree.

To us the family tree of the horse appears to be merely a scenario put together from non-equivalent parts. Nowhere, for example, are there intermediate forms documenting transition from a non-horse ancestor (supposedly a condylarth) with five toes on each foot, to *Hyracotherium* with four toes on the front foot and three on the rear. Neither are there transitional forms between the four-toed *Hyracotherium* and the three-toed *Miohippus*, or between the latter, equipped with browsing teeth, and the three-toed *Merychippus*, equipped with high-crowned grazing teeth. Finally, the one-toed grazers, such as *Equus*, appear abruptly with no intermediates showing gradual evolution from the three-toed grazers.

Thus, Birdsell tells this story in the following way (note that when an evolutionist uses such terms as "sudden," "abrupt," or "rapid" with reference to transitions he is usually inferring that no transitional forms have been found):

> The evolution of the foot mechanisms proceeded by rapid and abrupt changes rather than gradual ones. The transition from the form of foot shown by miniature *Eohippus* to larger consistently three-toed *Miohippus* was so abrupt that it even left no record in the fossil deposits . . . their foot structure changed very rapidly to a three-toed sprung foot in which the pad disappeared and the two side toes became essentially functionless. Finally, in the Pliocene the line leading to the modern one-toed grazer went through a rapid loss of the two side toes on each foot."[73]

He then goes on to say that this evolution was not gradual but that it had proceeded by rapid jumps.

In November of 1980, 150 evolutionists met for four days at the Field Museum of Natural History in Chicago to attack or defend the gradualistic evolutionary theory, or the new-Darwinian theory of evolution. More will be said of this later. Those attacking the new-Darwinian mechanism of evolution maintained there is little or no evidence of gradualism in the fossil record. Naturally the story of

---

[73] J. B. Birdsell, *Human Evolution*, p. 170.

the alleged evolution of the horse was discussed. Boyce Rensberger, in his report of the meeting, stated that:

> The popularly told example of horse evolution, suggesting a gradual sequence of changes from four-toed fox-sized creatures living nearly 50 million years ago to today's much larger one-toed horse, has long been known to be wrong. Instead of gradual change, fossils of each intermediate species appear fully distinct, persist unchanged, and then become extinct. Transitional forms are unknown.[74]

From the above literature it is evident that the continuity required by evolutionary theory cannot be documented from the fossil record. On the other hand, as Rensberger describes, each one of the horse kinds appears fully formed and no subsequent change takes place before it disappears from the record. This is the type of evidence predicted on the basis of creation.

A rather astounding and revealing fact is discovered when we compare North American ungulates to South American ungulates. All of us are familiar with the series shown in figure 15. These are the

Figure 15. The pes (hindfeet) of, a) *"Eohippus"*; b) *Merychippus*; c) *Equus*.

hindfeet (pes) of, (a) *"Eohippus"*; (b) *Merychippus*, with reduced lateral toes; and (c) modern *Equus*.

Now look at figure 16. Illustrated are the pes of the South American ungulates (order Litopterna), (a) *Macrauchenia*; (b) *Diadiaphorus*; and (c) *Thoatherium*. Again we see a three-toed hoofed ungulate *Macrauchenia*); a three-toed hoofed ungulate with reduced laterals (*Diadiaphorus*); and, in this case, a one-toed hoofed ungulate

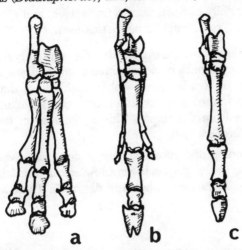

Figure 16. The pes of South American ungulates of the order Litopterna, a) *Macrauchenia*, b) *Diadiaphorus*; c) *Thoatherium*.

(*Thoatherium*) which, Romer says, seems even more horselike than any true horse, for it was single-toed with splints more reduced than those of modern equids.[75]

Do they not thus provide another nice, logical evolutionary series? No, not at all, for they do not occur in this sequence at all! *Diadiaphorus*, the three-toed ungulate with reduced lateral toes, and *Thoatherium*, the one-toed ungulate, were contemporaries in the Miocene epoch. *Macrauchenia*, with pes containing three full-sized toes, is not found until the Pliocene epoch, which followed the Miocene according to the geological column, and his fossils are even found in Pleistocene rocks. In fact, it is said that the one-toed *Thoatherium*

---

[74] Boyce Rensberger, *Houston Chronicle*, 5 November 1980), sec. 4, p. 15.
[75] Romer, *Vertebrate Paleontology*, pp. 260-261.

became extinct in the Miocene before the three-toed *Macrauchenia* made his appearance in the Pliocene.

Thus, if evolutionists would permit the fossil evidence and their usual assumptions concerning geological time to be their guide, they should suppose that in South America a one-toed ungulate gave rise to a three-toed ungulate with reduced lateral toes, which then gave rise to an ungulate with three full-sized toes. This is precisely the opposite of the supposed sequence of events that occurred with North American horses. We do not know any evolutionist who suggests such an evolutionary sequence of events, but why not? Perhaps it is because the three-toed to one-toed sequence for North American horses became so popularized in evolutionary circles that no one dare suggest the reverse transition. Of course, there is no more evidence for transitional forms in South America than there is in North America.

In the Rattlesnake Formation of the John Day Country of northeastern Oregon, the three-toed *Neohipparion* is found with the one-toed horse, *Pliohippus*.[76] No transitional forms between the two are found, In other cases "primitive" species of a genus, such as those of *Merychippus*, are found in geological formations supposedly younger than those containing "advanced" species.[77]

As a matter of fact, the idea widely promoted by evolutionists that three-toed horses evolved into one-toed horses is not supported by the evidence. Yes, only one-toed horses survive today, but not because they evolved from three-toed horses and then replaced them because they were evolutionarily advantaged. Three-toed horses and one-toed horses commonly co-existed together in North America. For example, in northeastern Nebraska there is a remarkable fossil graveyard in which are found a variety of birds, reptiles, and mammals. The deposit, said to represent a small pond, was discovered by Michael Voorhies, curator of vertebrate paleontology at the Nebraska State Museum.[78] More than 200 virtually complete fossil skeletons have been removed. The creatures, Voorhies believes, were killed over a period of months rather than in a sudden catastrophe, by ash falls from volcanic activity. Among the rich mammalian fauna were found five species of horses:

---

[76] S. Nevins, *Creation Research Society Quarterly* 10:196 (1974).

[77] J. T. Gregory, *University of California Publication of Geological Science* 26:428 (1942).

[78] M. R. Voorhies, *National Geographic* 159:66-75 (1981).

Pseudhipparion gratum, Cormohipparion occidentale, Protohippus supremus, Astrohippus sp., *Neohipparion,* and *Dinohippus.*[79] The *Dinohippus* varieties included a mix of tridactyl and monodactyl horses. MacFadden thus states,

> The recent discovery of an exquisitely preserved population of primitive *Dinohippus* [*Pliohippus* of Voorhies (1981)] from Ashfall Fossil Beds in northeastern Nebraska . . . suggests that some individuals were tridactyl, whereas others were monodactyl (Voorhies (1981). Although that also may have been the case for other primitive equine species previously thought to have been exclusively monodactyl. . .[80]

Later, MacFadden tells us that,

> Thus there were at least three different adaptive groups of fossil horses with diverse postcranial morphologies that coexisted during the middle and late Miocene. The anchiteres retained the primitive tridactyl foot structure, including a digital pad. The advanced three-toed horses evolved an unguligrade foot that in many ways was adaptively similar to the monodactyl forms. Finally, the monodactyl horses arose during that time, with a locomotory complex that also occurred later in *Equus.*[81]

Thus, there were three different groups of horses coexisting at this one time—"primitive" three-toed horses, "advanced" three-toed horses, and a one-toed horse. In publications by evolutionists, we see these arranged in a series, suggesting that the "primitive" three-toed horse evolved into the "advanced" three-toed horse, and the "advanced" three-toed horse finally evolved into a one-toed horse. Obviously, this is not the way it happened at all. As documented earlier, there are no transitional forms showing a three-toed horse

---

[79] M. Voorhies and J. R. Thomasson, *Science* 206:331-333 (1979); Bruce J. MacFadden, *Fossil Horses* (Cambridge: Cambridge University Press, 1992), p. 73.

[80] Macfadden, *Fossil Horses,* p. 255.

[81] *Ibid.,* p. 257.

evolving into a one-toed horse. They were actually living together. In a brief section on the litopterns in South America, MacFadden says they

> . . . were a group of extinct South American herbivores that became monodactyl during the early Miocene, about 8 myr earlier than did horses in North America.[82]

MacFadden fails to say a single word about the fact that three-toed litopterns supposedly appeared later, after the one-toed variety had become extinct.

Walter R. Barnhart, after his extensive study of the literature related to the origin and diversity of those creatures commonly referred to as horses, the Equidae, reached a number of surprising conclusions.[83] His research led him to conclude that the occurrence of mixed faunal groups of genera implies cohabiting populations which exhibit only relative minor fluctuations, or "microevolution," as it is often called. He reported that the geological range of taxa indicates that all genera of horses are found in the Miocene and thus the geological progress required by evolution does not exist. His final conclusion was that the fossil group of equini is made up of only three genera: *Hyracotherium*, *Mesohippus*, and *Equus*.

Under *Hyracotherium* he includes *Orohippus* and *Epihippus* as varieties. He contends that *Miohippus*, *Anchitherium*, *Hypohippus*, *Megahippus*, *Archaeohippus*, and *Parahippus* should be grouped as varieties or species under *Mesohippus*, and that *Merychippus*, *Hipparion*, *Stylohipparion*, *Neohipparion*, *Nannippus*, *Calippus*, *Pliohippus*, *Hippidion*, *Orohippidium*, and *Parahipparion* are all varieties or species under *Equus*. Barnhart also points out the lack of transitional forms required by the theory of evolution. He asserts that the notion that fossil horses (Equidae) form an evolutionary series that demonstrates macroevolution is falsified by a close, critical examination of the evidence.

Was *Hyracotherium* (Eohippus) really a horse? *Hyracotherium* was discovered in Europe before "Eohippus" was uncovered in North America, and was given the genus designation of *Hyracotherium* by the famous British anatomist and paleontologist, Richard Owen, who

---

[82] *Ibid.*, p. 262.

[83] Walter R. Barnhart, Thesis for Master of Science (El Cajon, California: Institute for Creation Research Graduate School, 1987), pp. 148-150.

was also its discoverer. Later, other specimens were discovered in North America and given the genus name *Eohippus*. It was subsequently concluded that the North American specimens were actually of the same genus as *Hyracotherium*. The latter thus has priority, so *Eohippus* is not a valid name for these creatures. It is most commonly used, however, undoubtedly because the name *Eohippus* means "drawn horse" while *Hyracotherium* was chosen by Owen because of the resemblance of this creature to creatures of the genus *Hyrax* (cony, daman).

Although *Hyracotherium*, or "Eohippus," was unlike modern horses, both morphologically and in habitat, this creature was chosen to stand at the base of the horses by the American paleontologist Marsh, and others, and this scheme became solidly entrenched both in popular circles and in scientific status after a lecture in New York City by Thomas H. Huxley and the publication of Marsh's studies.[84]

Nilsson has pointed out that while *Hyracotherium* has little or no resemblance to horses, it apparently was morphologically and in habitat similar to living creatures of the genus *Hyrax*.[85] *Hyrax*, like *Hyracotherium*, has four toes on the front feet and three on the rear. The cheek teeth of these two creatures share many similarities and are more like those of rhinoceros than those of horses. The habitat and way of life of *Hyrax* are also similar to those postulated for *Hyracotherium*. Thus, Nilsson maintains that while *Hyracotherium* does not resemble present-day horses in any way, they were, apparently, remarkably similar to the present-day *Hyrax*.

Others also doubt whether *Hyracotherium* was related to the horse. For example, Kerkut states:

> In the first place it is not clear that *Hyracotherium* was the ancestral horse. Thus Simpson (1945) states, "Matthew has shown and insisted that *Hyracotherium* (including Eohippus) is so primitive that it is not much more definitely equid than tapirid, rhinocerotid, etc., but it is customary to place it at the root of the equid group."[86]

---

[84] F. W. Cousins, *Creation Research Society Quarterly* 7:102 (1971).

[85] H. Nilsson, *Synthetische Artbildung* (Lund, Sweden: Vertag CWE Gleenrup, 1954). See Cousins, *Creation Resaerch Society Quarterly* 7:102 (1971), for a summary of Nilsson's section on the horse.

[86] G. A. Kerkut, *Implications of Evolution* (New York: Pergamon Press,

In other words, *Hyracotherium* is not any more like a horse than it is similar to a tapir or a rhinoceros, and thus just as justifiably it could have been chosen as the ancestral rhinoceros or tapir. It seems, then, that the objectivity of those involved in the construction of the phylogenetic tree of the horse was questionable from the very start, and that the "horse" on which the entire family tree of the horse rests was not a horse at all.

Furthermore, George Gaylord Simpson has admitted that nowhere in this world is there a trace of a fossil that would close the large gap between *Hyracotherium* and the Condylarthra, the order of mammals evolutionists have suggested as ancestral to *Hyacotherium*, and thus to all horses. William J. Morris, while stating his belief in the phylogeny of the equids from *Hyracotherium* to *Equus*, states,

> . . . the phylogenetic link between the earliest populations of *Hyracotherium* and possible condylarth ancestors has not been found. In fact, the very abrupt Eocene appearance of *Hyracotherium, even* in those areas where Late Paleocene faunas are well known, is disconcerting.[87]

No definitive work on horses has been published since the publication of Kerkut's book that would materially affect his conclusion that:

> In some ways it looks as if the pattern of horse evolution might be even as chaotic as that proposed by Osborn (1937, 1943) for the evolution of the Proboscidea, where "in almost no instance is any known form considered to be a descendant from any other known form; every subordinate grouping is assumed to have sprung, quite separately and usually without any known intermediate stage, from hypothetical common ancestors in the early Eocene or Late Cretaceous" (Romer, 1949).[88]

If indeed "horse evolution" is that chaotic and patchy, this classic case for evolution is without real merit. The actual evidence, on the other hand, neatly fits the creation model.

1960), p. 149.

[87] W. J. Morris, *Science* 153:1378 (1966).

[88] Barnhart, M. A. Thesis, pp. 148-150.

Marine Mammals

Evolutionists are desperate in their search to find transitional or intermediate forms to validate their theory of evolution. This situation is strikingly true concerning the origin of whales, dolphins, and other marine mammals. In one of Romer's concluding statements in his discussion of the subungulates (conies, elephants, sea cows), he says, "conies, proboscideans, and sirenians were already distinct groups at the time when they first appear in the fossil record."[89] Olson states that if we seek the ancestries of the marine mammals we run into a blank wall as far as intermediate stages between land and sea are concerned.[90] His remark included the seals, dolphins, and whales.

Speaking of whales, Colbert said:

> These mammals must have had an ancient origin, for no intermediate forms are apparent in the fossil record between the whales and the ancestral Cretaceous placentals. Like the bats, the whales (using the term in a general and inclusive sense) appear suddenly in early Tertiary times, fully adapted by profound modifications of the basic mammalian structure for a highly specialized mode of life. Indeed, the whales are even more isolated with relation to other mammals than the bats; they stand quite alone.[91]

Wursig has suggested that dolphins may have evolved from land mammals resembling the even-toed ungulates of today such as cattle, pigs, and buffaloes.[92] It is quite entertaining, starting with cows, pigs, or buffaloes, to attempt to visualize what the intermediates may have looked like. Starting with a cow, one could even imagine one line of descent which prematurely became extinct, due to what might be called an "udder failure!"

---

[89] Romer, *Vertebrate Paleontology*, p. 254.

[90] E. C. Olson, *The Evolution of Life* (New York: New American Library, 1965), p. 178.

[91] E. H. Colbert, *Evolution of the Vertebrates*, First ed. (New York: John Wiley and Sons, 1955), p. 303.

[92] Bernd Wursig, *Scientific American* 240(3): 136 (1979).

In a foldout accompanying an article on whales which appeared in *National Geographic Magazine* some years ago we are told,

> The whale's ascendency to sovereign size apparently began sixty million years ago when hairy, four-legged mammals, in search of food or sanctuary, ventured into the water. As eons passed, changes slowly occurred: hind legs disappeared, front legs changed into flippers, hair gave way to a thick, smooth blanket of blubber, nostrils moved to the top of the head, the tail broadened into flukes, and in the buoyant water world the body became enormous.[93]

In recent years a series of discoveries have been made of fossilized creatures which evolutionists have seized upon as virtual proof that some hairy four-legged animal really did venture into the water and gradually, over millions of years, evolve into a whale. Stephen Gould, whose favorite pastime is bashing creationists, rushed an article into print in which he described these finds in glowing terms.[94] He believes that evolutionists have finally scored a victory over creationists who declare that the fossil record fails to produce the transitional forms required by evolution. He declared:

> I cannot imagine a better tale for popular presentation of science or a more satisfying, and intellectually based, political victory over lingering creationist opposition.

Earlier in the article he had said:

> Those dogmatists who by verbal trickery can make white black, and black white, will never be convinced of anything, but *Ambulocetus* is the very animal that they proclaimed impossible in theory.

Creation scientists point out that evolutionists who believe that the origin of their human brain with its 12 billion brain cells and 120 trillion connections can ultimately be traced back to nothing but a mixture of hydrogen and helium gases plus gravitational energy are the ones who can believe, if needed to satisfy evolutionary theory, black is white, and white is black. As the Red Queen in Alice in Wonderland

---

[93] *National Geographic Magazine* (December 1976), Foldout.
[94] S. J. Gould, *Natural History* (May 1994), pp. 8-15.

stated, if one practices hard enough you can believe six impossible things before breakfast.

The consensus of evolutionists today has settled on the hairy, four-legged carnivorous mammal, *Mesonyx*, as the probable ancestor of all marine mammals. This opinion is based largely on dental evidence and shape of the skull. The mesonychids were wolf-like, hoofed carnivores that, as far as anyone knows, never went near water except to drink. Carroll states, *"Mesonyx* was the size and proportions of a wolf and perhaps, had a similar way of life."[95] Now let us push this wolf, or wolf-like creature, into the ocean and see where he leads us according to evolutionary scenario.

The first report concerned a new discovery of fossils of *Basilosaurus. Basilosaurus* was a large serpentine vertebrate found in Eocene rocks in the early 19th Century. Its name, which means "king lizard," was given to it by R. Harlan in 1834 because he thought it was a reptile. Later others considered it to be a mammal, but the name stuck. In 1990 Gingerich, Smith, and Simons announced that in 1987 and 1989 they had mapped 243 partial skeletons of *Basilosaurus* in the Reuglodon Valley in the desert of north central Egypt.[96] In addition to fairly large front feet and legs, this creature had a complete pair of hind legs, but tiny in size for such a creature. Although they reported that most joints were well-formed, that the patella and calcaneal tuber are large for insertion of powerful muscles, and that the knee has a complex locking mechanism, they believe the hind limbs were too small to assist in swimming and could not have supported the body on land. They therefore speculated that the hind limbs were probably used as accessories to assist in copulation. Evolutionists assume that the pelvic bones found in a few of the modern whales are vestiges left over from terrestrial ancestors. These pelvic bones are not vestigial structures that are on their way out, however. They serve a very important function. The pelvis of those modern whales that have them serves as the anchor for reproductive organs.[97]

Was *Basilosaurus* a whale, or on its way to becoming a whale? What makes a whale a whale? It all depends upon assumptions one

---

[95] Carroll, *Vertebrate Paleontology and Evolution*, p. 483.

[96] P. D. Gingerich, B. H. Smith and E. L. Simons, *Science* 249:154-157 (1990).

[97] W. M. A. de Smet, *Z. Saugetierkd* 40:299 (1975).

uses during his interpretation. We certainly have no whales today that have front and hind limbs. What was a whale doing with powerful front and hind legs? Whatever he was, creation scientists certainly do not believe *Basilosaurus* was a creature intermediate between a wolf or wolf-like animal and a whale.

In 1983, headlines in newspapers all over the world, based on an article published by Gingerish and coworkers,[98] trumpeted the discovery of a so-called primitive whale which established a link between whales and their hypothetical land-mammal ancestor, the hoofed mammalian carnivore, *Mesonyx*. The fossil material consisted solely of the posterior portion of the cranium, two fragments of the lower jaw, and isolated upper and lower cheek teeth. The creature was given the name *Pakicetus inachus*.

This fossil material was found in fluvial red sediments, or river-produced deposits colored by material leached from iron ores. This formation is thus a terrestrial or continental deposit. The fossil remains associated with *Pakicetus* are dominated by land mammals. Nonmammalian remains include other terrestrial remains such as snails, fishes (particularly catfish), turtles, and crocodiles. This evidence indicates a fluvial and continental, rather than a marine environment, as would be expected for a whale or whale-like creature. It is highly significant that the auditory mechanism of *Pakicetus* was that of a land mammal, rather than that of a whale, since there is no evidence that it could hear directionally under water, nor is there any evidence of vascularization of the middle ear to maintain pressure during diving. The authors stated that the teeth resemble those of the mesonychids, which possibly fed on carrion, mollusks, or tough vegetable matter. On the basis of this evidence, it seems most likely that *Pakicetus* was nothing more than a land mammal, with no relationship to marine mammals.

More recently, the claim concerning the possible discovery of a link between land mammals and marine mammals was contained in an article published in January 1994, in *Science*.[99] The article served as a basis, once again, for newspaper headlines throughout the U.S. For example, the Cleveland *Plain Dealer* featured the report in an article

---

[98] P. D. Gingerich et al., *Science* 220:403-406 (1983).
[99] J. G. M. Thewissen, S. T. Hussain, and M. Arif, *Science* 263:210-212 (1994).

published in that paper January 16, 1994, with the bold headline, "Fossil Thought to Belong to Walking Whale—Creature May Be Missing Link." Since whales don't walk on land, skeptics would immediately question the basis for designating this creature a whale, whatever it may have been. As a matter of fact, in a commentary published in the same issue of *Science* as the original scientific report, the writer states: "The authors provide some evidence for the seemingly preposterous conclusion that archaic whales were capable of walking on land."[100] The investigators gave their find the name *Ambulocetus natans*, from ambulare (to walk), cetus (whale), and natans (swimming). They thus believe that this creature both walked on land and swam in the water. In their report, the authors state: "Unlike modern cetaceans, *Ambulocetus* certainly was able to walk on land, probably in a way similar to modern sea lions or fur seals. In water, it combined aspects of the locomotion of modern seals, otters, and cetaceans. . . . As such, *Ambulocetus* represents a critical intermediate between land mammals and marine cetaceans."[101]

It is reported that Hans Thewissen, an assistant professor of anatomy at Northeastern Ohio Medical School; Tasseer Hussain, professor of anatomy at Harvard University; and M. Arif, a geologist of the Geological Survey of Pakistan, happened upon the fossil during a 1992 dig in hills west of Islamabad, Pakistan. The *Plain Dealer*, along with its article, has a good picture of the fossil. When some of the ICR staff looked at the picture with the knowledge that Thewissen and fellow workers called this creature a whale, they were naturally very skeptical having seen neither an elephant that flies or a whale that walks. In their article, Thewissen and coworkers state that *Ambulocetus* was about the size of a male sea lion, weighing about 650 lb. and had a robust radius and ulna (the two bones in the upper forearm). They report that the structure of the forearm would have allowed powerful elbow extension by triceps, and that, unlike modern cetaceans, elbow, wrist, and digital joints were flexible and synovial (lubricated). The hand was long and broad, with five digits. The femur was short and stout, and the feet were enormous. The toes were terminated by a short phalanx carrying a convex hoof. They suggest that unlike modern cetaceans, *Ambulocetus* had a long tail, and that it probably did not possess flukes. One wonders what in the world a

---

[100] Annalisa Berta, *Science* 263:180 (1994).

[101] Thewissen, Hussain, and Arif, *Science* 263:212 (1994).

whale was doing with hind limbs that terminated in a foot with hooves, or with any kind of powerful forelimbs and hind limbs that were designed to walk on land.

It is reported that the fossil of *Ambulocetus* was found in a silt and mudstone bed which contained impressions of leaves and abundant *Turritella*, a marine gastropod. This would suggest that it lived near the seashore, feeding possibly on land animals and/or plants, and perhaps foraging into shallow seas to feed on gastropods and molluscs. They report that the fossil beds are lower-to-middle Eocene beds, and about 120 meters (approximately 390 feet) higher than those in which *Pakicetus* was found. Berta, in her comments on the paper by Thewissen et al. gives an age of 52 million years for the sediments in Pakistan where *Ambulocetus* was found. Thewissen and his coworkers in their paper mention an age of 52 million years for the age of *Pakicetus*, which they refer to as the "oldest cetacean." *Ambulocetus*, bearing large forelimbs and hoofed hind limbs, was found in strata nearly 400 feet higher than *Pakicetus*. It therefore cannot be older. *Pakicetus* is called the oldest cetacean. Yet it is said that *Ambulocetus* documents transitional modes of locomotion in the evolution of whales. Confused? So are we. It is reported that the teeth resemble those of other archeocetes, which evolutionists believe were either archaic whales or ancestral to whales. The teeth of archeocetes are, however, so similar to mesonychid ungulates, believed to be wolf-like carnivorous mammals, that two of the archeocetes, *Gandakasia* and *Ichthylestes*, known only from teeth, were originally classified as mesonychids.[102]

G. A. Mchedlidze, a Russian expert on whales, while maintaining that Archeoceti occupy an intermediate position between terrestrial mammals and typical Cetacea, states that the problem of the phylogenetic relationship between Archeoceti and modern Cetacea is a highly controversial issue. He reports that a number of authors consider that the Archeoceti is a completely isolated group having nothing in common with typical Cetacea.[103] If this opinion is correct, then the archeocetes, supposedly archaic whales, were not whales at all and did not give rise to whales (cetaceans).

---

[102] *Ibid.*

[103] G. A. Mchedlidze, *General Features of the Paleobiological Evolution of Cetacea*, trans. from Russian (Rotterdam: A. A. Balkema, 1986), p. 91.

A search of texts on mammals for fossils of creatures resembling *Ambulocetus* failed to produce one closely resembling *Ambulocetus*, although *Allodesmus*, an extinct aquatic carnivore believed to have preceded walruses, bears some resemblance.[104]

Perhaps we should not be surprised that Thewissen and coworkers would dare to call *Ambulocetus* a "whale" when we note the fact that Robert Carroll, in his voluminous tome, *Vertebrate Paleontology and Evolution*, made the incredible statement that "Despite the extreme difference in habitus, it is logical from the standpoint of phylogenetic classification to include the mesonychids among the Cetacea."[105] Presto! These wolf-like animals are now whales! Who says

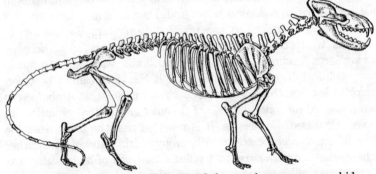

Figure 17. *Mesonyx.* Skeleton of the carnivorous mesonychid from the Eocene of North America. From W. B. Scott, *J. Acad. Nat. Sci. Philadelphia* 9:155 (1888).

Figure 18. *Basilosaurus,* which reached more than 80 feet in length. One of the suggested ancestors of whales. From Kellogg, *Carnegie Institute Washington Publication* 482:1-366 (1936).

Figure 19. *Askeptosaurus,* an aquatic reptile from the middle triassic of Switzerland. Approximately 6 feet long. From Kuhn Schnyder, *Neujahrsblatt Naturf. Ges. Zuerich* 176:1-119 (1974).

evolutionists do not have transitional forms? Anybody who can call a wolf a whale should have no trouble finding "transitional forms."

The final episode in this series (as of this writing) is a report by Gingerich, Raza, Arif, Anwar, and Zhore that they had discovered another fossil of a so-called archaeocete which they claim was intermediate between land mammals and whales.[106] They named the creature *Rodhocetus kasrani*. They found the fossil in the southwestern corner of Punjab Province of Pakistan and believe it to be 46–47 million years old. They describe features of this creature which they believe indicate that it could support its weight on land. They believe it also had features which would indicate it was a fairly efficient swimmer, thus constituting a creature intermediate between land mammals and marine mammals.

Were these creatures really intermediates whose evolutionary forebears were wolf-like creatures and whose evolutionary descendants ended up as whales, dolphins, and porpoises? Or were they, as Mchedlidze believes (and others he mentions) an isolated group that had nothing in common with ordinary whales? Here creation scientists and evolutionist Mchedlidze and his evolutionist colleagues find themselves in full agreement—they were creatures that had a mosaic of features, just as do the pinnipeds (seals, sea lions, walruses) and the sirenians (the sea cows, or manatees and dugongs—which appear fully-formed in the fossil record with no trace of transitional forms) and had nothing to do with any supposed ancestors for whales and dolphins.

Modern whales are of two major kinds—the toothed whales, the odontocetes (suborder Odontoceti), and the baleen whales, the mysticetes (suborder Mysticeti). The odontocetes include the killer whales, the narwhales (the male of which has a long, spirally twisted tusk extending from the upper jaw), the sperm whales, the dolphins and porpoises. The baleen whales, the largest of modern whales, include the right whales, the fin-back whales or norquals, and the blue whales, which may grow to as much as 100 feet in length and weigh as much as 150 tons.

---

[104] Carroll, *Vertebrate Paleontology and Evolution*, p. 483.

[105] *Ibid.*, p. 521.

[106] P. D. Gingerich, S. M. Raza, M. Arif, M. Anwar and X. Zhou, *Nature* 368:844-847 (1994).

The habitat and way of life of whales is vastly different than that of land-dwelling animals. To cope with these differences and many unusual life styles, whales are equipped with numerous incredibly specialized devices.[107] Evolutionists are forced to believe that whatever the need may be, no matter how complex and unusual, random genetic errors were able to produce the structures required in a perfectly coordinated manner.

For example, in order to feed on shrimp where the supply is abundant, as well as on the octopus, whales may have to dive to great depths. Ordinary animals cannot do that. None of the so-called intermediate types discussed earlier—*Basilosaurus, Pakicetus, Ambulocetus, Rodhocetus*—were equipped to do that. Bottlenose dolphins easily dive to depths of nearly 1200 feet. The beaked whale can dive to a depth of over 1600 feet. The largest of the toothed whales, the sperm whale (length about 65 feet and weight about 120,000 pounds) dives easily to 3,000 feet and can dive even to a depth of almost 10,000 feet, nearly two miles.

In order to withstand the enormous pressures at such great depths, which even at depths of about 3,000 feet reach pressures almost 100 times that at sea level, the cranial and auditory apparatus of the whale must be very specially modified, including greatly increased vascularization of the ear. The sperm whale has a huge chamber containing several hundred gallons of sperm oil, or spermaceti, which alters according to depth and temperature to permit adjustment in buoyancy. Before diving, this whale goes through a ten-minute breathing exercise in order for its muscles, blood, and lungs to store oxygen. Its blood contains 50% more hemoglobin than human blood, and while humans use only 10–20% of their breathed air for energy, this whale can utilize 80–90%. During a dive only 9% of its oxygen is derived from the lungs while 41% comes from blood and 50% from muscles and tissues. A number of other necessary modifications in the whale are required for these incredible dives. While at these great depths, these whales consume thousands of squid (28,000 were found in the stomach of one sperm whale), as well as giant octopuses.

In order to help them "see" at depths in the darkness, toothed whales are equipped with a sonar, or echolocation system. It is

---

[107] Werner Gitt, *If Animals Could Talk*, Eng. ed. (Brelefeld, Germany: Christliche Literatur-Verbreitung, D-33661, 1994), pp. 21-38.

reported that they can hear sounds emitted under water from distances of sixty miles. They also sing under water and have quite a repertoire.

The babies of whales are born under water. If they were delivered in the way human babies are normally delivered—head first—they would not survive. All whales are born tail first. Baby whales must nurse under water. If they had to nurse in the usual way they would either drown or starve to death. No problem. The mammary glands of the mother whale are equipped with muscles which enables her to rapidly squirt the milk into the babies mouth under such pressure it would create a fountain above water six feet high. Her mother's milk contains 42% fat and 12% protein, compared to 4.4% fat and 1% protein of human mother's milk. A baby blue whale drinks about 200 pounds of milk daily, gaining about 175 pounds each day.

Some evolutionists believe that the whalebone or baleen whales (Mysticeti) and the tooth whale (Odontoceti) had separate origins, while others believe they evolved from a common archaeocete ancestor. When odontocetes and mysticetes first appear in the fossil record, they are already clearly distinct, as predicted on the basis of creation.[108] Baleen whales are equipped with a whalebone or baleen which forms from ridges of hardened skin which extend down from the mouth in parallel crosswise rows. These whales filter enormous quantities of sea water to remove and feed on tiny plankton, organisms which float on the surface. The giant blue whale can gulp as much as seventy tons of water at one time, utilizing the huge pouch beneath its mouth, throat, and chest.

It is clear that the evidence weighs heavily on the creationist side concerning the origin of marine mammals. It requires an enormous faith in miracles, where materialist philosophy actually forbids them, to believe that some hairy, four-legged mammal crawled into the water and gradually, over eons of time, gave rise to whales, dolphins, sea cows, seals, sea lions, walruses, and other marine mammals via thousands and thousands of random genetic errors. This blind hit and miss method supposedly generated the many highly specialized complex organs and structures without which these whales could not function, complex structures which in incipient stages would be totally

---

[108] Carroll, *Vertebrate Paleontology and Evolution*, p. 524.

useless and actually detrimental. Evolution theory is an incredible faith.

Summary

As had been noted, there are a great number of fundamental differences between reptiles and mammals. There are structures in mammals, some that are incredibly complex, such as the organ of Corti, that have no homologous structures in reptiles and would thus have to be created *de novo*. The reproductive systems of mammals are fundamentally different from those of reptiles. Only mammals have mammary glands. Only mammals have diaphragms, and there is nothing homologous in the reptile from which it could have been derived. The origin of the complex echolocation systems in bats and whales defy an evolutionary explanation.

As it has been noted and thoroughly documented in this chapter, the gaps in the fossil record between the major kinds are systematic and usually large. The transitional forms, especially those that must be visualized as leading up to highly specialized mammals, such as bats, are not found in the fossil record. We heartily agree with the statement of Gould and Eldredge that:

> At the higher level of evolutionary transition between basic morphological designs, gradualism has always been in trouble though it remains the "official" position of most Western evolutionists. Smooth intermediates between *Baupläne* are almost impossible to construct, even in thought experiments; there is certainly no evidence for them in the fossil record (curious mosaics like Archaeopteryx do not count).[109]

---

[109] S. J. Gould and Niles Eldredge, *Paleobiology* 3:147 (1977).

Chapter VII

The Origin of Man

The Primates

Man, *Homo sapiens,* is placed in the order Primates, one of the thirty-two orders of mammals. Living primates include the prosimians (lemurs, lorises, and tarsiers); the New World monkeys; the Old World monkeys; and the apes (gibbons, siamangs, orangutans, gorillas, and chimpanzees). Man and these creatures have been placed together in the order Primates because they share certain characteristics in common. For example, all primates have grasping hands, keen eyesight, keen hearing, a relatively poor sense of smell, and relatively large brains (the average cranial capacity of humans is about three times that of any living ape). Evolutionists consider this to constitute a natural grouping, that is, these similarities exist because these creatures have arisen from a common ancestor. It will be seen in a later chapter, however, that the embryological, morphological, and genetic evidence contradicts the notion that the existence of similar structures in different animals (homologous structures) is due to inheritance from common ancestors. Creation scientists postulate that these similarities exist because the way of life of these creatures require these characteristics. Monkeys, apes, and prosimians require grasping hands for their arboreal activities. Man and these creatures need grasping hands for manipulating food and other objects. Since man and these other primates do not pursue prey by putting their noses to the ground they do not require a keen sense of smell, but their many activities do require keen eyesight and hearing. Their manner of life requires a higher level of intelligence, thus their larger, more efficient

brains. The father of taxonomy, Carolus Linnaeus, a special
creationist, was the one who first placed man and these other creatures
in the order Primates, certainly not because of any evolutionary
implications.

Order: Primates		
Suborder: Prosimii	**Suborder:** Anthropoidea	
Infraorder: Lemuriformes	**Infraorder:** Platyrrhine	**Infraorder:** Catarrhini
Superfamily: Lemuroidea	**Family:** Cebidae	**Family:** Cercopithecidae
Family: Lemuridae	New World Monkeys	Old World Monkeys
Lemurs		**Superfamly:** Hominoidea
Superfamily: Lorisoidea		**Family:** Pongidae
Family: Lorisidae		*Pan*: Chimpanzee
Lorises		*Gorilla*: Gorilla
Infraorder: Tarsiiformes		*Pongo*: Orangutan
Family: Tarsiidae		**Family:** Hominidae
Tarsiers		*Homo*: Man

Figure 20. Classification of Modern Primates

That man is fundamentally different from all other creatures, apes
included, seems undeniable to creation scientists and most people.
Though evolutionists argue that man has merely evolved a little higher
than the apes, even they recognize the vast difference. Cartmill,
Pilbeam, and Isaac put it this way:

Since the Darwinian revolution, when traditional Western
ideas about humanity's supernatural origins ceased to be
intellectually respectable, scientists have been struggling to
account for the human species as an effect of natural causes.
But they have generally taken their task to be one of
explaining how human beings came to differ so much and so
importantly from the other animals. In accepting this

persistently pre-Darwinian definition of their problem, scientists who study human evolution have saddled themselves with the paradoxical job of explaining how causes operating throughout nature have in the case of *Homo sapiens* produced an effect that is radically unlike anything else in nature.[1]

Yes, indeed, man is radically unlike anything else in nature, including apes; and evolutionists, ever since Darwin, have been very uncomfortably frustrated in their attempts to discover evidence of an animal ancestry for man. In their article entitled "Higher-Primate Phylogeny—Why Can't We Decide?" Holmquist, Mujamoto, and Goodman state that:

At present, no definitive agreement on either the correct branching order or differential rates of evolution among the higher primates exists, despite the accumulated integration of decades of morphological, immunological, protein and nucleic acid sequence data, and numerous reasonable theoretical models for the analysis, interpretation, and understanding of those data. Of the three distinct unrooted phylogenetic trees. . . .[2]

With all these data collected over many years of research by thousands of biologists, paleoanthropologists, immunologists, biochemists, and others, why is there no agreement concerning the pathway of man's evolution? Precisely because, as they acknowledge, the tree has no roots. Neither does it have trunk or branches. All that exists of the tree are tips of the branches.

Paleoanthropologist Bernard Wood expresses his frustration in this way:

It is remarkable that the taxonomy and phylogenetic relationships of the earliest known representatives of our own genus, *Homo*, remain obscure. Advances in techniques for absolute dating and reassessments of the fossils

---

[1] Matt Cartmill, David Pilbeam, and Glynn Isaac, *American Scientist* 74:410 (1986).

[2] Richard Holmquist, Michael Miyamoto, and Morris Goodman, *Molecular Biological Evolution* 5(3): 201 (1988).

themselves have rendered untenable a simple unilineal model of human evolution, in which *Homo habilis* succeeded the australopithecines and then evolved via *H. erectus* into *H. sapiens*—but no clear alternative consensus has yet emerged.[3]

Jerold Lowenstein and Adrienne Zihlman, after proclaiming their belief based on their interpretation of the fossil record, that man did walk on two legs before his brain became larger, state:

> But anatomy and the fossil record cannot be relied on for defining evolutionary lineages. Yet palaeontologists persist in doing just this. They rally under the banner of a methodology called cladistics, in which family trees of living and fossil primates are constructed on the basis of "primitive" and "derived" traits (mostly of teeth and bones), which are either shared or not shared. Shared primitive characteristics are shared because they come from a common ancestor; unshared derived characteristics reveal separate evolutionary paths. The subjective element in this approach to building evolutionary trees, which many palaeontologists advocate with almost religious fervour, is demonstrated by the outcome: there is no single family tree on which they agree. On the contrary, almost every conceivable combination and permutation of living and extinct hominoids has been proposed by one cladist or another.[4]

Lowenstein and Zihlman apparently fail to recognize the subjective element in their own conclusions even though a bit earlier in the article they acknowledge that:

> Imaginations run riot in conjuring up an image of our most ancient ancestor—the creature that gave rise to both apes and humans. This ancestor is not apparent in ape or human anatomy nor in the fossil record, but is evident only in the unseen world of the genome within the cell.[5]

---

[3] Bernard Wood, *Nature* 355:783 (1992).

[4] Jerald Lowenstein and Adrienne Zihlman, *New Scientist* 120:59 (1988).

[5] *Ibid.*, p. 58.

As other paleoanthropologists have acknowledged, Lowenstein and Zihlman reveal that:

> In the course of the past century, the discoverer of every new hominid or hominoid has nominated it as a potential human ancestor.[6]

In fact, practically every scrap of bone that is discovered is given a new species designation. What joy is there in plodding in someone else's footsteps, and what fame is there in paleoanthropology unless one does find a fossil pointing the true way to man's ancestry, especially if the claim is made that it is the very oldest in this field? And no field of science is more permeated with ideology than the search for man's ancestor. This is inevitable in this field of science where one's ultimate conclusion and every perception along the way is determined by his worldview.

Evolutionists assume that the first primates were similar to a lemur-like creature (adapids) or a tarsier-like creature (omomyids) referred to as "prosimians of modern aspect," although which one is a matter of dispute. Fossils of these creatures are found in North America, Europe, and Asia in rocks placed in the Eocene. Until recently three creatures whose fossils are found in Paleocene rocks, *Phenacolemur, Ignacius,* and *Plesiadapis,* were considered likely to be early ancestors of prosimians. Research has now shown that these creatures were not related to primates at all but were similar to *Cynocephalus,* a modern calugo or "flying lemur" (which is neither a lemur, nor does it fly, but glides only).[7] As one paleoanthropologist regretfully stated: "You might say that early primate evolution as we know it has just glided out the window." These facts have placed a wide gap between prosimians and any suggested ancestor.

Although the primates have supposedly evolved from an insectivorous ancestor, there are no series of transitional forms connecting primates to insectivores. Elwyn Simons, one of the world's leading experts in the field of primates, must admit that: "In spite of recent finds, the time and place of origin of order Primates remains shrouded in mystery."[8] Romer states that the early lemurs appear

---

[6] *Ibid.*, p. 59.

[7] K. Beard, *Nature* 345:340-341 (1990); Pat Shipman, *New Scientist* 126:60 (1990).

"apparently as immigrants from some unknown area."[9] He is forced to say this since paleontologists simply cannot tell from the fossils how lemurs arose. Kelso has stated,

> . . . the transition from insectivore to primate is not documented by fossils. The basis of knowledge about the transition is by inference from living forms.[10]

The situation has not changed since these publications appeared, for Carrol states:

> The specific origin of primates among more primitive eutherians has not been established. . . . No specific derived characters have been demonstrated as being uniquely shared between early primates and the early members of any other order.[11]

We can see, then, at the very outset the origin of the entire primate order cannot be determined from the fossil record. If primates evolved, there should be a series of transitional forms leading back to their insectivore ancestors, but no such transitional forms are found. This is exactly what creationists would expect the record to show, of course.

The particular insectivore that evolutionists have suggested as the ancestor of the primates is the tree shrew. This conclusion was based on the work in the 1920's of Wilfred Le Gros Clark on the Asian tree shrew, *Tupaia*. Le Gros Clark thought that he could see many similarities between the tree shrews and the primates. Studies over the past few decades have shown, however, that Le Gros Clark was simply wrong. As far back as 1966, C. B. G. Campbell, in his review of this alleged relationship, states:

> I have attempted to indicate the large number of recent studies whose results indicate that a close relationship between tupaiids and primates is unlikely.[12]

---

[8] E. L. Simons, *Annals of the New York Academy of Science* 167:319 (1969).

[9] A. S. Romer, *Vertebrate Paleontology*, 3rd ed. (Chicago: The University of Chicago Press, 1966), p. 218.

[10] A. J. Kelso, *Physical Anthropology*, 2nd ed. (New York: J. B. Lipincott, 1974), p. 142.

[11] R. L. Carroll, *Vertebrate Paleontology and Evolution* (New York: W. H. Freeman and Co., 1988), pp. 464, 467.

Campbell suggests that it was the innate attractiveness of the sequence: tree shrew–lemur–tarsier–ape–man that was in large measure responsible for its acceptance. No doubt another factor was the authoritative position in anthropology occupied by Le Gros Clark. When authority speaks, lesser lights hasten to fall in line.

More recently, R. D. Martin, based on his studies of the maternal behavior of tree shrews and of primates, has concluded that "the tree shrew is not on the roster of human ancestors."[13] In contrast to the primates, which uniformly exhibit elaborate maternal care, Martin found that the female tree shrew visits the nest for only about ten minutes of each forty-eight hours, during which she nurses the young. This is the only maternal care she gives the young. Furthermore, the fat content of tree shrew milk is 25%, while in primates it is typically only 1–3%, and never exceeds 5%. Martin also mentions the fact that a wide-ranging assessment of the tree shrews published in a recent book

Figure 21. The Philippine tarsier. From the Zoological Society of San Diego 1995. Used by permission.

edited by W. P. Luckett fairly well rules out any definite ties of tree shrews with primates.

Morphological and physiological evidence continues to accumulate that there is no connection between prosimians and tree shrews. In his 1990 publication on primate origins, Martin emphatically states: "There is now abundant evidence that tree shrews are simply unrelated to primates."[14]

An exciting discovery of a fossil graveyard, in what is believed to be a fissure filling near Shanghuang in southern Jiangsu Province in China, produced among the many mammalian fossils five new types of "early" primates, each representing a distinctive lineage.[15] The primates included adapids, omomyids, and a fossil of a creature practically indistinguishable from a modern tarsier. The living tarsier is thus now said to constitute a "living fossil." The discoverers of these fossils believe them to be about forty-five million years old, pushing the tarsier about thirty million years farther back into the past. Furthermore, since the adapids and omomyids are now known to be contemporary with modern tarsiers, neither could be ancestral to tarsiers.

Kelso, Martin, and others have made clear that there are no fossils of transitional forms that link primates to tree shrews (insectivores) or to anything else. Campbell, Martin, and many others have now documented the fact that there is no evidence from studies of living tree shrews to link them to primates. There is thus no evidence either in the present world or in the world of the past to link primates to any other creatures. Right at the very start, then, an evolutionary origin of man is invalidated by actual empirical scientific evidence. The primates, as a group, stand completely isolated from all other creatures.

As we have noted, the anthropoids include the New World Monkeys, the Platyrrhini, and Old World Monkeys, the Catarrhini. Supposedly, according to the evolutionary story, anthropoids evolved from one of the prosimian lines, the adapids or omomyids. Which one,

---

[12] C. B. G. Campbell, *Science* 153:436 (1966).

[13] R. D. Martin, *Natural History* 91:26 (1982).

[14] R. D. Martin, *Primate Origins and Evolution* (New Jersey: Princeton University Press, 1990), p. 710.

[15] K. C. Beard et al., *Nature* 368:604-609 (1994).

specifically, depends on who is telling the story. There is, however, a huge gap between the prosimians and monkeys or anthropoids. It is generally assumed that the New World monkeys, the broad-nosed monkeys, had a separate evolutionary origin from the Old World monkeys, the narrow-nosed monkeys. There is no fossil transitional forms to link monkeys to anything else, however. Anthropologist Susan Cachel states:

> The available fossil evidence does not document the prosimian-anthropoid transition . . . and so morphology of extant anthropoids becomes of paramount importance.[16]

Elizabeth Culotta reports that:

> At some point, one group diverged from the lower primates (or prosimians) and gave rise to the anthropoids. But no one can say with certainty what this ancestor looked like, because there's a large gap in the fossil record between primitive and advanced forms. "You put all the primates into a pile and you can always sort the anthropoids from the others," says John G. Fleagle of the State University of New York at Stony Brook. "They're so distinctive it's hard to figure out where they came from." . . . The lack of transitional fossil forms hasn't stopped paleoanthropologists from selecting their favorite candidates for the anthropoid's predecessors. . . .[17]

There are no transitional forms between the New World monkeys and their presumed ancestors, the prosimians. Thus Romer states, "little is known, unfortunately, of the fossil history of the South American monkeys."[18] Kelso states:

> The details of the evolutionary background of the New World monkeys, the Platyrrhinae, would doubtless be informative and interesting, but unfortunately we know very little about them.[19]

---

[16] Susan Cachel, *Science* 213:860 (1981).

[17] Elizabeth Culotta, *Science* 256:1516 (1992).

[18] Romer, *Vertebrate Paleontology*, p. 221.

[19] Kelso, *Physical Anthropology*, p. 150.

Concerning the New World monkeys, Carroll says:

> The Platyrrhinae are restricted to South and Central America throughout their history. The earliest known fossil is *Branisella*, a member of the modern family Cebidae from the middle to late Oligocene of Bolivia.[20]

R. D. Martin records that:

> The known fossil record of New World monkeys for South and Central America is, frankly, rather disappointing in many respects. All of the substantial primate fossils from North America are, as indicated above, included either among the "lemuroids" or among the "tarsioids" of the early Tertiary. The origins of the New World monkeys therefore remain a mystery, as the only substantial fossils are known from the late Oligocene and the Miocene, and by that stage they exhibit numerous characteristics clearly allying them with the modern forms. Indeed, without exception the substantial fossils that have been described resemble true New World monkeys (family Cebidae). . . .[21]

It is quite obvious that when the New World monkeys first appear, they are just that—monkeys.

The catarrhines include the Old World monkeys (narrow-nosed monkeys), apes, and man. Concerning their origins, Simons states: "Although the word has been used, there is actually no such thing as a 'protocatarrhine' known from the fossil record."[22] In a later publication he said,

> Not a single fossil primate of the Eocene epoch from either continent appears to be an acceptable ancestor for the great infraorder of the catarrhines, embracing all of the living higher Old World primates, man included.[23] [These "early" prosimians were found only in North America and Europe up until that time.]

---

[20] Carroll, *Vertebrate Paleontology and Evolution*, p. 471.

[21] Martin, *Primate Origins and Evolution*, p. 66.

[22] E. L. Simons, *Annals of the New York Academy of Science* 102:293 (1962).

[23] E. L. Simons, *Scientific American* 211(1): 50 (1964).

A. J. Kelso reports that:

> Clearly, the fossil documentation of the emergence of the Old World monkeys could provide key insights into the general evolutionary picture of the primates, but, in fact, this record simply does not exist.[24]

R. D. Martin states:

> Although early fossil evidence of New World monkeys may be described as disappointing, it is rich in comparison to that for Old World monkeys. . . . Overall, the fossil record can tell us very little about the early origins of Old World monkeys.[25]

The fossil record thus fails to produce any evidence for transitional forms between prosimians, allegedly the earliest primates, and either the New World monkeys or the Old World monkeys. Here we encounter another huge gap in the fossil record. Transitional forms are lacking where evolutionary theory urgently requires them.

The next step up the evolutionary ladder involves the origin of ape-like creatures from their presumed monkey-like ancestors. Here again a large gap is encountered. There are no identifiable transitional forms between monkeys and apes.

Man and the apes have been classified within the super-family, Hominoidea, and all such creatures are referred to as hominoids. One scheme suggested for the evolution of the hominoids is shown in figure 22. As can be seen from the diagram, the consensus among evolutionists is that the chimpanzee and the gorilla are our nearest kin among the apes.

Evolutionists believe that sometime in the past there existed a population of ape-like creatures that split into subpopulations, one of which gave rise to the gorilla and the other of which split once again to give rise to the chimpanzee and man. The time of this last common ancestor of ape and man is in much dispute. Current estimates vary all the way from four million years to about fourteen million years, depending on who is telling the story. Perhaps this is some indication

---

[24] Kelso, *Physical Anthropology*, p. 151.
[25] Martin, *Primate Origins and Evolution*, p. 68.

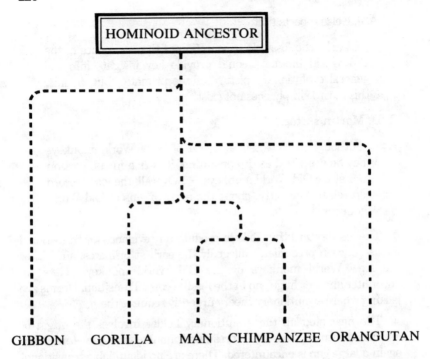

Figure 22. A suggested phylogenetic scheme for the hominoids.

of how little is really known about it. Since paleontologists have yet to find this assumed common ancestor of ape and man, he remains strictly a hypothetical creature.

As mentioned above, most evolutionists have considered that the chimpanzee (*Pan*) and the gorilla (*Gorilla*) are more closely related to man than is the orangutan (*Pongo*). This conclusion has been based on molecular, biochemical, and chromosomal data. For example, when the nuclear DNA of man and of the African apes (gorilla and chimp) are hybridized, there is a 1.1% base mismatch, while the mismatch between man and the orangutan is 2.4%.[26] The phylogeny based on this type of data is now, however, being challenged by Jeffrey Schwartz, Professor of Anthropology at the University of Pittsburgh.

---

[26] R. E. Benveniste and G. J. Todaro, *Nature* 261:101 (1976).

Schwartz points out that of twenty-six unique traits that man shares with the living hominoids, he shares all twenty-six with the orangutan, only nine with the chimpanzee and gorilla, and but five with the gibbon (*Hylobates*).[27] Some of the traits man shares with the orangutan but not with the African apes, according to Schwartz, include the longest hair, most widely separated mammary glands, the longest gestation period (equal in man and orangutan), thick molar enamel, low-cusped cheekteeth, copulation not confined to a specific part of the menstrual cycle, and highest oestriol levels during the menstrual cycle. Schwartz maintains that these data show that man is more closely related to the orangutan than he is to the African apes. Schwartz rejects the significance of much of the molecular and biochemical data that supposedly show a closer link between man and the African apes than that between man and the orangutan, and interprets some of the remainder as showing that man and the orangutan are more closely related than man and the African apes.

Creation scientists maintain that similarity does not necessarily establish a genetic relationship (homology, or similarities in morphological traits of man and the hominoids, will be discussed in the next chapter). They find it interesting, therefore, that evolutionists are able to reach quite contradictory conclusions depending upon which similarities are used to establish relatedness. This is especially so in this case because Schwartz is challenging the use of molecular and biochemical data to establish the phylogenetic relationships between man and the apes.

Having met with great frustration in their attempts to construct phylogenetic evolutionary trees based on the fossil record because of the systematic absence of transitional forms, evolutionists have of late been trumpeting loudly about the use of molecular data to establish relationships. Creation scientists have challenged conclusions based on such data, and they welcome help from within evolutionary circles, such as that provided by Schwartz.

The meaning of such relationships in establishing supposed evolutionary relatedness is actually confused in some ways by the work of Benveniste and Todaro reported in 1976.[28] As mentioned earlier, DNA hybridization studies by Benveniste and Todaro show that the

---

[27] J. H. Schwartz, *Nature* 308:501-505 (1984).
[28] Benveniste and Todaro, *Nature*, 261:101 (1976).

African apes, the gorilla, and the chimpanzee, are more closely related
to man than are the Asian apes, the orangutan, and the gibbon.
However, hybridization studies of the DNA of gorillas, chimpanzees,
orangutans, gibbons, and man versus the DNA transcript of baboon
type C virus revealed that the human DNA hybridized with the DNA
transcript of the baboon virus to the same extent as did the DNA of the
gibbon and the orangutan, and that the degree of hybridization of
human, gibbon, and orangutan DNA with the baboon type C virus
DNA transcript was less than that of gorilla and chimpanzee DNA.
Taken at face value, this would indicate that man is more closely
related to the orangutan than he is to the gorilla and the chimpanzee,
since the DNA of man and orangutan reacted similarly with baboon
type C virus while the reaction of the DNA of man and the gorilla and
chimpanzee with baboon type C virus was not equivalent.

Such a conclusion, although in agreement with the data considered
by Schwartz, nevertheless is contradictory to conclusions based on
other DNA hybridization studies and to the consensus of most
evolutionists that man is more closely related to the gorilla and the
chimpanzee than he is to the orangutan. Benveniste and Todaro,
therefore, suggest the notion that the results related to baboon type C
virus DNA transcripts do not really show that man is more closely
related to the orangutan and the gibbon than he is to the gorilla and
the chimpanzee, but that the similarities and differences are due to the
fact that the ancestors of man were of Asian origin while the ancestors
of the gorilla and the chimpanzee were of African origin. They suggest
that after the ancestor of man split off from the ancestor of the gorilla
and chimpanzee, he migrated to Asia and remained there for some
millions of years. Thus they postulate that much of man's evolution
occurred in a region remote from Africa, which is the home of the
baboon, the gorilla, and the chimpanzee, and that man, or man's
ancestors, migrated relatively recently to Africa. Not being exposed to
the baboon type C virus, which would be widespread in Africa but not
in Asia, supposedly allowed the virogenes of man, the orangutan and
the gibbon to diverge more than those of the gorilla and the
chimpanzee. This imaginative story-telling reminds us once more that
the theory of evolution has been rendered so plastic that no matter
what the data may be, the theory can be bent sufficiently to make
everything fit. Today most evolutionists accept an African origin for

man. We conclude that similarities or differences in such data tell us nothing about genetic relationships.

Romer refers to the chimpanzee and the gorilla as the "highest living members of the anthropoid group." What can he say about their origin? Romer states: "Our knowledge of the fossil history of these higher apes and of presumed human ancestors on this level is tantalizingly poor."[29] Some have imagined that the ancestors of the chimpanzee, gorilla, and orangutan may be found among species of *Dryopithecus*, fossil apes found in Africa, Europe, and Asia.[30] Just why this is so seems to be rather obscure, to say the least.

What can anthropologists say about man's ultimate origin from his imagined ape-like ancestor? Pilbeam says:

> It has come to be rather generally assumed, albeit in a rather vague fashion, the pre-Pleistocene hominid ancestry was rooted somewhere in the Dryopithecinae.[31]

When a scientist is forced to "assume" something "in a rather vague fashion," it is obvious that he is resorting to wholly unscientific methods to establish what he cannot do by a valid scientific method. What strange qualities could paleoanthropologists detect in an animal that allows them to decide on one hand that it was the progenitor of the chimpanzee, gorilla, and the orangutan, and yet on the other hand was the progenitor of the human race?

Pilbeam apparently does not agree with the general assumption that the dryopithecines were ancestral to man. He has expressed his conviction that the dryopithecines were too specialized, already too committed to ape-dom to have produced the hominids.[32]

The controversy about *Dryopithecus*, the first large fossil ape discovered, is as active today as ever. Begum has recently maintained that *Dryopithecus* is a close relative of the African great apes[33] (gorillas and chimpanzees are large African apes, the orangutan, an Asian great ape, is found in Borneo and Sumatra, and the small apes, the gibbons and siamangs—*Hylobates*—are found in the East Indies and southern

---

[29] Romer, *Vertebrate Paleontology*, p. 224.

[30] D. R. Pilbeam, *Nature* 219:1335 (1968).

[31] D. R. Pilbeam, *Advancement of Science* 24:368 (1968).

[32] E. L. Simons and D. R. Pilbeam, *Science* 173:23 (1971).

[33] D. Begum, *Science* 257:1929-1933 (1992).

Asia). On the basis of a new fossil cranium from middle Miocene rocks of Spain, supposedly 10–12 million years in age, Solà and Köhler, on the other hand, claim that *Dryopithecus* is particularly allied with the orangutan.[34] Regardless of any possible similarity to either the orangutan or the gorilla and chimpanzee, *Dryopitheous* did not possess the derived features (synapomorphies) for most known characters required as a possible ancestor for either the great apes or humans.[35]

What about the evidence in the fossil record for transitional forms leading up to the modern apes—gorillas, chimpanzees, orangutans, gibbons—and those leading up to man's putative ape-like ancestor, the australopithecines? They are nowhere to be found. Watson states that:

> Modern apes, for instance, seem to have sprung out of nowhere. They have no yesterday, no fossil record. And the true origin of modern humans—of upright, naked, tool-making, big-brained beings—is, if we are to be honest with ourselves, an equally mysterious matter."[36]

Unfortunately, most evolutionists are not as candid as Watson, but they do confirm Watson's statement. Carroll states:

> Unfortunately, there are no fossil hominoids known in Africa between 4 and 14 million years ago. The African apes *Gorilla* and *Pan* have no fossil record. Based on anatomical evidence, they might have diverged from the ancestors of humans any time from about 5 to 14 million years ago.[37]

Confirmation of these facts come also from R. D. Martin. He says:

> It should be noted at the outset that substantial fossil remains are known for all of the species listed below (a quite unusual situation with respect to the primate fossil record generally), but that there is virtually no fossil evidence relating to human evolution, other than a few fragments of dubious affinities, before about 3.8 Ma ago. The preceding period of human evolution therefore remains a complete mystery and an unfortunate major gap exists whatever view

---

[34] S. Moya Solà and M. Köhler, *Nature* 365:543-545 (1993).

[35] Lawrence Martin and Peter Andrews, *Nature* 365:494 (1993).

[36] Lyell Watson, *Science Digest* 90:44 (1982).

[37] Carroll, *Vertebrate Paleontology and Evolution*, p. 474.

one takes of the time of divergence of hominids and great apes.[38]

In an article entitled, "Where Have All the Primates Gone?" Pat Shipman relates that:

> Today there are only three genera and four species of great apes, and these are confined to fast-vanishing tropical rainforest or woodland habitats. But there are about a dozen genera and even more species of larger-bodied hominoids known from the Miocene. This means that anthropologists are confronted with many ancient apes with no known living counterparts.[39]

A bit later she quotes Mike Rose, an expert in primate movement, who says:

> When I look at the postcranial bones from the Miocene apes, I get a fairly clear and consistent pattern from many species. But it is nothing like we see in modern apes. Maybe we should consider the ones that survived as the bizarre ones.

The only reason evolutionists would want to consider modern apes as bizarre is that they can find no proper ancestors among what they consider earlier apes. Watson tells us that the origin of modern apes and modern humans are mysterious matters. Martin tells us that the long period of human evolution preceding about four million years ago is a complete mystery. Perhaps this long string of "missing links" are missing simply because they never existed.

Some evolutionists today firmly insist that we must never say that man has descended from the apes, but we must say that man and the apes have descended from a common ancestor. This is simply nonsense, and has been suggested in order to make the idea of man's origin from an ape ancestry more palatable to the public. While it is true that in the evolutionary view man has not descended from one of the modern apes but from a common ancestor of a modern ape and

---

[38] R. D. Martin, *Primate Origins and Evolution* (New Jersey: Princeton University Press, 1990), p. 82.

[39] Pat Shipman, *New Scientist*, 134:16 (1992).

man, if any of us saw this hypothetical common ancestor we would certainly call it an ape.

Today there is only a single species in the Hominidae, the family of man—*Homo sapiens*, or modern man. In the creationist view, man has always been separate and distinct from all other creatures, a unique created being. In the evolutionist view, man has had a long evolutionary history, his particular line of descent having split off from the apes millions of years ago. All creatures intermediate between man and the apes would be considered as members of the Hominidae and are thus referred to as hominids. Evolutionists thus believe that there were many species intermediate between modern man and his last common ancestor with the apes, and ever since Darwin the search for these supposed transitional forms has been intense.

Nothing excites our interest more than that which offers some hint concerning the origin of our own species. More than one obscure paleoanthropologist has become famous overnight by announcing sensational and extravagant claims following the find of some fragmentary remains of a creature he believes to be related to man's origin, especially if the find was made in some remote area of Africa or Asia. As we shall see, most such claims eventually fade into obscurity as further research and discoveries invalidate the claims, and in a few cases sensational "finds" have even been exposed as hoaxes.

In figure 23 are indicated the creatures that evolutionists have suggested as intermediates between the apes and man. Considering that this supposed evolutionary history is believed to have spanned many millions of years, the roster of suggested intermediates is exceedingly slim, especially since some of these have already begun to slip down out of the family tree.

Ramapithecus Loses its Status as a Human Ancestor

David Pilbeam, formerly of Yale and now at Harvard University, Elwyn Simons, now of Duke University, two of the leading paleoanthropologists in the United States, and others had in recent years strongly championed *Ramapithecus* as an early hominid, a creature in the direct line leading to man.[40] During that time it was

---

[40] Simons, *Annals of the New York Academy of Science* 167:319 (1969);

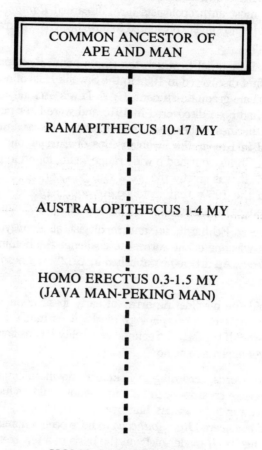

COMMON ANCESTOR OF
APE AND MAN

RAMAPITHECUS 10-17 MY

AUSTRALOPITHECUS 1-4 MY

HOMO ERECTUS 0.3-1.5 MY
(JAVA MAN-PEKING MAN)

HOMO SAPIENS 0.1 MY
(NEANDERTHAL MAN, CROMAGNON MAN,
MODERN DAY MAN)

Figure 23. Suggested intermediates in the evolutionary line leading from apes to man with dates currently suggested by evolutionists.

frequently stated in the anthropological literature and textbooks that
there was general agreement that *Ramapithecus* and related fossils
(referred to as ramapithecids) were ancestral to all true hominids,
including man. Today, in the light of additional material that has been
discovered, most anthropologists have discarded *Ramapithecus* as a
hominid. He is no longer considered to have been a creature in the line
leading to man.

The fossil material to which the genus name *Ramapithecus* was
given was first discovered in 1932 in the Siwalik Hills of northwestern
India by a Yale graduate student, G. E. Lewis. Actually a few other
fragments had been discovered in 1915 and were later placed among
the ramapithecines. Other fossilized remains of this creature have also
been found in Kenya, the Swabian Alps of Europe, and in Yunnan
Province of China, so it had a wide range, being found in places 2,000
miles apart. It was chiefly the work and publications of Simons and
Pilbeam in the 1960s that installed *Ramapithecus* in man's family
tree. Challenges to this notion were not long in forthcoming, however.

Dr. Robert Eckhardt, an anthropologist at Pennsylvania State
University, was one of the earliest to challenge the hominid status of
Ramapithecus. An article he published in 1972[41] was headlined by the
statement:

> Amid the bewildering array of early fossil hominoids, is
> there one whose morphology marks it as man's hominid
> ancestor? If the factor of genetic variability is considered, the
> answer appears to be no.

In other words, according to Eckhardt, nowhere among the fossil
apes or ape-like creatures can be found what could be judged to be a
proper ancestor for man. As had been noted, Simons, Pilbeam, and
others had considered *Ramapithecus* to have been a hominid, and this
judgment had been made solely on the basis of a few teeth and a few
fragments of the jaw. Eckhardt made twenty-four different
measurements on a collection of fossil teeth from two species of
Dryopithecus (fossil apes) and one species of *Ramapithecus* (a

---

Simons, *Scientific American* 211(1): 50 (1964); Pilbeam, *Nature* 219:1335
(1968); Pilbeam, *Advancement of Science* 24:308 (1968); Simons and
Pilbeam, *Science* 173:23 (1971).

[41] Robert Eckhardt, *Scientific American* 226 (1): 94 (1972).

supposed fossil hominid) and compared the range of variation found for these fossil species to similar measurements made on a population of chimpanzees at a research center and on a sample of wild chimpanzees in Liberia.

The range variation in the chimpanzee populations was actually greater than those in the fossil samples for fourteen of the twenty-four measurements, the same for one, and less for nine of the measurements. Even in the minority of cases where the range of variation of the fossil samples exceeded those in living chimpanzees, the differences were very small. Thus, in the tooth measurements made, there was greater variation among living chimpanzees, or a single group of apes, than there was between *Dryopithecus*, a fossil ape, and Ramapithecus, which was supposed to have been a hominid. And remember, *Ramapithecus* was judged to be a hominid solely on the basis of its dental characteristics!

Eckhardt extended his calculations to five other species of *Dryopithecus* and to *Kenyapithecus*, which according to Simons and Pilbeam[42] is equivalent to *Ramapithecus*. After stating that on the basis of tooth-size calculations, there is little basis for classifying the dryopithecines in more than a single species, Eckhardt goes on to say:

> Neither is there compelling evidence for the existence of any distinct hominid species during this interval, unless the designation "hominid" means simply any individual ape that happens to have small teeth and a corresponding small face.

Eckhardt's conclusion is that *Ramapithecus* seems to have been an ape—morphologically, ecologically, and behaviorally.

Recently, Walker and Andrews[43] have described a reconstruction of the dental arcades of *Ramapithecus* based on a sample that was more complete than those studied previously. This reconstruction made it clear that *Ramapithecus* did not have the parabolic dental arcade postulated on the basis of earlier reconstructions. The reconstruction showed that the dental arcades from both the upper and lower jaws

---

[42] Pilbeam, *Nature* 219:1335 (1968); E. L. Simons and D. R. Pilbeam, *Folia Primatol* 3:81 (1965).

[43] Alan Walker and Peter Andrews, *Nature* 244:313 (1973).

were very similar, if not identical, to that which would be expected of an ape.

Even more recent discoveries by Pilbeam[44] and by Alan Walker and Richard Leakey[45] have definitely established that *Ramapithecus* was a pongid and not a hominid. These discoveries have included not only jaw fragments and teeth but also fragments of the skull, face, and a few limb bones.

In his book, *The Evolution of Man*,[46] published in 1970, Pilbeam had warned:

> Locomotion, like body size, cannot be inferred without some post-cranial bones. It would be unwise to speculate about Ramapithecus' locomotion from a knowledge solely of its jaws and teeth!

Yet, as he admitted in his 1984 article,[47] he had come to believe that *Ramapithecus* walked bipedally solely on the basis of fragments of the jaws and teeth and had publicly proclaimed it. He has now acknowledged that this conclusion was based more on his preconceived ideas than the actual data.

The fossils discovered by Pilbeam in Pakistan and by Walker and Leakey in Kenya have actually been assigned to the genus *Sivapithecus*, fossils of which had first been discovered in India in 1910. However, it is now recognized that *Ramapithecus* and *Sivapithecus* are most likely similar enough to be of the same species, or at least to be of the same genus.[48] One of Pilbeam's finds was dated at about eight million years, and the other at thirteen million years. Pilbeam reports that his recently discovered fossils of *Sivapithecus* reveal specializations of anatomical features of the face and skull identical to those of the orangutan. On the basis of this evidence,

---

[44] D. R. Pilbeam, *Nature* 295:232 (1982); W. Herbert, *Science News* 121:84 (1982); D. R. Pilbeam, *Natural History* 93:2 (1984).

[45] Alan Walker and Richard Leakey, as recorded by Boyce Rensberger, *Science 84* 5(1):16 (1984).

[46] D. R. Pilbeam, *The Evolution of Man* (New York: Funk and Wagnalls, 1970). p. 107.

[47] Pilbeam, *Natural History* 93:2 (1984).

[48] Pilbeam, *Nature* 295:232 (1982); Herbert, *Science News* 121:84 (1982); Pilbeam, *Natural History* 93:2 (1984).

Pilbeam has declared that *Ramapithecus* (also *Sivapithecus*, of course) must be stripped of its rank as a hominid.[49]

Walker and Leakey report that their fossils of *Sivapithecus*, which they say are seventeen million years old, reveal an uncanny resemblance to the modern-day orangutan.[50] In fact, Walker is quoted as saying: "It's heretical to say so, but it may be that orangs are 'living fossils.'" In other words, what Walker is saying is that living orangutans are so similar to these *Sivapithecus* fossils that the orangutan is a living embodiment of *Sivapithecus*. They cannot quite bring themselves to say that *Sivapithecus was* an orangutan, of course, for that would be rank heresy.

Thus, *Sivapithecus-Ramapithecus* turns out to be a creature that is very orangutan-like and not a creature that was on its way to becoming human. Having established that *Sivapithecus-Ramapithecus* was not a hominid but was uncannily similar to modern orangs, it is incredible that Walker is now suggesting that this creature was the ancestor of orangutans, chimpanzees, gorillas, *and* man![51] What is the basis for such an astounding claim? The basis for this claim is that the fossils were found in Africa (where the gorilla and the chimpanzee supposedly originated) and the assumed age of the fossil (many evolutionists believe that the age of the presumed common ancestor of all apes and man must have been at least seventeen million years or more). Thus, even though their fossils look just like an orangutan, they are declared to be candidates for the ancestor of all apes and man simply because they supposedly are old enough and were found in the right location!

About twenty years ago a flesh model of *Ramapithecus* was on display in the San Diego Museum of Man. There before you stood almost in the flesh "living" proof of evolution. He wasn't a man; he wasn't an ape. He stood upright in a fully human manner. He was definitely an intermediate. As eager-eyed students viewed this highly visible "proof" of evolution, not one would have any idea it was based solely on a few teeth, a few fragments of a jaw, and a barrel full of evolutionary preconceived ideas. We are reminded that Mark Twain once remarked that science is such a fascinating subject because you

---

[49] Pilbeam, *Natural History* 93:2 (1984).
[50] Walker and Leakey, *Science 84* 5(1):16 (1984).
[51] *Ibid.*

Figure 24. The modern day orangutan. From the Zoological Society of San Diego 1995. Photo by Ron Garrison. Used by permission.

can get such a remarkable production of conjectures from such a trifling investment of facts!

As we will see later, *Ramapithecus* is just one of a long series of creatures that have been suggested at one time or another as "missing links" but which, when more complete evidence became available, were relegated to the ape family. Two that met their demise before *Ramapithecus* were *Dryopithecus* and *Oreopithecus*. Both were at one time declared to be hominids (*Oreopithecus* was, in fact, declared by various investigators to be a monkey, an ape, a hominid, and even a pig!),[52] but now are recognized as apes.[53]

As mentioned earlier, the assumed common ancestor of ape and man has yet to be discovered. Many evolutionists believe that this common ancestor existed about twenty million years ago, or even longer. Eliminating *Sivapithecus-Ramapithecus* as a possible ancestor for man leaves the supposed evolutionary history of man a blank all the way from the hypothetical split of ape and man down to the

---

[52] Pilbeam, *The Evolution of Man*, p. 99.
[53] Pilbeam, *Nature* 295:232 (1982); Herbert, *Science News* 121:84 (1982); Pilbeam, *Natural History* 93:2 (1984).

Figure 25. Flesh model of *Ramapithecus* in the
San Diego Museum of Man. Photo by the author.

australopithecines, dated from about one million years to about four
million years on the evolutionist's time scale.

Australopithecus—Ape or Ape-Man?

The next, and much more recent, candidate, chronologically
speaking, as one of man's hominid ancestors, is *Australopithecus*,
whose existence, evolutionists believe, spanned a period from almost
4.5 million years to as recently as one million years. The first find of
this creature was by Raymond Dart in 1924,[54] to which he gave the
name *Australopithecus africanus*. He pointed out the many ape-like
features of the skull, but he believed that some features of the skull,
and particularly of the teeth, were man-like. The name
Australopithecus means "southern ape," but after Dart examined the
teeth further, he decided *A. africanus* was a hominid. This claim

---

[54] Raymond A. Dart, *Nature* 115:195-199 (1925).

created considerable controversy, most workers at that time claiming that *A. africanus* was an ape with some interesting but irrelevant parallel features with man. Additional finds of *Australopithecus* were made in later years by Robert Broom, John T. Robinson, and by Dart.

The find by Louis Leakey and his wife of what they called *Zinjanthropus boisei*, or "East-Africa Man," at Olduvai Gorge in Tanzania[55] has attracted great attention. As it turned out, they really found nothing essentially different than had been discovered by Dart many years earlier. Their research, however, was sponsored by the National Geographic Society, and a combination of rather extravagant claims by Leakey for his find combined with publicity through the pages of the National Geographic Society magazine succeeded in conveying the idea that Leakey had made a unique and momentous discovery at Olduvai. Even Leakey admitted later, however, that his *Zinjanthropus boisei* is a variety of *Australopithecus*, discovered years previously in South Africa. *Zinjanthropus boisei* is now classified as *Australopithecus boisei* (some place it in the genus *Paranthropus*) and is even believed by some to be a sub-species of *Australopithecus robustus*.

The australopithecines until recently have generally been classified into two species. One is more gracile with somewhat smaller jaws and teeth and has been designated *Australopithecus africanus* (figure 26). The other has more massive teeth and jaws and possesses sagittal and supramastoid crests (bony ridges), found in gorillas and orangs, and has been named *Australopithecus robustus* (figure 27).

All of these animals possessed small brains, the cranial capacity averaging 500 c.c. or less, which is in the range of a gorilla, and about one-third of that for man. These animals thus unquestionably had the brains of apes, regardless of what else can be said about them. Both of them had ape-like skulls and jaws, these features being particularly obvious in the case of *A. robustus*.

The dentition, above all, it is said, is what makes these animals distinctive and which has served to cause paleoanthropologists to claim a hominid status for them (figure 28). The front teeth (incisors and canines) are relatively small, and the dental arcade, or curve of the jaw, is more parabolic and less U-shaped than is typical of modern apes. It

---

[55] L. S. B. Leakey, *Nature* 188:1050 (1960); 189:649 (1961).

is also claimed that the morphology, or shape, of the teeth is in many features more man-like than ape-like. The cheek teeth (premolars and molars), however, are massive, even in the gracile, or *africanus* form. *A. africanus*, even though only about sixty to seventy pounds, or about the size of a smallish chimpanzee, had cheek teeth larger than chimps and orangs and as large as gorillas, some of the latter of which reach 400 pounds in size. As a consequence, the jaws are very large, particularly in *A. robustus*.

Some fragments of the pelvis, limb, and foot bones of these animals have been recovered, and, based on studies of these fragments, it has been the consensus among evolutionists that the australopithecines

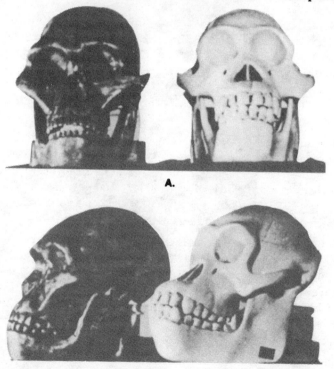

A.

B.

Figure 26. Frontal (A) and diagonal (B) views of *Australopithecus africanus* (left) and cast of an orangutan skull (right). From Rusch's Human Fossils, in *Rock Strata and the Bible Record*, P.A. Zimmerman, Ed., Concordia Pub. House, St. Louis, 1970.

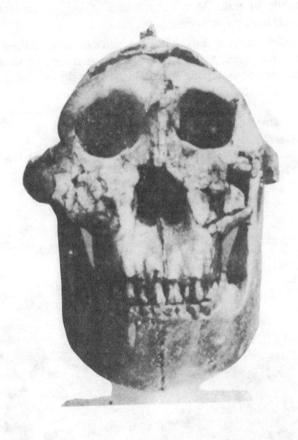

Figure 27. Reconstruction of the *Australopithecus boisei*
(*Zinjanthropus*) skull.

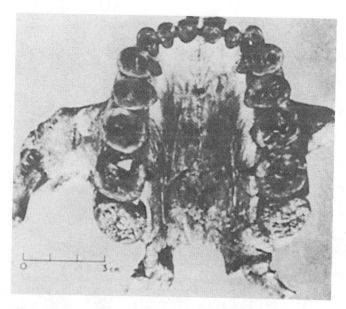

Figure 28. The palate and dentition of *Australopithecus boisei*.

walked habitually upright. This was especially so after such authorities as Broom[56] and Le Gros Clark[57] strongly supported this conclusion.

Evaluation of the Australopithecines by Lord Zuckerman and Charles Oxnard

In more recent years, however, this view has been challenged by Solly Lord Zuckerman,[58] famous British anatomist, and by Dr. Charles Oxnard,[59] for some years Director of Graduate Studies and Professor of Anatomy at the University of Southern California Medical School, and now at the University of Western Australia, Perth.

---

[56] Robert Broom and G. W. H. Schepers, *Transv. Mus. Mem.* 2:1 (1946).

[57] W. E. Le Gros Clark, *J. Anatomy* (London) 81:300 (1947).

[58] Solly Zuckerman, *J. Roy Col. Surg. Edinburgh* 11:87 (1966); S. Zuckerman, *Beyond the Ivory Tower* (New York: Toplinger Pub. Co., 1970), pp. 75-94.

[59] C. E. Oxnard, *Nature* 258:389-395 (1975); C. E. Oxnard, *Homo* 30:243 (1981); C. E. Oxnard and F. P. Lisowski, *American Journal of Physical Anthropology* 52:116 (1980); See B. Wood, *Nature* 262:331 (1976).

Zinjanthropus drawn by Neave Parker for Dr. L. S. B. Leakey. Copyright, *the Illustrated London News & Sketch, Ltd.*, 9/1/60.

Zinjanthropus drawn by Maurice Wilson for Dr. Kenneth P. Oakley.

Figure 29. Two contrasting views by evolutionists of *Zinjanthropus* (*A. robustus*).

For over fifteen years a research team headed by Lord Zuckerman studied the anatomical features of man, monkeys, apes, and the australopithecine fossils. Practically all available important fossil fragments of *Australopithecus*, along with anatomical specimens from hundreds of monkeys, apes, and humans were compared.

Concerning the claim by Le Gros Clark and others that *Australopithecus* should be classified as a genus of the Hominidae (family of man) rather than as a genus of the anthropoid apes, Lord Zuckerman has said:

> But I myself remain totally unpersuaded. Almost always when I have tried to check the anatomical claims on which the status of *Australopithecus* is based, I have ended in failure.[60]

Lord Zuckerman's conclusion is that *Australopithecus* was an ape, in no way related to the origin of man.

Oxnard's research has led him to say:

> Although most studies emphasize the similarity of the australopithecines to modern man, and suggest, therefore, that these creatures were bipedal tool-makers at least one form of which (*Australopithecus africanus*—"*Homo habilis*," "*Homo africanus*") was almost directly ancestral to man, a series of multivariate statistical studies of various postcranial fragments suggests other conclusions.[61]

From his results Oxnard concluded that *Australopithecus* did not walk upright in human manner. He states:

> Multivariate studies of several anatomical regions, shoulder, pelvis, ankle, foot, elbow, and hand are now available for the australopithecines. These suggest that the common view, that these fossils are similar to modern man or that on those occasions when they depart from a similarity to man they resemble the African great apes, may be incorrect. Most of the fossil fragments are in fact

---

[60] Zuckerman, *Beyond the Ivory Tower*, p. 77.
[61] Oxnard, *Nature* 258:389, 394 (1975).

uniquely different from both man and man's nearest living genetic relatives, the chimpanzee and gorilla.

To the extent that resemblances exist with living forms, they tend to be with the orangutan. . . .[62]

Finally, the quite independent information from the fossil finds of more recent years seems to indicate absolutely that these australopithecines, of half to 2 million years and from sites such as Olduvai and Sterkfontein, are not on a human pathway.[63]

More recently, and following some studies on Johanson's "Lucy" (*Australopithecus afarensis*), Oxnard had this to say:

. . . the australopithecines known over the last few decades from Olduvai and Sterkfontain, Kromdrai, and Makapans-gat, are now irrevocably removed from a place in the evolution of human bipedalism, possibly from a place in a group any closer to humans than the African apes and certainly from a place in the direct human lineage.[64]

Relative to recent studies on *Australopithecus afarensis* ("Lucy"), Oxnard states:

Though the standard idea is that some of the australopithecines are implicated in a lineage of humanlike forms, the new possibility suggested in this book, a radiation separate from either humans or African apes, has received powerful corroboration. It is now being recognized widely that the australopithecines are not structurally closely similar to humans, that they must have been living at least in part in arboreal environments, and that many of the later specimens were contemporaneous or almost so with the earliest members of the genus *Homo*.[65]

---

[62] C. E. Oxnard, *University of Chicago Mag.* (Winter 1974), pp. 11-12.

[63] Oxnard, *Homo*, p. 225 (1981).

[64] C. E. Oxnard, *The Order of Man* (New Haven: Yale University Press, 1984), p. 332.

[65] *Ibid.*, pp. *iii* and *iv* of *Nota Bene*.

Oxnard's conclusions are, then, that *Australopithecus* is not related to anything living today, man or ape, but was uniquely different. If Oxnard and Lord Zuckerman are correct, certainly *Australopithecus* was neither ancestral to man nor intermediate between ape and man. Oxnard is convinced that the australopithecines were unique, not related to anything living today. As we will see later, the research of many others tend to strongly support the conclusions of Lord Zuckerman and Oxnard.

Donald Johanson's "Lucy"

Donald Johanson, at one time an assistant professor of anthropology at Case Western Reserve University and Curator of Physical Anthropology at the Cleveland Natural History Museum, is one of those once obscure anthropologists who have become famous overnight following extravagant and sensational claims concerning the discovery of fossil remains of alleged human ancestors. While working in the fall of 1973 near Hadar in the Afar Triangle of Ethiopia with a team headed jointly by Johanson, Maurice Taieb, a French geologist, and Alemayehu Asfaw of the Ethiopian Antiquities Administration, Johanson discovered the knee joint of a small primate which he at first assumed was that of a monkey. After fitting the parts together and noting the angle the joint appeared to form, he declared that it was the knee joint of a hominid, that is, of a creature intermediate between ape and man. He furthermore believed, on the basis of the fossils of animals that had been found in the area, that his fossil knee joint was three million years old. He thereupon declared on the spot that he had discovered a three million year old human ancestor.[66]

On the way back to the United States after the close of the fossil-hunting season, Johanson stopped off in Nairobi to show his fossil knee joint to Richard Leakey and Mary Leakey, the son and the widow of Louis Leakey. They both declared it to be hominid. On his return to America, Johanson showed the knee joint to C. Owen Lovejoy, a professor of anthropology at Kent State University and an authority on locomotion. After a brief examination of the fossils, Lovejoy declared it to be from a fully bipedal creature, a "modern knee joint."[67]

---

[66] Donald Johanson and M. A. Edey, *Lucy, the Beginnings of Mankind* (New York: Simon and Schuster, 1981), pp. 155-156.

During the second season at Hadar in October of 1974, Asfaw discovered a lower jaw which he thought was from a baboon. Johanson, however, declared it to be from a hominid. Two days later Asfaw discovered two additional similar jaws. One was a palate (upper jaw) with all of the teeth intact. Johanson's announcement concerning this material at a press conference in Addis Ababa on October 25, 1974, included the following statement:

> These specimens clearly exhibit traits which must be considered as indicative of the genus *Homo*. Taken together, they represent the most complete remains of this genus from anywhere in the world at a very ancient time.

> All previous theories of the origin of the lineage which leads to modern man must now be totally revised. We must throw out many theories and consider the possibility that man's origins go back to well over four million years.[68]

Similar bold and imaginative language was used by Richard Leakey concerning his find of Skull 1470, as we will see later.

In November of that same year while prospecting for fossils a few miles from camp with graduate student Tom Gray, Johanson found what he declared on the spot to be "a bit of a hominid arm."[69] Soon they had discovered other remains, including vertebrae, ribs, and parts of a skull and pelvis, all declared to be hominid. After three weeks of collecting at the site, about 40% of a fossilized skeleton had been recovered. It was that of a female and was named "Lucy" by Johanson. This creature was only about three and one half feet tall and had a very small brain, from 380 c.c. to 450 c.c.[70] Johanson announced in press conferences that his "Lucy" was a three and one-half million year old hominid that walked upright just like modern humans. This brought instant fame to "Lucy" and her discoverer. The National Geographic Society promised funds and assigned a photographer to Johanson's expedition. Money came from several sources. Johanson's future was secure.

---

[67] *Ibid.*, p. 163.

[68] Anonymous, *Nature* 253:232 (1975).

[69] Johnson and Edey, *Lucy, the Beginnings of Mankind*, p. 16.

[70] *Ibid.*, p. 271.

In a paper received for publication in September of 1975 and published in March of 1976,[71] Johanson and Taieb tentatively assigned the material found by Asfaw to the genus *Homo*, and suggested that "Lucy" showed affinities to *Australopithecus africanus*, while other fragments (a right proximal femur and a temporal fragment) bore affinities to *Australopithecus robustus*.

In the fall of 1975 during the third season at Hadar, members of Johanson's team discovered a group of fossils that included fragments from at least thirteen individuals, including those of four juveniles and nine adults. This find was unprecedented, as the discovery of so many fossilized primates of any kind in a single small area had never occurred before. As with all earlier finds of primate remains at Hadar, Johanson immediately declared them to be hominids, even ascribing them to the genus *Homo*.[72] Johanson dubbed them the "First Family." The use of such terms as "human," "Lucy," the "First Family," "child," and similar anthropomorphic terms helps to convey the notion that the human-like status of these fossils is firmly established.

To assist him in his interpretive studies of the Hadar fossils, Johanson enlisted the services of Tim White, at that time a post-doctoral student in anthropology from the University of Michigan. White had worked with both Richard Leakey at Lake Turkana in Kenya and with Mary Leakey at Laetoli in Tanzania. From the beginning of their discussion, Johanson argued that there were two species at Hadar, including one that should be placed in the genus *Homo*, while White argued for a single species. White's views prevailed, and their final conclusion was that the Hadar fossils represented a very primitive species of *Australopithecus*, to which they assigned the name *Australopithecus afarensis*.[73]

According to the analyses of Johanson and White, assisted by Owen Lovejoy's conclusions on locomotion, as well as the support of others, "Lucy" and her fellow creatures walked upright in the human manner, although they were essentially ape-like from the neck up.[74] They were thus portrayed as creatures with smallish, powerful, human-like bodies topped with the heads of apes. This had been more

---

[71] D. Johanson and M. Taieb, *Nature* 260:293 (1976).

[72] Johnson and Edey, *Lucy, the Beginnings of Mankind*, pp. 213, 223.

[73] D. Johanson and T. D. White, *Science* 203:321 (1979); 207:1104 (1980).

[74] Johnson and Edey, *Lucy, the Beginnings of Mankind*, p. 352.

or less the view generally held by evolutionary anthropologists concerning the australopithecines for several decades. This consensus has become a fixture in textbooks and has been widely disseminated in the scientific literature as well as in all forms of the mass media.

Johanson's special claim to fame rested not only on the large number of individuals his fossils represented and the fact that one ("Lucy") was about 40% complete, but that the date assigned to these fossils, about three and one half million years, made them the oldest candidates for human ancestors. The family tree constructed by Johanson and White thus places A. afarensis at the base of the tree. Their tree branches, with one branch from A. afarensis giving rise successively to A. africanus and A. robustus and the other branch giving rise successively to Homo habilis, Homo erectus, and Homo sapiens (see figure 30).

A Skull of Afarensis at Last!

All early reconstructions of the skull of "Lucy" and her fellow creatures were based on fragmentary remains pooled from several individuals. This skull was reported as resembling a small female gorilla. In 1994, however, Kimbel, Johanson, and Rak reported the recovery of an additional fifty-three specimens of A. afarensis from the Hadar Formation in Ethiopia,[75] the site where "Lucy" had been discovered. Among these fossils was the nearly complete skull of an adult male. It is grossly ape-like. Also recovered was the most complete Australopithecus ulna (one of the bones of the forearm) yet discovered and a humerus (the upper arm bone). The relative length of the forearm compared to the upper arm, the ulna/humerous length index, was 91% (that of "Lucy" was even greater, 92.5%). This is distinctly closer to that of the chimpanzee (95%) than to that of the human (80%). Kimbel, Johanson, and Yak state that:

> The combination of a relatively short, but robust humerus and a long forearm is unlikely to resolve the debate about locomotion in A. afarensis.

This is Johanson's roundabout way of admitting that his claims that "Lucy" and her fellow australopithecine creatures walked upright in a human manner is in trouble. Not only did these ape-like creatures

---

[75] W. H. Kimbel, D. C. Johanson and Yoel Rak, *Nature* 368:449-451 (1994).

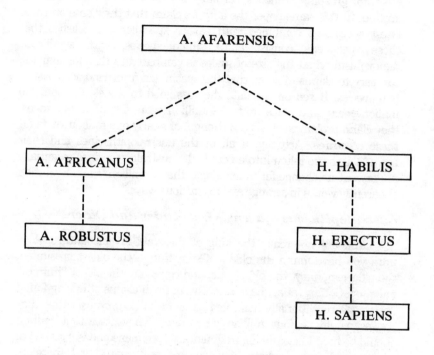

Figure 30. The family tree of man as suggested by Johanson and White.

have relatively long powerful forearms and short, robust hindlimbs similar to the apes, but they had long curved fingers and long curved toes. Long curved fingers and toes are designed for locomotion in the trees, for grasping branches, certainly not for walking around on the ground. In this same paper the authors claim that their data on these latest specimens combined with earlier specimens establishes that these specimens consist of a single species, with significant dimorphism when the size of males is compared to that for females, contrary to claims of some that the specimens from Hadar consist of two species. Based on the date they assigned to the skull, about 3.0 million years, and dates up to 3.9 million years for other specimens, they claim prolonged stasis (no change) of nearly one million years for these creatures. Actually, if all of the australopithecines and their reputed ages are taken into account, the australopithecines essentially underwent no change for much longer than a million years. Evolution apparently works in strange and mysterious ways.

Australopithecus afarensis Gets Older and Older

You are not really the king of the walk in paleoanthropology until you have found the oldest of something—the oldest prosimian, the oldest monkey, the oldest ape, and especially the oldest "human" ancestor. Coffing, et al., have recently set forth claims of having found specimens conditionally identified as those of *A. afarensis* that they suggest could be four million years old.[76] They state that caution should be used in classifying fragmentary specimens and isolated teeth as hominid (intermediate between ape and man), and therefore suggest that these specimens be called "hominoid indeterminate." Actually numerous specimens in paleoanthropology (recall *Ramapithecus*) have been identified as hominid on the basis of fragmentary specimens and/or one or two teeth, and hundreds of specimens in paleontology in general have been classified on the basis of one or two teeth or other very fragmentary evidence. Coffing et al. report that the other fossils collected at the site, which included a variety of fish (including lungfish), reptiles, antelopes, gerbils, rats, and arboreal colobines (monkeys) indicate a diverse habitat, from aqueous, to forests, to dry savanna, to woodland on a floodplain. This would

---

[76]Katherine Coffing et al., *American Journal of Physical Anthropology* 93:55-65 (1994).

suggest that paleontologists should be extremely cautious when attempting to visualize a habitat on the basis of fossils. Their scenarios may be grossly in error.

Claims Are Made for the Ultimate "Missing Link"

Tim White of U.C. Berkeley, Gen Suwa of the University of Tokyo, and Berhane Asfaw of the Paleontology Laboratory, Addis Ababa, Ethiopia, have put in a claim to have found evidence of a creature that they say could represent the population of apelike creatures that gave rise to modern apes and man,[77] a fossil they date at 4.4 million years, a full half-million-years older than *A. afarensis*. They named it *Australopithecus ramidus*. In the concluding statement in their paper, after acknowledging that more fossils are needed, they say:

> The fossils already available indicate that a long-sought link in the evolutionary chain of species between humans and their African ape ancestors occupied the Horn of Africa during the early Pliocene.

It is just possible that this claim is based more on desire for fame and fortune than on substance. Early in their paper they state that:

> Because details of the ape and human divergence are poorly understood, taxonomically diagnostic hominoid fossil evidence antedating the existing record of *A. afarensis* has been eagerly anticipated.

That they may have been a bit overeager to claim that eagerly anticipated bit of paleontological history is indicated by the vigorous opposition voiced in some quarters. Their claims have received support as well.[78]

An especially critical analysis appeared in the *CEN Technical Journal*.[79] A total of 17 fossils were collected. The holotype (the fossils on which definitive characters are based) consisted of an alleged set of associated teeth of one individual—two incisors, two canines, five premolars, and one molar. Other fossils included two fragments from

---

[77] T. D. White, Gen Suwa, and B. Asfaw, *Nature*, 371:306-312 (1994).

[78] Bernard Wood, *Nature* 371:280 (1994).

[79] Anonymous, Perspectives section, *CEN Technical Journal* 8(2): 129-130 (1994).

cranial bases, a mandible from an immature creature, associated upper limb fragments, and other teeth. The fossils were collected from numerous sites in an area stretching along about one mile.

Much was made of the single temporary (deciduous) molar tooth found in the immature mandible about one mile from the holotype. They report that this "apelike" molar is "far closer to that of a chimpanzee than to any known hominid." The other teeth examined had many chimpanzee or other apelike characteristics, with few exceptions which they claimed pointed in the hominid direction. The fossil skull material also points to a chimpanzee. They report that "The Aramis cranial fossils evince a strikingly chimpanzee-like morphology. . . ." Concerning the arm fragments, they state: "The arm displays a mosaic of characters usually attributed to hominids and/or great apes." If it is said that these characters are usually attributed to hominids or great apes, as their statement permits, then it could be said that these characters are usually attributed to great apes. In fact, after declaring that the fossil possesses "probable derived characters shared with other hominids" they state that: "The specimen also shows a host of characters usually associated with modern apes."

Wood, in his defense of the attribution of these fossils to a primitive ancestor of ape and man, argues that the three "hominid" characteristics are derived while the many similarities to chimpanzees and other great apes are either "primitive retentions" or the result of convergent evolution.[80] It seems obvious that what one believes to be true has a powerful, even decisive influence on his conclusions. Whatever this creature was (or creatures were), it could not have been ancestral to man, because as has already been pointed out in this chapter, neither were the australopithecines, the supposed descendants of *A. ramidus*, ancestral to man. One of the editors of *Nature* in the issue in which *A. ramidus* was reported offered a cautionary note:

> The attractive epithet of the "missing link" had better be avoided until it is possible to answer with some clarity the question "With what?"[81]

---

[80] Wood, *Nature* 371:280 (1994).
[81] Anonymous, *Nature* 371:269-270 (1994).

The author of the critical article in *CEN Technical Journal* closes out his comments in appropriate fashion. He says:

Like many previous claims about new fossil evidence for the evolution of mankind, this one seems like another case of "much ado about nothing."[82]

Challenges to the Johanson-White Interpretation of the Hadar Fossils

Chapter 14 of the book, *Lucy, The Beginnings of Humankind*, by Johanson and Edey is entitled "The Analysis is Completed." This title reflected Johanson's confidence that his analysis of the Hadar fossils as creatures that were essentially ape from the neck up but which walked in a fully human manner, was correct and would stand the test of time. This confidence was a bit premature, to say the very least. First, it flies directly in the face of the conclusions of Lord Zuckerman and Charles Oxnard concerning the status of the australopithecines. Lord Zuckerman and Oxnard worked on fossils of australopithecines that were supposedly two million years younger, or more recent, than "Lucy" and the other Hadar fossils of Johanson. Certainly, then, if Johanson's Hadar creatures walked erect, the creatures studied by Lord Zuckerman and Oxnard must have walked erect. As we have noted earlier, however, Lord Zuckerman and Oxnard concluded that the australopithecines they studied did not walk erect in a human manner.

Furthermore, while not denying that the Hadar creatures may have had some measure of bipedal locomotion, a number of investigators have challenged the claims of Johanson, White, and Lovejoy that these Hadar creatures were fully bipedal in the human manner. In our attempt to analyze and evaluate these analyses by various investigators, we have discovered that "there is a jungle out there."

First, almost all investigators have changed their minds at one time or another, and yet no consensus is in sight. Richard Leakey has been most candid in this respect. In an article published in March of 1982 in *New Scientist*, he is reported to have said, "I am staggered to believe that as little as a year ago I made the statements that I made."[83]

---

[82] Anonymous, *CEN Technical Journal* 8(2): 130 (1994).

Although there is little doubt that Leakey believes that the australopithecines walked erect, he is quoted in this same article as saying that paleontologists do not know whether *Australopithecus* walked upright. "Nobody has yet found an associated skeleton with skull." We should be reminded that this statement was made after all recent major discoveries had been reported, including those of the teams headed by Johanson, by Mary Leakey, and by Richard Leakey. In his book, *The Making of Mankind*,[84] published in 1981, Leakey had stated (p. 71) that "we can now say that the australopithecines definitely walked upright."

As reported earlier in this section, Johanson had at first believed that his Hadar specimens included those with affinities with *Australopithecus robustus* and *Australopithecus africanus*, and that some were definitely of the genus *Homo*. Later he changed his mind and not only grouped all of them into a single new species, *Australopithecus afarensis*, but declared that his *afarensis* creatures were the most primitive of all the australopithecines, in fact, the most primitive of all known hominids. If these creatures were really that *primitive*, how is it that Johanson in his early discussions with White, and after many months of studying these fossils, still insisted that some must be included in the genus *Homo*, the most *advanced* of all hominid genera?

Jack T. Stern and Randall Susman, anatomists of State University of New York at Stony Brook, have published a detailed study of the postcranial skeleton of Johanson's Hadar specimens.[85] In this paper Stern and Susman suggest that the larger specimens were the males and the smaller specimens were the females of a single species. In a paper detailing the current squabbling among evolutionists concerning the status of "Lucy" and the other Hadar specimens published July 2, 1983, one year after Stern and Susman had submitted their paper to the *American Journal of Physical Anthropology*, Stern is reported to have changed his mind and is now

---

[83] R. E. F. Leakey, as quoted by Jeremy Cherfas, *New Scientist* 93:695 (1982).

[84] R. E. F. Leakey, *The Making of Mankind* (New York: E. P. Dutton, 1981).

[85] J. T. Stern, Jr. and L. R. Susman, *American Journal of Physical Anthropology* 60:279 (1983).

suggesting that the Hadar specimens represent two species.[86] In this same issue of *Science News* it is reported that Yves Coppens, Director of the Musee de l'Homme in Paris, and one of the co-authors of the paper published by Johanson identifying the Hadar specimens as a single species, is now suggesting on the basis of the premolars found among these specimens that two species are represented. Also in this same paper it is reported that Phillip Tobias of the University of Witwatersrand of Johannesburg, South Africa, on the basis of comparative studies of the Hadar specimens with nearly 100 new specimens found during the last few years at Sterkfontein, South Africa, the site of Raymon Dart's first find of *Australopithecus africanus* in 1924, asserts that the species designation of *afarensis* should be abandoned and that Johanson's Hadar specimens should all be included within *A. africanus*. This is also recommended by Noel T. Boaz, a New York University anthropologist.

As already mentioned, Stern and Susman have published a detailed analysis of the postcranial material from the Hadar specimens.[87] Although these investigators believed that their studies revealed that the Hadar creatures were adept tree climbers and thus were either partially or fully arboreal, they believe that these creatures also possessed some mode of bipedality. They thus state:

> ... we must emphasize that in no way do we dispute the claim that terrestrial bipedality was a far more significant component of the behavior of *A. afarensis* than in any living nonhuman primate (p. 280).

Stern and Susman point out many ape-like features of the Hadar specimens. Concerning the hands, which are long and curved, they say:

> A summary of the morphologic and functional affinities of the Hadar hand fossils heads inexorably to an image of a suspensory adapted hand, surprisingly similar to hands

---

[86] W. Herbert, *Science News* 124:8 (1983).

[87] Stern and Susman, *American Journal of Physical Anthropology* 60:279 (1983); Herbert, *Science News* 124:8 (1983); R. H. Tuttle, *Science* 220:833 (1983); For a description of the analysis of Stern and Susman in layman's terms, see J. Cherfas, *New Scientist* 97:172 (1983).

found in the small end of the pygmy chimpanzee-common chimpanzee range (p. 284).

Concerning the foot, which was long, curved, and heavily muscled, they state:

> In summary, the foot and ankle remains reveal to us an animal that engaged in climbing as well as bipedality. . . . *There is no evidence that any extant primate has long, curved, heavily muscled hands and feet for any purpose other than to meet the demands of full or part-time aboreal life* (p. 308). (Emphasis added.)

With reference to the scapula, they report:

> We conclude that the glenoid cavity of *A. afarensis* was directed far more cranially than is typical of modern humans and that this trait was an adaptation to use of the upper limb in elevated positions as would be common during climbing behavior (p. 284).

In the section on the innominate, after pointing out that the innominate of "Lucy" shows:

> . . . the distinctly human traits of a low broad ilium, a deep sciatic notch, a prominent anterior inferior iliac spine, and an ischial surface for the origin of the hamstring muscles. . .

they go on to describe a number of features that are ape-like (pp. 284–290), and with reference to the possibility of a weak or absent sacrotuberous ligament they state: "One possible explanation is that the bipedal gait was like that of chimpanzees or spider monkeys. . . ." Later they say:

> The possibility that the sacrotuberous ligament of *A. afarensis* was not as powerfully developed as in humans suggests either a lesser frequency or a different manner of terrestrial bipedality than typifies modern humans (p. 290).

Of the sacrum, Stern and Susman state that: "The AL 288–1an sacrum is distinct from modern human sacra in that the first segment lacks well-developed transverse processes" (p. 291). With reference to the pelvis, after pointing out that the anterior portion of the iliac blade of "Lucy" (AL 288–1) does not face laterally as in humans but that the alignment of the blade seems to be even more coronal than in chimpanzees, they say:

> The fact that the anterior portion of the iliac blade faces laterally in humans but not in chimpanzees is obvious. The marked resemblance of AL 288–1 to the chimpanzee is equally obvious.

Later, with reference to this fact they state that: "It suggests to us that the mechanism of lateral pelvic balance during bipedalism was closer to that in apes than in humans" (p. 292).

To Stern and Susman, the proximal femur of one of the large individuals (AL 333–3) is much more human-like than that of one of the small individuals (AL 288–lap). They conclude:

> The overall impression gained by a study of the well-preserved large proximal femur (AL 333–3), is that this specimen is very similar to the modern condition. . . . On the other hand, the articular coverage of the femoral head in AL 288–lap suggests the conclusion that the hip excursion of this small representative of A. *afarensis* was more ape-like than man-like (p. 295).

Later (p. 296) they say:

> The small proximal femur is much less human-like in overall appearance and probably came from an individual with the ability to abduct the hip in the manner of pongids.

With reference to the distal tibia of the small specimens, Stern and Susman state:

> Preuschoft's analysis would suggest that AL 288–1, like non-human primates with an anterior trunk center of gravity, had difficulty maintaining a vertical orientation of the trunk and might have progressed bipedally in a manner unlike that of humans and more like that of an African ape (p. 300).

They conclude:

> The evidence of the distal tibiae from Hadar then indicates
> that the small-bodied form was distinct from modern
> humans in locomotor behavior, while the larger specimens
> evince no sign of such distinction (p. 301).

Their studies of the fibula led to the statement:

> We can summarize the morphologic status of the Hadar
> fibulae by stating that they seem to be derived from a
> population with an average structure different from that of
> the typical human.

After discussing a number of traits they had considered, they
say:

> Each of these traits is a structural similarity to pongids.
> The overall configuration of the AL 188–1at distal fibula is
> far more similar to that of an ape than that of a human
> (p. 305).

> Their analysis of the knee joint is especially interesting since
> Johanson, White, and Lovejoy had cited the structure of the knee joint
> as being particularly significant in establishing a fully human bipedal
> mode of locomotion for "Lucy" and the other Hadar creatures. Stern
> and Susman state:

> In summary, the knee of the small Hadar hominid shares
> with other australopithecines a marked obliquity of the
> femoral shaft relative to the bicondylar plane, but in all
> other respects it falls either outside the range of modern
> human variation (Tardieu, 1979) or barely within it (our
> analysis). Since, aside from the degree of valgus, the knee of
> the small Hagar hominid possesses no modern trait to a
> pronounced degree, and since many of these traits may not
> serve to specify the precise nature of the bipedality that was
> practiced, we must agree with Tardieu that the overall
> structure of the knee is compatible with a significant degree
> of arboreal locomotion (p. 298).

Furthermore, the degree of valgus of the knee joint of Lucy may not be a human trait at all. The valgus angle is a measure of the extent that the leg above the knee bends outward or laterally (thus in humans a larger than normal valgus angle gives rise to the "knock-kneed" condition). With chimpanzees and gorillas, the valgus angle is about 0°. The upper and lower legs of these apes thus form a straight line and the center of gravity of the body falls inside of the legs. With humans, the degree of valgus is about 9°, the upper leg angling outward or laterally from the knee. This places the lower legs and feet more directly under the center of gravity of the body. "Lucy" and the South African australopithecines have a high degree of valgus, about 15°.

As the reader will recall, it was this angle of the knee joint that led Johanson to declare on the spot that the knee joint that he found in 1973 was from a hominid. As mentioned both by Stern and Susman (p. 298) and by Cherfas,[88] Jack Prost of the University of Illinois at Chicago Circle takes just the opposite view. He maintains that the high degree of valgus exhibited by the australopithecines supports the fact that they were adept tree climbers.[89] In favor of this theory is the fact that among monkeys and apes the highest degree of valgus (equal to that of humans) is found in the orangutan and the spider monkey, both extremely adept tree climbers. On page 313 of their article, Stern and Susman state their overall conclusions:

> We discovered a substantial body of evidence indicating that arboreal activities were so important to *A. afarensis* that morphologic adaptations permitting adept movement in trees were maintained. This conclusion in and of itself, does not ineluctably lead to a second deduction that the nature of terrestrial bipedality, when it was practiced, was different from modern humans. However, we do believe this second conclusion to be reasonable even though the evidence in its favor is much less compelling than that indicating a significant degree of arboreality.

Earlier on that same page concerning the nature of the bipedal gait of these creatures, they had stated, however, that:

---

[88] Cherfas, *New Scientist* 97:172 (1983).

[89] Jack Prost, *American Journal of Physical Anthropology* 52:175 (1980).

Finally, if deductions about poorly developed sacroiliac and
sacrotuberous ligaments in the Hadar hominid are correct,
then one possible explanation is that the bipedal gait was
like that of chimpanzees or spider monkeys, in which the
maximum vertical force is, on the average, a smaller fraction
of body weight than characterizes humans.

Thus, while retaining the notion that "Lucy" and the other *A.
afarensis* creatures walked upright, although not necessarily in a fully
human manner, Stern and Susman maintain that these creatures
were highly adapted to an arboreal, or tree-climbing, mode of
locomotion. In the light of the many ape-like features of these
creatures described by Stern and Susman, and in view of the
conclusions of Oxnard and Zuckerman and their co-workers
concerning the mode of locomotion of the australopithecines, it may be
that *A. afarensis* and other australopithecines were actually no more
adapted to a bipedal mode of locomotion than are chimpanzees and
gorillas, which do occasionally walk bipedally.

There is even a case known in which a monkey adopted habitual
upright bipedal locomotion.[90] A "black ape" of the Celebes
(*Cyanopithecus niger*), kept isolated from other primates in the Hong
Kong Zoological and Botanical Gardens, copied human movement at a
very early age and moved almost entirely in a bipedal mode, quite
unlike the way such Old World monkeys walk when they occasionally
walk bipedally.

We have quoted extensively from Stern and Susman in order to
emphasize that even some who believe that, in contrast to the
conclusions of Lord Zuckerman and Oxnard, the australopithecines
had attained a certain mode of bipedality, they still detect many
ape-like features in the postcranial anatomy of these primates.
Furthermore, the conclusions of Stern and Susman contrast sharply
with those of Johanson and Owen Lovejoy, the latter of whom is
quoted as proclaiming that *A. afarensis* was fully adapted to bipedal
locomotion in "excruciating detail."[91]

---

[90] C. E. Oxnard and F. P. Lisowski, *American Journal of Physical
Anthropology* 52:116 (1980).

[91] I. Anderson, *New Scientist* 98:373 (1983).

Russell Tuttle, an anthropologist at the University of Chicago, leans toward Johanson and his supporters concerning the mode of bipedality of "Lucy," as opposed to the views of Stern and Susman, but does agree with Stern and Susman that "Lucy" must have been arboreal.[92]

Since that time Susman has not backed off from his convictions concerning the mode of locomotion of "Lucy" and fellow australopithecines. At the 63rd Annual Meeting of the American Association of Physical Anthropologists he stated his belief that *A. afarensis* walked funny, not like humans. He argued that their odd gait implies they slept, ate, and lived primarily in the trees.[93]

Several recent papers support the contentions of Stern and Susman that the australopithecines, rather than walking in the same manner as modern humans, as Johanson has contended, at the most had a limited and nonhuman type of bipedal locomotion Christine Berge of the Laboratoire d'Anatomie Comparée, Paris, reports that her biomechanical study of the pelvis and lower limb of *Australopithecus afarensis* (AL–288–1, Johanson's "Lucy") shows that only the reconstruction of the gluteal musculature on the basis of the pongid pattern is consistent with the bony structure of the fossil and would have permitted effective movement of bipedalism.[94] She mentioned an earlier study which showed that the structure of the pelvis could provide some arguments for an arboreal locomotion.[95]

Excavations over the past eight years at Sterkfontein, where the original discovery of *Australopithecus africanus* was made in 1924, has yielded almost 600 alleged hominid fossils. Lee R. Berger of the University of Witwatersrand in Johannesburg, South Africa, in his paper at the 65th Annual Meeting of the American Association of Physical Anthropologists reports that the most significant find is of a partial skeleton of an *A. africanus* creature whose "apelike" body was capable of only limited two-legged walking.[96] The fossil includes bones

---

[92] W. Herbert, *Science News* 122:116 (1982).

[93] Ann Gibbons, *Science* 264:350 (1994).

[94] Christine Berge, *Journal Human Evololution* 26:259-273 (1994).

[95] C. Berge, in *Gravity, Posture and Locomotion in Primates*, F. K. Jouffroy, M. H. Stack and C. Niemitz, eds. (France: 11 Sedicesimo, Firenze, 1990), pp. 97-108.

[96] Bruce Bower, *Science News* 147:253 (1995).

from the shoulder, arm, spine, and pelvis. Anatomical analysis indicates that this creature used powerful arms to climb in trees much of the time, according to Berger, and that the pelvis was generally apelike in shape. He suggests that they might have had some degree of bipedality as suggested by others but in a distinctly non-human manner. Of course modern apes and many monkeys have a limited ability to walk bipedally, but certainly not in a human manner.

Of Faces, Teeth, Ears, and Things

Earlier we described the almost complete skull of *A. afarensis* that was discovered by Kimbel, Johanson, and Rak[97] and the grossly apelike nature of the teeth, jaws, face, and brain of this creature. Even earlier studies by Yoel Rak had revealed that the face of *A. africanus* was very different from any possible hominoid ancestral pattern. In his review of Yak's book, *The Australopithecine Face*, Peter Andrews states:

> It is shown that, contrary to wide-spread belief, the face of *A. africanus* is extremely specialized and widely divergent from the hominoid ancestral pattern. Far from providing a good model for human ancestry, it is very different from the common pattern shared by *Homo* and the African apes, the chimpanzees, and gorillas.[98]

Dental developmental patterns in humans and apes differ significantly, and the determination of that pattern in modern apes, humans, and alleged subhuman ancestors can reveal significant relationships, if any, between putative ancestors of man and humans. Using computerized tomography on the Taung skull, the first fossil of an australopithecine ever found (by Raymond Dart in 1924 at Sterkfontein), Glenn Conroy and Michael Vannier reported that:

> The dental development pattern revealed here by CT (computerized tomography) are clearly comparable to those of a 3–4-year-old great ape. In addition, the precocious development of the paranasal sinuses, particularly the intrapalatal extensions of the maxillary sinuses, combined

---

[97] Kimbel, Johanson and Rak, *Nature* 368:449-451 (1994).

[98] Peter Andrews, review of *The Australopithecine Face* (Academic Press, 1993), in *Nature* 308:758 (1984).

with the horizontal alignment of the developing permanent incisors, confirm the retention of some great-apelike growth mechanism in the Tuang facial skeleton.[99]

Holly Smith used a method she calls central tendency discrimination (CTD) to distinguish patterns of development of the teeth of alleged subhuman ancestors—gracile australopithecines, *Homo habilis*, and *Homo erectus* (the latter two will be considered shortly)—as compared to teeth developmental patterns of humans and apes.[100] After describing appropriate criteria to be used in the method, she states:

> Restricting analysis of fossils to specimens satisfying these criteria, patterns of dental development of gracile australopithecines and *Homo habilis* remain classified with African apes. Those of *Homo erectus* and Neanderthals are classified with humans, suggesting that patterns of growth evolved substantially in the Hominidae.

It is clear from these studies that patterns of dental development in young australopithecines clearly place them with creatures very similar to gorillas and chimpanzees rather than any similarity to humans. These conclusions are also supported by Timothy Bromage and Christopher Dean of University College in London, who have identified a rapid, apelike rate of tooth development in what are alleged to be 1.5 million to 3.5 million year old infant hominids.[101] Any claims, in spite of all this contrary data, that Dart did find a few human-like aspects in the Taung skull, such as lack of brow ridges, adaptations in tooth shape, smaller canines, and an alleged cranial base that could hold the head in an erect position must be balanced by the fact that the Taung infant was only about three years old. The skull of a baby ape must never be compared to that of an adult ape. Of course the Taung skull did not have brow ridges but did have smaller canines, just as one would expect in a three-year old ape, and Lord Zuckerman in his studies could not confirm the notion that the cranial base of the australopithecines indicated an upright mode of locomotion. The

---

[99] G. C. Conroy and M. W. Vannier, *Nature* 329:625-627 (1987).

[100] B. Holly Smith, *American Journal of Physical Anthropology* 94:307-325 (1994).

[101] Bruce Bower, *Science News* 132:408 (1987).

evidence to be discussed next definitely contradicts the notion that these creatures walked erect.

Fifteen years ago, Rak and Clarke reported their studies on an ear ossicle, the right incus discovered in the *Australopithecus robustus* specimen SK 848.[102] This was the first ear ossicle discovered in any of the australopithecines. Their research showed that it was substantially different from modern man and the dissimilarity actually exceeded the difference between the ear bones of modern man and the African apes. They emphasized the unique advantages that ear ossicles have for taxonomic and phylogenetic studies, and the fact that this bone provides at least a notion of how great a phylogenetic deviation is represented by *A. robustus*.

In 1994 Fred Spoor, Bernard Wood, and Frans Zonneveld reported their research on the morphology of the vestibular system (the bony labyrinth, which includes the semicircular canals) of modern humans, modern apes, and suggested human ancestors, including the australopithecines, *Homo habilis*, and *Homo erectus*, using high-resolution computerized tomography, or CT scanning.[103] In this procedure the object is "sectioned serially" radiographically, which builds up a series of images by radiographic "slicing" through a skull or other fossil. This permits the production of an accurate three-dimensional picture of the bony labyrinth of the skull (or any other fossil) without disturbing the fossil or sample. Spoor and his coworkers reasoned that the size and/or shape of the labyrinth might be significantly altered to accommodate the differences in balance that correlate with differences in speed and mode of locomotion.

This was indeed the case. They found that humans have relatively significantly larger posterior and anterior semicircular canals but relatively smaller lateral canals than the great apes (taking body size into consideration). In contrast, *Australopithecus africanus* and *Paranthropus (Australopithecus) robustus* showed proportions similar to the great apes. This is another important character that indicates that the australopithecines did not walk upright in a human manner but spent as much time in the trees as do modern apes and probably, when they did walk upright in a limited fashion, their mode of locomotion was similar to modern apes. Kevin Hunt of Indiana

---

[102] Yoel Rak and R. J. Clarke, *Nature* 279:62-63 (1979).

[103] F. Spoor, B. Wood, and F. Zonneveld, *Nature* 369:645-648 (1994).

University noted from his study of chimpanzees in Tanzania that they usually stand on two legs when gathering fruit from small trees. When they move a short distance from one patch to another the chimpanzees may walk bipedally.[104]

The vestibular system of *Homo erectus* (OH2, Sangiran 2, Sangiran 4) shows modern humanlike proportions. Very significantly, and disconcerting to those who would place *Homo habilis* in the genus *Homo* rather than in the genus *Australopithecus*, the vestibular system of the *H. habilis* they studied (Stw 53) was not humanlike at all but had a particularly large lateral canal, this morphology being most similar to cercopithecoids (Old World monkeys). The sample examined was a perfectly preserved left labyrinth. This, along with the data on tooth development by Holly Smith[105] and other data which will be shortly presented, indicates that the so-called *Homo habilis* is just another variety of *Australopithecus*.

Charles Oxnard has studied the foot bones of two fossils of the robust australopithecines recovered by Louis Leakey at the Olduvai Gorge in Tanzania in the 1960's.[106] After their analysis of the foot bones of OH8, Day and Napier declared that these studies indicated that this creature walked bipedally.[107] According to Oxnard and Lisowski their research revealed that the original rearticulation of the OH8 foot bones by Day and Napier was wrong due to a series of incorrect osteological alignments. Their rearticulation revealed that the foot bones of OH8 were from a creature that resembles those of arboreal creatures and that when it walked bipedally it did so with flattened arches, like a gorilla or chimpanzee, and not with high arches as does man.[108]

Most assessments of the foot bones of OH 10 implied that it was the foot of a creature that walked bipedally in the human manner. In a series of studies involving multivariate morphometric analyses of the talus (ankle bone) and rearticulation of the entire suite of foot bones,

---

[104] As reported by Pat Shipman, *New Scientist* 143:26 (1994).

[105] Smith, *American Journal of Physical Anthropology* 94:307-325 (1994).

[106] Michael H. Day, *Guide to Fossil Man*, 4th ed. (Chicago: The University of Chicago Press, 1986), pp. 169-170.

[107] M. H. Day and J. R. Napier, *Nature* 201:967-970 (1964).

[108] C. E. Oxnard and F. Peter Lisowski, *American Journal of Physical Anthropology* 52:107-117 (1980).

Oxnard showed that the original assessments were in error and the foot was entirely different from that of man. Although it shared features with modern apes, it was not entirely like that of any present-day ape but was uniquely different in some aspects.

It seems that the multitude of data on the mode of locomotion, the pattern of tooth development, the structure of the incus, the structure of the labyrinth of the ear, the relatively long and powerfully built forearms and short, robust hindlimbs with their long curved fingers and long curved toes, the overall structure of the feet, the ape-sized brains, and the very apelike jaws, teeth, face, and skulls of the australopithecines establishes beyond reasonable doubt that these creatures were simply apes. They were apes that were uniquely different than any ape now living, but nevertheless, just apes, in no way related to the ancestry of man.

Richard Leakey and His Lake Turkana Specimens—Homo or Australopithecus?

As a prospector for fossils, Richard E. F. Leakey may be compared to a prospector for gold who has had little education, yet was able to strike it rich. Richard Leakey is the son of the famous Louis and Mary Leakey, both of whom earned doctoral degrees. Richard Leakey has never been to college. As a fossil prospector, he did have several advantages, however. The years of experience he had with his parents and his lifelong residence in Kenya were practical advantages. The Leakey name and his position as Director of the Kenya National Museums helped to generate funds and to provide the equipment and opportunities necessary to hunt for fossils. Added to this were his keen intelligence and Leakey ambition.

Leakey's first fossil hunting excursion in Kenya occurred in 1968 when, aided by a grant from the National Geographic Society, he led a team to prospect an area east of Lake Turkana (then named Lake Rudolph) known by the name of Koobi Fora and located just south of the Ethiopian border. The area turned out to be rich in fossils. During the first expedition, three "hominid" jaws were discovered, and in 1969 Leakey found an excellent specimen of an *Australopithecus boisei* skull, similar to the one his father and mother had discovered at Olduvai in Tanzania ten years earlier. In 1972, Bernard Ngeneo, one of the Kenyans in Leakey's team, made the discovery that was to make Richard Leakey famous.

The discovery was of the famous cranium, KNM-ER 1470, popularly known as Skull 1470. The official designation stands for #1470 of the Kenya National Museum's East Rudolph collections. Descriptions of this material were published by Leakey in the British journal *Nature*[109] and in the *National Geographic*,[110] and descriptions may be found in books authored by Leakey.[111] Descriptions of earlier material found at East Turkana are referenced in Leakey's 1973 publication,[112] and material found in this area in 1973 was described by Leakey in 1974.[113] A good survey of the East Turkana specimens was published in 1978 by Alan Walker and Leakey.[114] It was interesting to note that in the paper reporting the discovery of Skull 1470 and several leg bones, Leakey congratulates Ngeneo and paleontologist John Harris for making the discoveries, thanks anatomist Bernard Wood for spending many hours at the site screening for fragments, and thanks Wood, anthropologist Alan Walker and Leakey's wife Meave, for reconstructing the material. In addition, Leakey must have relied heavily on others for the anatomical analyses, since he has no professional training in anatomy or anthropology. Yet Leakey's name is listed as the sole author on the paper.

It may be recalled that Johanson, in a press conference held in October of 1974, had stated, concerning the discovery of several jaws, that in view of these finds, "All previous theories of the origin of the lineage which leads to modern man must now be totally revised."[115] In Leakey's *National Geographic* article he is quoted as saying: "Either we toss out this skull or we toss out our theories of early man. . . . It simply fits no previous models of human beginnings."[116] Lord Zuckerman spent fifteen years with a team of scientists that rarely numbered less than four studying *Australopithecus* fossils, using the

---

[109] R. E. F. Leakey, *Nature* 242:170 (1973); 242:447 (1973).

[110] Leakey, *National Geographic* (June 1973), p. 819.

[111] Leakey and R. Lewin, *Origins* (New York: E. P. Dutton, 1977); Leakey, *The Making of Mankind.*

[112] Leakey, *Nature* 242:447 (1973).

[113] Leakey, *Nature* 248:653 (1974).

[114] Alan Walker and R. E. F. Leakey, *Scientific American* 239(2): 54 (1978).

[115] Anonymous, *Nature* 253:232 (1975).

[116] Leakey, *National Geographic* (Nune 1993), p. 819.

best methods of anatomy available, before finally declaring whether these creatures were or were not hominids. Johanson and Richard Leakey were not only willing to declare on the spot that their finds were hominids but were both bold enough, with little study or time for independent evaluations, to declare that their discoveries made all previous theories of man's origin obsolete. With the cooperation of today's mass media, young anthropologists have found a short cut to fame—call a press conference, display your fossils, and make bold and imaginative statements. Fifteen years of detailed anatomical studies in the laboratory is simply considered unnecessary drudgery.

In his *National Geographic* article,[117] Leakey refers to Skull 1470 as "this surprisingly advanced early man." In press conferences and public lectures Leakey emphasized that his Skull 1470 had many advanced human-like features, in some respects, such as the absence of large eyebrow ridges, the possession of a high-vaulted dome and the absence of any indication of a nuchal crest, even more advanced than *Homo erectus*. Yet, he declared, this creature was nearly three million years old. The postcranial remains which had been found in the Koobi Fora Formation and which Leakey believed displayed evidences of habitual bipedal locomotion, had been found at too great a distance from Skull 1470 to definitely associate these postcranial remains with the owner of the skull, according to Leakey. The estimated cranial capacity of 800 c.c. (other estimates have been somewhat lower), and the morphology of the calvaria (skull cap), Leakey believed, warranted inclusion of the fossil in the genus *Homo*, but he saw no compelling reason to attribute this creature to *Homo habilis*. He therefore designated it *Homo* sp. indet.[118]

A thorough evaluation of the Lake Turkana specimens is found in the paper published by Walker and Leakey.[119] In this paper (published five years after the paper just referred to above), and in the book he published in 1981,[120] Leakey declares that his Skull 1470 should be attributed to *Homo habilis*, although his co-author of the paper, Alan Walker, an anthropologist now at Johns Hopkins University, believes that it should be placed in the genus *Australopithecus*.

---

[117] *Ibid.*, p. 820.

[118] Leakey, *Nature* 242:447 (1973).

[119] Walker and Leakey, *Scientific American* 239(2): 54 (1978).

[120] Leakey, *The Making of Mankind*, p. 17.

In attributing his 1470 specimen to *Homo habilis* Leakey has backed down considerably from earlier claims, and Walker's suggestion that it should be placed among the australopithecines certainly lowers its status considerably. As mentioned above, Leakey had declared in his 1973 *National Geographic* article that "either we toss out this skull or we toss out our theories of early man." In a lecture delivered in San Diego not long after this, the author heard Leakey declare that the discovery of Skull 1470 invalidated all current theories on the origin of man but that he had nothing to put in their place. If, however, Skull 1470 may be attributed to *Homo habilis*, certainly not all theories on the origin of man current at that time would have been invalidated.

The species *Homo habilis* had been declared to be a valid species by his father, Louis Leakey, in 1964,[121] and the elder Leakey had incorporated *Homo habilis* into a suggested lineage for the origin of man. According to Louis Leakey, among the known fossils, *Homo habilis* stands alone in the lineage leading to man. In his view, the australopithecines, *A. africanus* and *A. boisei* (*robustus*), were aberrant side branches, not in the direct line of man's ancestry.

The specimens that Louis Leakey designated *Homo habilis* had been discovered by his team at Olduvai Gorge not long after the discovery of his "Zinjanthropus" (*A. boisei*).[122] Leakey, Tobias, and Napier believed that these specimens were sufficiently advanced to place them in the genus *Homo*. This generated considerable controversy, some supporting Leakey and coworkers, and others insisting that *Homo habilis*, even though its cranial capacity (about 650 c.c.) was larger than that of the smaller varieties of australopithecines, was an invalid taxon and that these fossils should be retained in the genus *Australopithecus*.

No paleoanthropologist has succeeded in sorting out all the creatures that are put into the taxon *Homo habilis* by some and taken out by others. Some insist that *H. habilis* is a bona fide taxon, including creatures intermediate between the australopithecines, either *afarensis* or *africanus*, and *Homo erectus*. Others argue just as strenuously that those creatures classified as *H. habilis* are no more than variants of the australopithecines. In his review of two books on

[121] L. S. B. Leakey, P. V. Tobias, and J. R. Napier, *Nature* 202:7 (1964).
[122] L. S. B. Leakey, *Nature* 188:1050 (1960); 189:649 (1961).

Homo habilis (his article was entitled, "The Many Faces of *Homo habilis*"), Ian Tattersall began his review with the statement that,

> ... it is increasingly clear that *Homo habilis* has become a wastebasket taxon, little more than a convenient recipient for a motley assortment of hominid fossils from the latest Pliocene and earliest Pleistocene ... [123]

Near the end of his review, Tattersall states,

> Of course, if we were to take as a rough guide to generic allocation the fact that among mammals it is the genus that tends to be the basic "Gestalt" category, we would have no problem in excluding the entire group of *habilis* and related fossils from the genus whose type species is *Homo sapiens*. After all, the original assignment of the gracile Olduvai specimens to *Homo*, no less than the specific epithet *habilis*, depended on little more than the presumption of tool manufacture (together, perhaps, with that of some fractional enlargement in brain size). And what we have learned since 1964 about the gracile Olduvai hominid species has tended to make these beasts appear less and less like ourselves, both cranially and in their body proportions.

A group headed by Johanson reported in 1987 that they had discovered the fossils of a creature in the Olduvai Gorge that they identified as *Homo habilis*.[124] The fossil remains (designated OH 62) included fragments of the cranium and limb bones, including a proximal (upper) fragment of the tibia, portions of the femur, most of the ulna, an almost complete humeral shaft, and most of the radial shaft. These are the first limb bones recovered that could definitely be associated with *Homo habilis*. These fossil remains dated at about 1.8 million years. The analysis of these fossil remains provided a real shock to those who had suggested an evolutionary line proceeding from *A. afarensis* to *H. habilis* to *H. erectus* to *H. sapiens*. According to their research, the fossil remains were of an adult female about 3½ feet tall that had long, heavily built arms. Its anatomy was much more apelike than expected. The teeth are as big, relative to body size, as those of

---

[123] Ian Tattersall, *Evolutionary Anthroplogy* 1(1): 34-36 (1992).
[124] D. C. Johanson et al., *Nature* 327:205-209 (1987).

"Lucy." Tim White, one of the members of the team of ten, remarked that "What we see is a creature whose body size and anatomy are strikingly similar to 'Lucy.'"[125]

A very thorough analysis of OH 62 was carried out by Sigrid Hartwig-Scherer and Robert D. Martin of the Anthropological Institute and Museum of the University of Zurich.[126] According to their research, this *Homo habilis* specimen is even more apelike than AL 288-1 ("Lucy"). They report that,

> This study has failed to corroborate earlier expectations concerning postcranial similarities between *Homo habilis* and later members of the genus *Homo*. On the contrary, as reported here, a variety of measurements indicate that OH 62 displays much stronger similarities to African ape limb proportions than does AL 288-1 (Figures 1 and 2; see also Leakey *et al.*, 1989). Computerized tomography scanning revealed that the cortex of the arm bones of OH 62 is amazingly thick and more robust than that of many chimpanzees.

Tim Bromage, who studies facial development at Hunter College in New York City, rotates a laser beam around fossil specimens and uses a computer to convert the reflections into an image. One similarity between *A. afarensis* and humans is the way the cheekbones are swept back relative to the upper jaw. However, when he analyzed the way the cheekbones of *A. afarensis* and humans are built during development, he found that they do not develop in the same way at all.[127] He commented that,

> So although the two faces have some similarities, they are built in very different ways during development. This particular characteristic cannot be used in support of an ancestral relationship between *A. afarensis* and humankind.

---

[125] Bruce Bower, *Science News* 131:340 (1987).
[126] S. Hartwig-Scherer and R. D. Martin, *Journal of Human Evolution* 21:439-449 (1991).
[127] Tim Bromage, *New Scientist* 133:38-41 (1992).

Earlier in the article, he stated concerning KNM-ER 1470 (Richard Leakey's famous skull of *Homo habilis*),

> One of the most complete (and best known) of the early specimens of *Homo* is ER 1470, a fossil cranium and face 1.9 million years old from east of Lake Turkana, in northern Kenya. When it was first reconstructed, the face was fitted to the cranium in an almost vertical position, much like the flat faces of modern humans. But recent studies of anatomical relationships show that in life the face must have jutted out considerably, creating an ape-like aspect, rather like the faces of *Australopithecus*.

Thus, the reconstruction of the skull and face of KNM-ER 1470 that was displayed in *National Geographic*, science journals, and newspapers world-wide was actually incorrect and made the specimen look humanlike rather than apelike. In the same article, Bromage revealed that his analysis of the face of the Taung infant (Dart's initial find) resulted in a pattern that was typical of a monkey or an ape rather than humanlike.

In considering the status of *Homo habilis*—is it a valid taxon or should it be included in the australopithecines; is it advanced sufficiently to suggest it is intermediate between "Lucy" (*A. afarensis*) and *Homo erectus* or is it even more apelike than "Lucy"—it is informative to examine the estimated cranial capacities and alleged ages of various fossils of the robust forms of *Australopithecus* (*A. boisei, A. robustus*), the more gracile forms of *Australopithecus* (*A. afarensis, A. africanus*), those specimens designated *Homo habilis*, and *Homo erectus*. In Table 1 are found the estimated cranial capacities and suggested ages for some of these fossil creatures.

From the table it can be seen that those creatures designated as *Australopithecus africanus* are spread over a time span of three million years and distances of several thousand miles, yet they show essentially no change in cranial capacity or general morphology and thus are readily grouped together in a single species. It is also noted that there is a very considerable overlap in the alleged ages of the species of *Australopithecus* and those designated as *Homo habilis*, and, in fact, some species of *Australopithecus africanus* overlap considerably the reported ages of *Homo erectus*.

Specimen	Attribution	Age (m.y.)	Cranial Capacity (c.c.)	Reference
Table 1. A comparison of fossil specimens attributed to various alleged hominids				
OH 5	*A. boisei*	2.1–1.7	530	1
ER 406	*A. robustus*	2.4–1.5	500	2
Many Specimens	*A. africanus*	4–1	350–400	1, 2
AL 288–1	*A. afarensis*	3–1	350–400	1
OH 7	*H. habilis*	2.1–1.7	675	1
OH 13	*H. habilis*	1.7	650	1
OH 62	*H. habilis*	1.8	?	5
ER 1470	*H. habilis*	1.9	775	2
ER 3733	*H. erectus*	1.5	850	2
ER 3883	*H. erectus*	1.5	850 (?)	2
KNM–WT 15000	*H. erectus*	1.6	800	3
MOJOKERTO 1	*H. erectus*	1.8	?	4

References:

[1] M. H. Day, *Guide to Fossil Man*, 3rd. ed. (Chicago: University of Chicago Press, 1977).

[2] A. Walker and R. E. F. Leakey, *Scientific American* 239:54 (1978).

[3] F. Brown et al., *Nature* 316:788 (1985).

[4] C. C. Swisher, III, et al., *Science* 263:1118 (1994).

[5] D. Johanson et al., *Nature* 327:205-209 (1987); S. Hartwig-Scherer and R. D. Martin, *Journal of Human Evol.* 21:439-449 (1991).

A correspondent for *Nature* remarked:

Such sympatry of *Homo* with one, and quite possibly two, forms of australopithecines could mean that there is little information about the direct and immediate ancestors of *Homo*. These known australopithecines, contemporary with *Homo*, obviously cannot fill the ancestral role.[128]

While certainly not entertaining any doubts about the fact of evolution, Stephen J. Gould, Harvard University paleontologist, has the following to say concerning this state of affairs:

> What has become of our ladder if there are three coexisting lineages of hominids (*A. africanus*, the robust australopithecines, and *H. habilis*), none clearly derived from another? Moreover, none of the three display any evolutionary trends during their tenure on earth: none become brainier or more erect as they approach the present day.[129]

Gould believes that the old idea of straight-line evolution, with the various fossil creatures representing rungs in a ladder leading to man, is wrong and that the true picture is more like a bush with a number of parallel branches. But this leaves unanswered what gave rise to the bush? How and why does evolution occur in fits and starts?

The fact that creatures classified as *Homo* were contemporaneous with the australopithecines has been known for some time. Richard Leakey and Alan Walker, for example, noted that,

> There is evidence from East Africa for late-surviving small *Australopithecus* individuals that were contemporaneous first with *H. habilis*, then with *H. erectus*.[130]

Louis Leakey had reported more than two decades ago the contemporaneous existence of *Australopithecus, Homo habilis,* and *Homo erectus,* fossils of which he had found in Bed II of the Olduvai Gorge.[131] Extremely startling, and a fact very difficult for evolutionists

---

[128] Anonymous, *Nature* 261:541 (1976).

[129] S. J. Gould, *Natural History* 85:30 (1976).

[130] R. E. F. Leakey and Alan Walker, *Science* 207:1103 (1980).

[131] A. J. Kelso, *Physical Anthropology*, 1st ed. (New York: J. B. Lipincott Co., 1970), p. 221; M. D. Leakey, *Olduvai Gorge, Vol. 3* (Cambridge: Cambridge

to assimilate, was Louis Leakey's claim that he had found the remains of a circular stone habitation hut at the bottom of Bed I.[132] Deliberate manufacture of such shelters has long been attributed only to *Homo sapiens*, and can be observed in Africa today.

If *Australopithecus, Homo habilis,* and *Homo erectus* existed contemporaneously, how could one have been ancestral to another? *And how could any of these creatures be ancestral to man, when man's artifacts are found at a lower level than these supposed ancestors of man?* If the facts are correct as Leakey has reported them, then obviously none of these creatures could have been ancestral to man, and that leaves man's ancestral tree absolutely bare. Certainly scratch *Homo habilis*, whatever it was, and all australopithecines from the family tree of man.

Absolute Dates that Are Not Absolute

"Lucy: The Trouble with Dating an Older Woman" is the title of an article[133] discussing challenges to the date of 3.6 million years that Johanson assigned to "Lucy." Francis Brown, a geologist from the University of Utah, believed that the date should be reduced to three million years, based on correlation of volcanic tuffs at Hadar with similar tuffs at Lake Turkana which he believed are reliably dated at about three million years.[134] Noel Boaz, New York University anthropologist, and his co-workers believed also that the date should be reduced to about three million years.[135] Boaz based his argument on the animal fossils found at Hadar. Johanson and Tim White, while defending the older date, maintained that a reduction in age for the Hadar specimens to three million years would not affect their theory of man's lineage, and they eventually settled on the three-million-year age.

Challenges to the nearly three million year old date that Richard Leakey assigned to his Skull 1470 and other specimens found at the same level have come from various sources.

University Press, 1971), p. 272.

[132] Kelso, *Physical Anthropology*, p. 221; M. D. Leakey, *Olduvai Gorge, Vol. 3*, p. 24.

[133] W. Herbert, *Science News* 123:5 (1983).

[134] F. H. Brown, *Nature* 300:631 (1982).

[135] N. T. Boaz, F. C. Howell, and M. L. McCrossin, *Nature* 300:633 (1982).

In his 1973 article,[136] Leakey seemed sure of this date, which was based on potassium-argon dating of the KBS Tuff, under which these fossils were found. The date derived for the tuff was about 2.6 million years, which he proclaimed was "securely dated." Paleomagnetic investigations, Leakey reported, provided "a result which supports the 2.61 m.y. date." In this same paper, Leakey states:

> Collections of vertebrate fossils recovered from below the KBS Tuff in areas 105, 108 and 131 all show the same stage of evolutionary development, and this evidence supports the indicated age for this phase of deposition at East Rudolph.

After mentioning that evidence from pig fossils had been cited as supporting a younger date for the KBS Tuff, Walker and Leakey state that "the fission-track studies of zircons from the KBS tuff indicate that the older dates are correct."[137]

Thus, based on potassium-argon dating, supported by fission-track dating, paleomagnetic dates, and fossil vertebrates, the KBS Tuff was declared to be firmly dated at 2.6 million years. Leakey added approximately another 300,000 years for the deposition of the sediment between the level where ER 1470 was found and the overlying KBS Tuff to come up with an estimate of 2.9 m.y. for the age of this skull and other specimens found at the same level.

The combination of Leakey's claim that his Skull 1470 was a "surprisingly advanced early man," even more modern in several respects than *Homo erectus*, along with the suggested age of almost three million years, was too much for many evolutionists to digest. The age of three million years made Leakey's suggested "early man" older than many of his supposed ape-like ancestors. Both the man-like status and the suggested three million year age of this specimen, therefore, came under attack. Cronin et al. have cited faunal studies, potassium-argon redating of the KBS Tuff, tuff chemistry studies, and fission-track dating as establishing an age of about 1.8 million years for the KBS Tuff.[138] They believe that the most likely date for Skull 1470, therefore, is two million years.

---

[136] R. E. F. Leakey, *Nature* 242:447 (1973).

[137] Alan Walker and R. E. F. Leakey, *Scientific American* 239(2): 65 (1978).

[138] J. E. Cronin et al., *Nature* 292:113 (1981).

Concerning the relative status of Skull 1470, Cronin and his co-workers state:

> . . . its relatively robustly constructed face, flattish naso-alveolar clivus (recalling australopithecine dished faces), low maximum cranial width (on the temporals), strong canine juga and large molars (as indicated by remaining roots) are all relatively primitive traits which ally the specimen with members of the taxon *A. africanus*.

They agree, nevertheless, to the placement of Skull 1470 in *Homo habilis*.

When sufficient pressure is applied, so-called absolute radiometric dates seem to be anything but absolute as the data is massaged and dates are adjusted to fit current conventional wisdom.

Concerning the accepted notion that these fossils are greater than one to two million years in age, it is interesting to note that Walker and Leakey state:

> The Turkana hominid fossils are often so little mineralized that a preservative must be applied to the bone as excavation progresses in order to keep it from fragmenting further. Indeed, sometimes the preservative fluid must be applied with painstaking care because the impact of a falling drop can cause breakage.[139]

Heavy mineralization is, however, generally expected of fossils of these suggested ages.

With reference to KNM-ER 1510, which includes cranial and mandibular fragments, Richard Leakey states, "The specimen is poorly mineralized and further geological investigation at the site indicates a Holocene rather than an early Pleistocene provenance as originally thought."[140] The early Pleistocene is thought to be about 1.8 million years in age, while the Holocene is assumed to have begun about 10,000 years ago. Leakey has thus reduced his estimated age for KNM-ER 1510 by almost 1.8 million years! The fact that the specimen was poorly mineralized, Leakey seems to be implying, lends support for the younger age. Why is it, then, that the fact that the Turkana

---

[139] Walker and Leakey, *Scientific American* 239(2): 58 (1978).
[140] R. E. F. Leakey, *Nature* 248:653 (1974).

specimens are often lightly mineralized causes no concern for Leakey? Another puzzling aspect of this story is that while Walker and Leakey state that the Turkana hominid fossils (most of which are assumed to be greater than a million years in age) are often lightly mineralized, Leakey in his 1973 paper on KNM-ER 1470, 1472, 1475 and 1781 states that "All specimens are heavily mineralized. . . ."[141] This seems to pose a contradiction unless it just so happened that by coincidence all these specimens became heavily mineralized. Leakey, in any case, finally conceded that Skull 1470 is 1.8–1.9 million years old.

The Laetoli Footprints

Laetoli is a site in Tanzania about twenty-five miles south of the Olduvai Gorge. Mary Leakey, the widow of Louis Leakey (Louis Leakey died in 1972), had begun work there with a team in 1974. Many so-called hominid fossils have been found there by her team.[142] In 1976 some animal footprints were discovered and in 1977 footprints were found which were said to have been made by a creature that walked upright in a human manner.[143] Interesting accounts of the discovery and investigation of the prints may be found in the book by Richard Leakey,[144] and especially in the book by Johanson and Edey.[145] In the latter publication, this assessment of the prints is given by White:

> Make no mistake about it, . . . They are like modern human footprints. If one were left in the sand of a California beach today, and a four-year old were asked what it was, he would instantly say that somebody had walked there. He wouldn't be able to tell it from a hundred other prints on the beach, nor would you (p. 250).

In a technical paper published in *Science*, White states:

> The uneroded footprints show a total morphological pattern like that seen in modern humans. . . . Preliminary observations and experiments suggest that the Laetoli

---

[141] R. E. F. Leakey, *Nature* 242:447 (1973).

[142] M. D. Leakey et al., *Nature* 262:460 (1976).

[143] M. D. Leakey and R. L. Hay, *Nature* 278:317 (1979).

[144] R. E. F. Leakey, *The Making of Mankind*, pp. 40-42.

[145] Johanson and Edey, *Lucy, the Beginnings of Mankind*, pp. 245-252.

hominid trails at site G do not differ substantially from modern human trails made on a similar substrate.[146]

Others have similar opinions.[147]

Who made the prints? This is the subject of a lively controversy, but none of the participants in the discussion may have the right answer. The dispute is whether the footprints were made by creatures similar to Johanson's "Lucy" or whether they were made by creatures of the genus *Homo*. Russell Tuttle argues that "Lucy," or a similar creature, with her long curved toes, could not have left these prints, concerning which he said,

> A small barefoot *Homo sapiens* could have made them. . . .
> In all discernible morphological features, the feet of the
> individuals that made the trails are indistinguishable from
> those of modern humans.[148]

More recently, after considerable research on these footprints by several paleoanthropologists, Tuttle had this to say:

> In sum, the 3.5 million-year-old footprint traits at Laetoli
> site G resemble those of habitually unshod modern humans.
> None of their features suggest that the Laetoli hominids
> were less capable bipeds than we are. If the G footprints
> were not known to be so old, we would readily conclude that
> there were made by a member of our genus *Homo*. . . . In
> any case, we should shelve the loose assumption that the
> Laetoli footprints were made by Lucy's kind,
> *Australopithecus afarensis*.[149]

Tuttle does not, of course, argue that a creature of the species *Homo sapiens* actually made the prints, because, as do all evolutionists, he believes them to be about 3.7 million years old, about 3.5 million years before modern man evolved. Tim White, Don Johanson, and others in the Johanson camp argue that rather than *Homo*, creatures similar to "Lucy" left the footprints.

---

[146] T. D. White, *Science* 208:175 (1980).

[147] Johanson and Edey, *Lucy, the Beginnings of Mankind*, pp. 245-252.

[148] I. Anderson, *New Scientist* 98:373 (1983).

[149] R. H. Tuttle, *Natural History* (March 1990), pp. 61-64.

Footprints of antelopes, pigs, giraffes, elephants, rhinos, hares, ostriches, and other animals were found at Laetoli. In artists' conceptions of the scene, we see pictures of giraffes for the giraffe footprints, elephants for the elephant footprints, ostriches for the ostrich footprints, etc. And—humans for the human footprints? Oh, no! Occupying the human footprints we see a sub-human creature, half-ape and half-man. While evolutionists concede that a giraffe must have made the giraffe prints, an elephant must have made the elephant prints, etc., their preconceived ideas about evolution and the age of these formations do not allow them to concede that a human made the human prints. Creationists, accepting the plain facts as revealed by the empirical scientific evidence, believe that the prints were made by modern man—*Homo sapiens*. It is thus the creationist who is the empiricist, allowing the evidence to speak for itself, while it is the evolutionist who models the facts to fit his preconceived notions.

Natural Variability, Hybridization and Other Factors

There is considerable variability within species among primates, including man. Adolph H. Schultz of the Anthropology Institute of the University of Zurich has studied this problem extensively, and his publications on the subject are especially informative.[150] In his 1968 publication, Schultz states:

> This quite unusual lack of intraspecific stability in so many different characters of the recent man-like apes has unfortunately not always been taken into consideration in the interpretation and classification of fossil hominoid fragments.[151]

This failure to take into account the considerable variability among primates has led some anthropologists to attribute great evolutionary significance to differences between fossil specimens that lie well within the range of variability of a single species.

---

[150] A. H. Schultz, "Age Changes, Sex Differences, and Variability as Factors in the Classification of Primates," *Classification and Human Evolution*, ed. S. L. Washburn (Chicago: Aldine Pub. Co., 1963), pp. 85-115; A. H. Schultz, "The Recent Hominoid Primates," *Perspectives on Human Evolution*, vol. 1 (New York: Holt, Rinehart, and Winston, 1968), pp. 122-195.

[151] Schultz, "The Recent Hominoid Primates," p. 186.

Schultz describes the extraordinary variability of the cranial proportions and the even great variability of the perfectly normal chimpanzees that differ in so many details that formerly they might have been classified as different species.[152] The range in cranial capacity of the great apes and man is enormous, ranging (in c.c.) from 175-540 for orangutans, 275-500 for chimpanzees, 340-752 for gorillas and 1100-1700 for man, according to Schultz.[153] There are actually reports in the literature of cranial capacities for man from as little as 800 c.c. to as much as 2000 c.c. Tooth sizes, both absolute and relative, vary greatly among primates.[154] Even the number of vertebrae vary significantly.[155]

It can be seen from an examination of Table 2 that there is considerable variation within species of the combined number of thoracic and lumbar vertebrae. Note also the very significant difference between the closely related gibbons and siamangs, species that are capable of hybridization.

Table 2. Percentage distribution of variations in the number of thoracic and lumbar vertebrae and average numbers of these vertebrae in hominoids and macaques (from Schultz, note 155).

Number of Vertebrae	Macaque (216)	Gibbon (319)	Siamang (29)	Orang (127)	Chimp (162	Gorilla (81)	Man (125)
15			4	19			
16			10	74	29	43	7
17		5	48	7	68	56	91
18	5	72	38		3	1	2
19	91	23					
20	4						
Average	19	18	17	16	17	16.6	17

The presence or absence and the size of the sagittal crest (the bony ridge that runs longitudinally along the midline of the skull, varies both intraspecifically and interspecifically among the apes. The characteristics mentioned here are only a few of those that vary considerably in man and the apes.

---

[152] *Ibid.*
[153] *Ibid.*, p. 168.
[154] *Ibid.*, p. 186.
[155] *Ibid.*, p. 149.

In addition to the natural variability found within species, there is considerable variability due to sex and age. Sexual dimorphism is significant in man and chimpanzees, very pronounced in gorillas and orangutans (the adult body weight of the male being double that of the female) and insignificant in gibbons and siamangs. The male generally tends to be more robust. Thus, the frequency of occurrence and the size of the sagittal crest is greater among males in species possessing this structure.

Differences due to age are especially significant with reference to the structure of the skull in apes. Very pronounced changes occur during the transition from juvenile to adult in apes, but not in man.[156] The skull of a juvenile ape is somewhat like that of man, but the skull of adult apes is drastically different from that of man. We may remember that the first specimen of *Australopithecus* that was discovered by Raymond Dart, the Taung "child," was that of a three year old juvenile. This juvenile skull should never have been compared to those of adult apes and humans.

The joint between the skull and the vertebral column, and thus the center of the occipital condyles and of the foramen magnum, lies well back toward the rear of the skull in all adult apes. These structures lie much farther forward in fetal and infantile life of these apes, but move toward the rear during postinfantile growth. In man, the relative position of these structures changes very little, if at all, during growth. Thus, the relative position of these structures lies farther forward in adult humans as compared to adult apes, and this relationship is used as a diagnostic feature in deciding whether or not a particular fossil creature walked upright (in cases where sufficient material is available). One can easily see that it would be a serious mistake, in this respect, to compare a juvenile ape skull to a human skull.

Several anomalies (from an evolutionary point of view) might be mentioned. First is the fact that the birth weight as per cent of maternal weight in man is almost twice that of the great apes (5.5 vs. 2.4–4.1), but about the same or less than that found in monkeys (5–10) and in gibbons. 7.5).[157] Furthermore, the order of eruption of the teeth is the same in Old World monkeys, gibbons and man, but differs from that of the great apes.[158] Adding to this the fact that while on the

---

[156] *Ibid.*, pp. 170-172.
[157] *Ibid.*, p. 177.

ground the gibbon walks habitually upright, an evolutionist might have some basis for arguing that man is more closely related to gibbons and monkeys that he is to the great apes.

Another factor of considerable importance that is completely ignored by evolutionists in assessing evolutionary significance to differences between fossil specimens is hybridization between species. Berstein reports that two members of a troop of wild *Macaca irus* in Malaysia have been tentatively identified as hybrids of *M. irus* and *M. nemestrina*. Mentioning the variety of primate taxa which will hybridize in the laboratory, he suggests that it is necessary to be extra cautious in evaluating evidence of intergradation.[159] This caution would apply to fossil specimens as well as to living creatures.

The Status of Australopithecines: Summary

We conclude that the australopithecines (*A. africanus, H. africanus, H. habilis, A. boisei, A. robustus, A. afarensis*) were apes, with no genetic relationship either to man or to any of the extant apes. Their mode of locomotion, while unique in some respects, was probably more similar to that of the orangutans than that of any other living creature.

Suggested intermediates for the origin of man all seem to eventually experience a similar fate. Immediately following the announcement of the discovery comes sharp disagreement among the experts; this is followed by gradual acceptance by the majority; then skeptical voices begin to be heard in increasing volume; finally, the creature is cast out of the family tree. This process required about fifty years for *Ramapithecus* and for Piltdown Man, and about 100 years to dethrone Neanderthal Man. It has now been seventy years since Dart announced his discovery of *Australopithecus*. His claim for an intermediate status for this creature met harsh criticism from many fellow evolutionists soon after his announcement, but for the past three or four decades conventional wisdom has given the australopithecines a central place in human evolutionary schemes. Now an increasing number of skeptics are being heard, but several decades more will probably pass before *Australopithecus* loses its status as a human ancestor. Not to worry. Several new

---

[158] *Ibid.*
[159] I. S. Berstein, *Science* 154:1559 (1966).

"intermediates" will have been "discovered" by that time to generate endless arguments among the experts.

Homo Erectus—An Enigma

The creature designated *Homo erectus* has had a checkered history. Experts have vacillated relative to the authenticity of this or that fossil, much of the original evidence disappeared completely, and authorities have argued over the status of creatures so designated—whether they were giant apes, apelike men, or fully human, *Homo sapiens*. Most evolutionists would retain all or most of the fossils that have been classified as *Homo erectus* in that taxon, and would maintain that it was the most recent species that was antecedent to true man, *Homo sapiens*. Others have argued, such as the great French expert Marcellin Boule, for example, that the Peking Man creature was very possibly a large ape which was killed and eaten by modern humans. It is very possible that various fossils that have been collected around the world—Africa, Europe, and Asia—are actually a mixed bag, some being remains of *Homo sapiens* and others, as Boule concluded, and even Dubois finally tended to believe, constituting fossiliferous remains of giant apes.

Fossils originally assigned to the taxon *Pithecanthropus erectus* (erect ape-man), popularly called Java Man, along with fossils originally assigned to *Sinanthropus pekinensis* (Chinese Man from Peking), commonly known as Peking Man, and others found in more recent years in Africa have now all been lumped together in a single species designated *Homo erectus*. The story of *Homo erectus* begins with Eugene Dubois.

Java Man

Dubois was a Dutch physician who, convinced that man had evolved, also became convinced that man's emergence from the apes had taken place somewhere in Asia. Lacking the means to fund an expedition, Dubois joined the Dutch army and asked for and received an assignment to the Dutch East Indies, now Indonesia. In 1887 he and his wife and child sailed for Sumatra. His superiors in the East Indies gave him considerable freedom to search for his "missing link." After two years or so of disappointing results in Sumatra, Dubois was transferred to Java. There in the fall of 1891 along the banks of the

Solo River near the village of Rinil, Dubois found a skull cap. A year later and fifty feet from where he had found the skull cap, he found a femur. Subsequently, Dubois added three teeth to his collection.

The skull cap was very thick-walled and was long and low with no forehead, and had enormous eye-brow ridges. Dubois estimated the cranial capacity to be 900 c.c. The femur was essentially identical to a human femur. Dubois believed that all of the specimens were from a single individual and constituted a true "missing link"—a creature with a very primitive, or ape-like skull, and which, based on the human-like femur, walked erect just like man. He, therefore, named the creature *Pithecanthropus erectus* (erect ape-man).

Dubois exhibited these fossils at the International Congress of Zoology at Leyden in 1895. Authorities greeted Dubois' announcement with considerable skepticism and divided opinion. British zoologists tended to view the remains as human, the Germans as those of an ape, and the French as those of something between ape and man.

Dubois failed to publish the fact that he had also discovered at nearby Wadjak two human skulls (known as the Wadjak skulls) with a cranial capacity of about 1500–1650 c.c., somewhat above the present human average. To have revealed this fact at that time would have rendered it difficult, if not impossible, for his Java Man to have been accepted as a "missing link." It was not until 1922, when a similar discovery was about to be announced, that Dubois published the fact that he had possessed the Wadjak skulls for over thirty years. His failure to reveal this find to the scientific world at the same time he exhibited the *Pithecanthropus* specimens was unfortunate, since this repressed important evidence. One evolutionist anthropologist excused it by stating that it would have been too much of a meal for most anthropologists to digest if the human skulls had been exhibited along with his *Pithecanthropus erectus*.

About fifteen years before his death, and after most evolutionists had become convinced of the man-like status of *Pithecanthropus*, Dubois himself dealt it the unkindest blow of all—he changed his mind and declared that it was nothing more than a giant gibbon![160]

---

[160] W. S. Howell, *Mankind in the Making* (Garden City, New York: Doubleday, 1967), pp. 155-156; Marcellin Boule and H. V. Vallois, *Fossil Men* (New York: Dryden Press, 1957), p. 126; Niles Eldredge, *Fossils—The Evolution and Extinction of Species* (New York: Harry N. Abrams, Inc.,

Actually, Dubois was not the only one bold enough to assert this possibility. Marcellin Boule (then Director of the French Institute of Human Paleontology and one of the world's foremost experts on human fossils) and H. V. Vallois (Boule's successor) stated:

> Following Dubois, several naturalists have laid stress on the resemblance between the *Pithecanthopus* remains and the corresponding portions of a Gibbon's skeleton. In that case, why not assume that *Pithecanthropus* represents a large form, a giant Ape, related to the Gibbon group?

Later they go on to say:

> A certain number of facts can be adduced in support of this hypothesis. In all countries, during Pliocene and Quaternary times, there were giant forms of mammals whose living representatives are now greatly reduced in size. This is the case—to limit ourselves to the Primates—with *Megaladapis*, a giant Lemur of the Quaternary in Madagascar, and *Dryopithecus giganteus*, a fossil Anthropoid of great size from the Siwalik Hills. *Pithecanthropus*, discovered in the same zoological region as the modern Gibbons, may have been no more than a particularly large representative of a genus more or less closely allied to the same group.[161]

Following a discussion of many features of the skull-cap, Boule and Vallois remark: "Taken as a whole, these structures are very similar to those of chimpanzees and gibbons."[162] They report that von Koenigswald, a German paleontologist who also spent time in Java and discovered some additional material, attributed the two molar teeth that Dubois had discovered to an orangutan and the premolar tooth to a true man.[163]

A 1906 expedition at the exact site of Dubois' excavation failed to produce a single scrap of similar material, although 10,000 cubic yards of soil were removed. During 1936–1939, G. H. R. von Koenigswald

---

1991), p. 66.

[161] Boule and Vallois, *Fossil Men*, p. 126.

[162] *Ibid.*, p. 118.

[163] *Ibid.*, p. 121.

carried out an extensive search at Sangiran, about forty miles from Trinil. His efforts were rewarded by the discovery of fragments of jawbones, including teeth, fragments of skulls, and a skullcap. No limb bones were found. Von Koenigswald labeled his finds *Pithecanthropus* II, III, and IV.

Boule and Vallois report that the skulls found at Sangiran present the same general character as Dubois' *Pithecanthropus*.[164] In the case of the Sangiran finds, several teeth were intact in the mandible. Every characteristic of these teeth given by Boule and Vallois is simian rather than man-like.[165]

In the following quotation from the book by Boule and Vallois, it will be noted that they point out the many ape-like features of the teeth in the mandible found by von Koenigswald at Sangiran and then assert that these facts confirm what has been discovered from the study of the cranium of *Pithecanthropus*:

> The true molars are extremely large and increase in size from the first to the third, a simian feature that does not occur in Humans. The point of the canine rises about the biting surface of the premolars, another simian character only found in Man in the fossil jaw from Wadjak. No less important is the presence of a diastema or gap between the upper canine and the lateral incisor of 5 millimetres on the right and 6.2 millimetres on the left. In about fifty per cent of cases the diastema is no larger in Anthropoids; this feature, which proves that the lower canine must have been particularly highly developed, has never been encountered in the genus *Homo*.
>
> To these characteristics may be added the fact that the upper premolars and true molars are arranged almost in a straight line, so that the form of the palate was more reminiscent of the U-shaped palate of the Anthropoids than of the horseshoe-shaped human palate. *All these facts provide singularly unambiguous confirmation of those that emerged from a study of the cranium*[166] [Emphasis added].

---

[164] *Ibid.*, p. 123.
[165] *Ibid.*

Indeed, if the facts mentioned here about the teeth "provide singularly unambiguous confirmation" of the facts which were derived from an analysis of the cranium, then the cranium must have been decidedly simian-like and not human-like. Earlier in their book, Boule and Vallois had stated:

> . . . in its principal characters, the Trinil skull-cap is really intermediate between that of an ape-like chimpanzee, and that of a Man of really low status, such as Neanderthal Man.[167]

Boule had given Neanderthal Man a very low sub-human status.

The assessment by Boule and Vallois of the femur found by Dubois at Trinil (plus a few other fragments of femur found later by Dubois) was that it was essentially indistinguishable from that of a human. They conclude:

> If we possessed only the skull and the teeth, we should say that we are dealing with beings, if not identical with, at least closely allied to the Anthropoids. If we had only the femora, we should declare we are dealing with Man.[168]

Boule and Vallois thus assert that if one looked only at the skull one would say, "Ape," while if one looked only at the femur one would say, "Man." Perhaps this is the true assessment of these specimens—the femur was that of a true man and the skull, as Dubois himself finally concluded and to which, as noted earlier, Boule and Vallois gave at least qualified assent, was that of an exceptionally large ape. From the first, doubt was expressed that the femur belonged to the owner of the skull cap and doubt has remained to the present. Boule and Vallois state, "and whatever the presumptions in favor of the femur belonging to the cranium, some doubt remains. . . ."[169] Concerning the association of the femur with the skull cap, Tim White states:

> Many were reluctant to accept the validity of the association, and some workers [M. H. Day and T. I.

---

[166] *Ibid.*

[167] *Ibid.*, p. 118.

[168] *Ibid.*, p. 123.

[169] *Ibid.*

Molleson, in *Human Evolution*, M. N. Day, Ed. (Taylor and Francis, London, 1973), Vol. 11, p. 127] are still hesitant.

Harry Shapiro remarked that,

> The *Pithecanthropus* femur was so human that it seemed to some of the experts of the day to be incongruous with so apelike skull. . .. But here was a creature who stood and walked as we do, but with a skull remarkably primitive and apelike, a massive protruding jaw and a brain but little more than half the size of ours. The apparent incongruity led some scientists to suggest that the femur did not belong to the skull and that their juxtaposition was simply fortuitous.[170]

At the time, firmly believing in and fervently hoping to find the intermediate form his former professor, Ernst Haeckel, had declared must exist (Haeckel had even named the imaginary link "Pithecanthropus alalus," or speechless ape-man), Dubois naturally jumped to the conclusion that the femur and skull cap belonged to the same individual and that this individual was thus an ape-man who walked erect—a true "missing link." As noted earlier, the three teeth that Dubois also associated with the skull cap did not belong to the owner of the skull cap, and there appears little justification in attributing the femur to the owner of that skull cap.

Whatever the status accorded to other specimens found in other parts of the world which have been attributed to *Homo erectus*, it is very likely that Dubois' final assessment of his *Pithecanthropus erectus* may be the correct one—a very large primate of some kind within the generalized group called apes, possessing no genetic relationship to man whatsoever.

Peking Man

If one accepts uncritically the evidence usually presented in texts and treatises on Peking Man, the case for the existence of near-man, or a man with many very primitive features, would seem established. For example, the skull model and flesh reconstructions based on this model shown in figure 31 reveal a remarkable resemblance to modern man and could hardly be called less than human. A close examination of the

---

[170] H. L. Shapiro, *Peking Man* (New York: Simon and Schuster, 1974), p. 30.

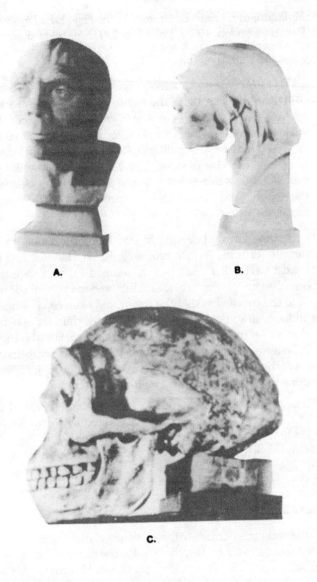

A.   B.

C.

Figure 31. Flesh model (A, B) and skull model (C) of *Sinanthropus pekinensis* (so-called Peking Man). From Rusch's *Human Fossils*, in *Rock Strata and the Bible Record*, P. A. Zimmerman, Ed., Concordia Publishing House, St. Louis, 1970.

reports related to Peking Man, however, reveal a tangled web of contradictions, highly subjective treatment of the data, a peculiar and unnatural state of the fossil bones, and the loss of essentially all of the fossil material.

At Choukoutien (now renamed Zhoukoudian), about twenty-five miles from Peking (now Beijing), China, in the 1920's and 1930's, were found fragments of about thirty skulls, eleven mandibles (lower jaws), and about 147 teeth. Except for a very few and highly fragmentary remains of limb bones, nothing else from these creatures was found. One of the initial finds was a single tooth, and without waiting for further evidence, Dr. Davidson Black, Professor of Anatomy at Union Medical College, Peking, declared that this tooth established evidence for the existence of an ancient hominid, or man-like creature, in China. He designated this creature *Sinanthropus pekinensis*, which soon came to be known as Peking Man.

The story is told that this tooth and the subsequent finds were recovered from a cave in the limestone cliff. This came to be known as the "lower cave" after fragments of ten other creatures, all identified as the remains of modern man, were found higher up on the cliff in what was allegedly the "upper cave." As we shall see, there is serious doubt that a cave existed at either level.

Of most critical importance to an evaluation of this material is the fact that all of this material except two teeth disappeared sometime during the period 1941–1945, and none of it has ever been recovered. Many stories concerning the disappearance of this material have circulated, the most popular being that it was either lost or seized by the Japanese during an attempt to move it from Peking to a U.S. marine detachment that was evacuating China. None of these stories has been verified. No living person apparently knows what happened to the material.

As a result, we are totally dependent on models and descriptions of this material left by a few investigators, all of whom were totally committed to the idea that man had evolved from animal ancestors. Even if a scientist is as completely objective as humanly possible, the model or description he fashions on the basis of scanty and incomplete material will reflect to a critical degree what he thinks the evidence ought to show. Furthermore, there is ample evidence that objectivity was seriously lacking in the treatment and evaluation of the material recovered at Choukoutien. If the type of evidence we have today relating to Peking Man were brought into a court of law, it would be ruled as hearsay and inadmissible as evidence.

With these considerations in mind, let us review the evidence related to Peking Man. First, the evaluation of the evidence by evolutionists will be examined, and then a creationist view will be described. For the evolutionist viewpoint, we will use the publication *Fossil Man*, an English translation of *Les Hommes Fossiles* by Marcellin Boule and H. V. Vallois, which has been referred to earlier.[171] Boule and Vallois devote an extensive section (pp. 130-146) of the English translation) to *Sinanthropus*, or Peking Man.

The first evidence related to *Sinanthropus* was discovered in 1921, when two molar teeth were recovered from a pocket of bone-remains at the site near the village of Choukoutien. A third molar was found in 1927 and given to Dr. Davidson Black. As related earlier, it was on the basis of this tooth that *Sinanthropus pekinensis* was erected. In 1928, the Chinese paleontologist in charge of the excavations, Dr. W. C. Pei, recovered fragments of crania, two pieces of lower jaw and numerous teeth, which were immediately described in a publication by Black. In 1929, Pei unearthed a well-preserved skullcap resembling that of *Pithecanthropus*. Since that time the site has been systematically explored under the supervision of the Geological Survey of China. Eventually the collection described at the beginning of this section was recovered.

It is claimed that a vast cavern once existed in the face of the limestone cliff, since the "cave filling" appears on the surface along a distance of 450 feet and is about 150 feet thick. It is said that the roof of the cavern collapsed, burying the old cave-filling.

The *Sinanthropus* fragments are found at many different levels of the fillings. The fossil fauna (the bones of about 100 different animals were found) did not vary from the top to the bottom of the deposit, and the *Sinanthropus* remains found at the various levels had everywhere the same characteristics. If these remains were actually found in a real cave-filling as alleged, then this means that during all the time it would have taken to lay down 150 feet of filling, no change in *Sinanthropus* or the animals of the area took place.

[171] Boule and Vallois, *Fossil Men*, p. 126.

All of the skulls were damaged and lacked their lower jaws. After the discovery of the skulls described earlier, three other skulls were reported to have been recovered in 1936 while Dr. Franz Weidenreich, an American paleontologist of German extraction, was in charge.

Skull III, actually the first to be discovered, is described in some detail by Boule and Vallois (Boule had visited Peking and Choukoutien and had examined the originals). It was ascribed by Black to an adolescent and by Weidenreich to an individual of eight or nine years of age. Boule and Vallois say that, viewed from the top and side, it bears a striking resemblance to *Pithecanthropus*, and that Skull II in its general contour was even more like that of *Pithecanthropus*. They conclude that "In its totality, the structure of the *Sinanthropus* skull is still very ape-like" (p. 136). A bit later they report that the three crania from Locus L (found in 1936) present the same characters as the skulls just mentioned, but in more accentuated form.

The cranial capacity of the skulls, although admittedly very approximate, was estimated to be about 900 c.c. for the skulls discovered earlier and up to about 1200 c.c. for two of the skulls found in 1936. Boule and Vallois point out that these values are about midway between the higher apes and man.

The features of the lower jaws described by Boule and Vallois were all ape-like except for the shape of the dental arcade (curve of the jaw), which was parabolic as in man, apparently, rather than U-shaped as in the apes. Likewise, all of the features for the teeth given by these authorities were ape-like except that no diastema (space) separates the canine teeth from neighboring incisors, as is the case in some species of apes (but not all). Furthermore, though the upper canine teeth were "particularly large," rising appreciably above the level of the other teeth as in the apes and being described as "small tusks," the lower canines look rather like large incisors. Thus, with very few exceptions, the structural features of the jaw and teeth were ape-like, but the presence of these few exceptions led Boule and Vallois to state that the mandibles and teeth of *Sinanthropus* denote a large primate more closely allied to man than any other known great ape.

After comparing a table of measurements of *Sinanthropus* to one for *Pithecanthropus*, Boule and Vallois say that the differences are less than those within a single species (namely, Neanderthal Man). They, therefore, insist at the very least that these two creatures be included within a single genus, although they are willing to permit the species differentiation to stand. Since *Pithecanthropus* enjoys priority, they would assign the name *Pithecanthropus pekinensis* to the Choukoutien creature. Since, as noted earlier in their discussion of *Pithecanthropus*, these authorities had said that, based on the skull and teeth alone, we are dealing with beings, if not identical with, then closely allied to the anthropoids, we wonder if by this close linkage of *Sinanthropus* with *Pithecanthropus*, Boule and Vallois wish to downgrade *Sinanthropus* to a creature, if not identical with, at least closely allied to the anthropoids, or if they wish to upgrade *Pithecanthropus*. Today most evolutionists have elevated *Pithecanthropus* and place *Pithecanthropus* and *Sinanthropus* in a single species, *Homo erectus*.

In their discussion of the relationship of *Sinanthropus* to *Pithecanthropus* (p. 141), Boule and Vallois accuse Black of lack of objectivity and of twisting facts. Specifically, they say:

> Black, who had felt justified in forging the term *Sinanthropus* to designate *one* tooth, was naturally concerned to legitimize this creation when he had to describe a skull cap. While acknowledging the great resemblance of this piece to the Javan counterpart, he stressed the differences and demonstrated them by numerical data. Now, on studying his tables of measurements, it is quite evident that the differences observed between *Pithecanthropus* on the one hand, and the various fragments of *Sinanthropus* on the other, far from possessing generic value, are less than the variations recorded with the very natural specific group of *Homo neanderthalensis*.

In other words, since Black had stuck his neck out on the basis of a single tooth and had erected the *Sinanthropus* category around that tooth, he felt compelled to model the facts to fit his scheme. We should, therefore, be very cautious in accepting the descriptions or models of *Sinanthropus* from the hand of Dr. Black.

A section entitled "A New Discussion of the Facts" appears at the end of the chapter devoted to the discussion of *Sinanthropus* by Boule and Vallois. It is based mainly on a model of *Sinanthropus* constructed by Weidenreich (fig. 31) allegedly on the basis of the material found in 1936. This model is so glaringly different from the earlier descriptions of *Sinanthropus* and from a model of *Pithecanthropus* fashioned elsewhere by Boule, that it is probable that this section was written by Vallois after the death of Boule (the 1952 edition of *Les Hommes Fossiles* was published after the death of Boule in 1942 and was a revision by Vallois of an earlier edition of this book authored solely by Boule). In fact, there can be no doubt that this section was written by Vallois after Boule's death, since it displays and refers to a model of a skull of *Sinanthropus* by Weidenreich. Weidenreich did not publish his description[172] of the skull of *Sinanthropus* until 1943, which is the year following Boule's death.

Davidson Black died in 1934 and was replaced by Franz Weidenreich. Dr. Pei continued to be in charge of the excavations, and it was his duty to submit his finds to Weidenreich for evaluation. It is reported that he found portions of three skulls in 1936. It was these three skulls (referred to by Boule and Vallois as those from Locus L) on which Weidenreich supposedly based his model.

In the section, "A New Discussion of the Facts," no new data are introduced, but the reader is asked to examine three photographs by Weidenreich showing several views of three skulls or models: a skull of a female gorilla; Weidenreich's model of his female *Sinanthropus*; and the skull of a Northern Chinese. The reader is then invited to verify for himself that *Sinanthropus* occupies a position intermediate between the Anthropoid apes and man. If one accepts uncritically Weidenreich's model of *Sinanthropus*, then he could hardly reject the above appraisal. As a matter of fact, on the basis of this model, some have been led to believe that *Sinanthropus* should not be considered as near-man, but should be judged to be fully human.

It should be emphasized that in these photographs, skulls of a gorilla and of a man are being compared to a *model* of the *Sinanthropus* skull fashioned by Weidenreich. When a complete skull is available, the specimen is completely reliable, especially if no distortions took place since burial and the reconstruction was accurate. Almost always the remains of a skull are fragmentary. In this case, the paleontologist attempts to reconstruct the skull based on the fragments, using filler material to fill in missing fragments and to

---

[172] Franz Weidenreich, *Paleont. Sinica*, New Ser. D. 10:1 (1943).

model missing parts. The reconstruction is more or less reliable depending on how fragmentary the fossil remains are and on the objectivity of the paleontologist. Models are casts of reconstructions or are fashioned according to what the investigator feels the skull should look like.

Today we have no skulls or fragments of *Sinanthropus* (except two teeth and a few fragments that have been recovered during the past few decades), no reconstructions which include actual fossil material. All we have available are the *models* fashioned by Weidenreich. How reliable are these models? Are they accurate casts of the originals, or do they reflect what Weidenreich *thought* they should look like? Why do his models differ so greatly from the earlier descriptions? These models of Weidenreich should be considered totally inadmissible as evidence related to the taxonomic affinities of *Sinanthropus*. If such a case were ever brought to court, there would not be the slightest doubt that such hearsay evidence would be ruled inadmissible.

Finally, a most peculiar characteristic of the *Sinanthropus* remains is discussed by Boule and Vallois. As they put it (p. 145):

> How are we to explain the almost complete absence of long bones and this kind of selection of bony parts all belonging to the skull, in which lower jaws predominate? Weidenreich believed that these selected parts did not come into the cave by natural means, but that they must have been brought there by hunters who chiefly attacked young individuals and chose for preference, as spoils or trophies, heads or parts of heads. In itself, this explanation is thoroughly plausible. *But the problem is to name the hunter* [Emphasis added].

All authorities agree that every one of the *Sinanthropus* individuals had been killed by hunters and eaten. All of the skulls had been bashed in near the base so that the brains might be extracted and eaten. Practically nothing of these creatures was found except fragments of the skull, and that in spite of the fact that fragments of almost forty different individuals were recovered. The only question remaining unanswered in respect to these circumstances was, *who was the hunter*?

Weidenreich, as do almost all other evolutionists, concludes that the hunter must be *Sinanthropus* himself! He was both the hunted and the hunter! This hypothesis is necessary to preserve the status of *Sinanthropus* as the evolutionary ancestor of man.

Boule and Vallois express serious doubts as to the validity of this theory. They say (p. 145):

> To this hypothesis, other writers preferred the following, which seemed to them more in conformity with our whole body of knowledge: the hunter was true Man, whose stone industry has been found and who preyed upon *Sinanthropus*.

Later on, they say:

> We may therefore ask ourselves whether it is not overbold to consider *Sinanthropus* the monarch of Choukoutien, when he appears in the deposit only in the guise of a mere hunter's prey, on a par with the animals by which he is accompanied.

There is thus very good evidence, "more in conformity with our whole body of knowledge," that the *Sinanthropus* creatures were the victims of hunters who were true men. If this is so, then *Sinanthropus* could not have been the evolutionary ancestor of man, but must have been a large monkey-like or ape-like creature.

The evaluation of *Sinanthropus* by a creationist, the Roman Catholic priest, Rev. Patrick O'Connell, will now be considered. To pit the evaluation of a priest against those of eminent evolutionary paleontologists seems akin to pitting David against Goliath. But perhaps in this case, also, David has found a weak spot in Goliath.

O'Connell was in China during all of the time the excavations at Choukoutien were being carried out, including the Japanese occupation and for several years after their departure. Although he did not make an on-site investigation, O'Connell had the advantage of seeing the accounts published in China in both Chinese and foreign languages. He became convinced that the public had not been given all the facts and that no "missing link" had been found at Choukoutien. He published his conclusions in his book, *Science of Today and the Problems of Genesis*.[173]

O'Connell believed that the disappearance of the *Sinanthropus* remains was by design rather than an accident of war. The Japanese did not interfere with the work at Choukoutien, and Weidenreich and Pei continued the excavations until Weidenreich left in 1940. O'Connell believes that Pei may have destroyed the fossils before the Chinese government returned to Peking in order to conceal the fact that the models did not correspond to the fossils.

In an article published in the Peking periodical *China Reconstructs* in 1954, Dr. Pei says that the material from Choukoutien was then on display. This included the *casts* or *models* of a few of the skulls of *Sinanthropus* (made by Black and Weidenreich), *fossil remains* of various animals, and a selection of the stone instruments found. It appears, then, that of the material related to *Sinanthropus*, only the fossil remains of *Sinanthropus* are missing.

The almost universally accepted version of the Choukoutien setting is that the fossils of *Sinanthropus* were found in the cave-filling of a huge cavern, the roof of which had collapsed. The human fossils found at the same site at an upper level supposedly were recovered from an upper cave. There seems to be little evidence that a cave existed at either level. As noted earlier, a huge cavern must be postulated for the lower cave, since the "cave filling" extended along the surface for at least 450 feet. The "upper cave" would have had to be as large or larger, since the debris was scattered over even a larger area. Weidenreich never claimed that a cave existed at the upper level, but referred to it as the "so-called upper cave."

According to O'Connell's reconstruction of the events of Choukoutien, a large-scale industry of quarrying limestone had been carried out there in ancient times. That lime-kilns had been constructed and operated there is indicated by the fact that thousands of quartz stones brought from a distance (no quartz is found at Choukoutien) were found in the debris at both levels. The stones had a layer of soot on one side. Enormous heaps of ashes were found at both levels.

The quarrying had been carried on at the two levels on a front of about 200 yards and to a depth of about fifty yards into the hill. The limestone hill was undermined and collapsed, burying everything at

---

[173] Patrick O'Connell, *Science of Today and the Problems of Genesis*, Book I (Hawthorne, California: Christian Book Club of America, 1969).

both levels under thousands of tons of stone. It was in these heaps of buried ashes and debris that the skulls of *Sinanthropus* were found.

Stones brought from a distance and dressed for building found beside a limestone quarry and enormous heaps of ashes can only mean one thing according to O'Connell: lime-burning was being carried out. Furthermore, lime production on the scale carried out at Choukoutien must mean houses were being built on a considerable scale.

Regardless of whether O'Connell is right concerning a lime-burning industry at Choukoutien, no other explanation has been given for the extensive stone industry found there. H. Breuil, an authority on the Old Stone Age, was invited to Choukoutien. His report, published in the March, 1932, issue of *L'Anthropologie*, tells us that in a section on the lower level of 132 square meters, twelve meters deep, 2,000 roughly shaped stones were found at the bottom of a heap of ashes and debris which contained the skulls of *Sinanthropus* and the bones of about 100 different animals.

The nature of the tools found at the site according to Breuil was not primitive. The graders and scrapers and other tools, sometimes of fine workmanship, had many features not found in France until the Upper Paleolithic.[174] The Upper or Late Paleolithic is supposed to have begun about 35,000 years ago, while the Peking Man fossils are assumed to date somewhere between one and two million years. This evidence could hardly be used, therefore, as an argument for a great antiquity for *Sinanthropus*.

O'Connell points out that very little attention has been paid to the fact that fossil remains of ten human individuals of modern type were found at an upper level of the same site where the skulls of *Sinanthropus* were found. Some books, for example, Romer's *Man and the Vertebrates*, make no mention of the fact. Others make no mention of this in the section on *Sinanthropus*, but place this information elsewhere. O'Connell believes that these individuals were killed by a landslide caused by undermining of the limestone cliff during quarrying operations, and that this same landslide buried the skulls of *Sinanthropus*. The bones found at the upper level made up the usual assortment expected for such remains.

---

[174] Boule and Vallois, *Fossil Man*, p. 145.

An examination of a diagram of the site from which the *Sinanthropus* skulls were recovered (p. 132 of *Fossil Men*) tends to support O'Connell. The disposition of the remains, especially those found in the "vertical offshoot of the main pocket" does not seem to correspond to that expected for a cave-filling.

O'Connell points out that some of the early descriptions of *Sinanthropus* by certain investigators differ quite significantly from the later descriptions and models of Black and Weidenreich. He quotes Teilhard de Chardin as saying (*L'Anthropologie*, 1931) that "*Sinanthropus* manifestly resembles the great apes closely."

There seems to be a progression through the two descriptions of *Sinanthropus* by Black and the third description by Weidenreich based on the skulls found in 1936 (see model shown in fig. 31) during which *Sinanthropus* becomes more and more man-like. Perhaps this is the only evolution involved in this whole affair!

O'Connell concludes that *Sinanthropus* consisted of the skulls of either large macaques (large monkeys) or large baboons killed and eaten by workers at an ancient quarry. There does seem to be considerable evidence that a lime-burning site was buried under rock and debris at Choukoutien. Whether the creatures whose skulls were discovered were macaques or baboons (or gibbons as Dubois suggested for *Pithecanthropus*), they were ape-like. Finally, Boule and others had leaned to the belief that *Sinanthropus* had been killed and eaten by true man.

O'Connell terms the representation of *Sinanthropus* as a near-man an outright fraud. We believe at the very least a combination of prejudice, preconceived ideas, and a zeal for fame have been responsible for elevating an ape-like creature to the status of an ape-like man.

Homo erectus from Africa

As mentioned earlier in the section on the australopithecines, Louis Leakey had reported that in Bed II of the Olduvai Gorge he had found fossils of *Australopithecus*, *Homo habilis* and some specimens which were attributed to *Homo erectus*.[175] The *H. erectus* fossils included the

---

[175] L. S. B. Leakey, *Nature* 188:1050 (1960); 189:649 (1961); A. J. Kelso, *Physical Anthropology*, 1st ed. (New York: J. B. Lippincott Co., 1970), p. 221; M. D. Leakey, *Olduvai Gorge, Vol. 3* (Cambridge: Cambridge U. Press, 1971),

greater part of a skull cap[176] (OH 9) and part of a femur (the shaft) and a hip bone[177] (OH 28). In 1975 Richard Leakey's team recovered a relatively complete cranium and parts of the maxilla and facial skeleton of a creature that was attributed to *H. erectus*.[178] The fossil specimen, designated KNM-ER 3733, was found in the Upper Member of the Koobi Fora Formation, and is believed by Leakey to be at least 1.5 million years old and to be very similar to the *H. erectus* material from China.[179]

Beginning with an initial discovery in 1973, many fragments of the skull and postcranial skeleton of a creature designated KNM-ER 1808 were recovered from the Upper Member of the Koobi Fora Formation by Leakey's team.[180] An age of 1.6 ± 0.1 million years was attributed to this creature, which was for some time the most complete *Homo erectus* fossil skeleton known. The fossil specimen displayed pathological changes that are consistent with chronic excessive intake of vitamin A (hypervitaminosis A).

A very exciting discovery was made by Kamoya Kimeu on the west side of Lake Turkana in August of 1984. Working with a team headed by Richard Leakey and Alan Walker, Kimeu made the initial discovery, a small piece of skull protruding from the ground just outside of camp. About a month of digging and sifting produced an almost complete skeleton of a male, estimated to have died at about twelve years of age. The skeleton, known as the Nariokotome *Homo erectus* skeleton for its location at Nariokotome III, west Lake Turkana, Kenya, is complete except for its left arm, lower right arm, and most of the foot bones (thus no hand or foot bones have yet been recovered. The fossil was dated at 1.6 million years.

Popular accounts of the discovery were published[181] and a brief technical report was published.[182] In 1993 a description of the history of

p. 272.

[176] Leakey, *Nature* 188:1050 (1960).

[177] M. H. Day, *Nature* 232:383 (1971).

[178] R. E. F. Leakey and A. Walker, *Nature* 261:572, 574 (1976).

[179] *Ibid.*, 261:574.

[180] Donald Johanson and M. A. Edey, *Lucy, the Beginnings of Mankind* (New York: Simon and Schuster, 1981), p. 163; M. D. Leakey and R. E. F. Leakey, *Kooby Fora Research Project*, vol. 1 (Oxford: Clarendon, 1978); A. Walker, M. R. Zimmerman, and R. E. F. Leakey, *Nature* 296:248 (1982).

[181] R. E. F. Leakey and A. C. Walker, *National Geographic* 168:624-629

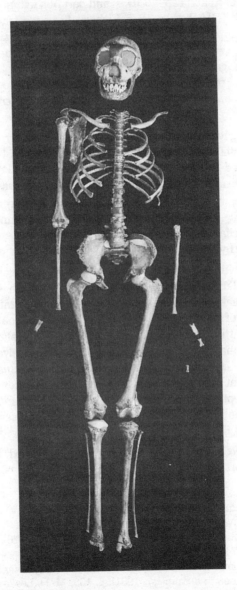

Figure 32. The Nariokotome *Homo erectus* skeleton. © 1985 by David
L. Brill, Atlanta. Used by permission.

the find, an exhaustive description of all the fossil remains that had been recovered, a comparison to the fossils of other creatures, and an analysis and conclusions were published.[183] There were several very surprising aspects of this individual. Although only about twelve years of age, his height was estimated to be almost five feet six inches. Based on this height and his age, it is estimated that he would have been six feet tall at maturity. The postcranial skeleton is so similar to modern humans that Walker was quoted as saying that he doubted that the average pathologist could tell the difference between the fossil skeleton and that of a modern human.[184] Concerning the skull, Walker was stated to have said, "When I put the mandible on the skull, Leakey and I both laughed because it looked so much like a Neanderthal."[185]

In the extensive technical report, Alan Walker states that "The overall similarity between early *H. erectus* skeletons and those of modern humans is striking" (the African *H. erectus* fossils are said to be from early *H. erectus* and the Asian *H. erectus* fossils are said to be from late *H. erectus* because the African fossils were dated at 1.5–1.8 million years and, at that time, the Asian fossils were dated at about one million years and less). A bit later Walker says: "The facial skeleton seems remarkably modern in many aspects."[186] The face is, as a whole, however, more prognathic (protruding) than those of modern humans. The cranial capacity has been estimated to be about 880 c.c.,[187] which is at the very low end of that of modern humans. The size and shape of the braincase and a few other characteristics of the postcranial skeleton were the only exceptions when the skeleton of this young boy was compared to those for modern humans.[188]

At present, most paleoanthropologists classify all of the African, Asian, and European fossils within the taxon *Homo erectus*, although a few would sink all *H. erectus* fossil creatures into *H. sapiens*.[189]

(1985); J. M. Harris, *Terra* 24:21-24 (1986).

[182] F. Brown et al., *Nature* 316:788-792 (1985).

[183] A. C. Walker and R. E. F. Leakey, eds., *The Nariokotome Homo Erectus Skeleton* (Cambridge: Harvard U. Press, 1993).

[184] Boyce Rensberger, *The Washington Post* 19 October 1984), p. A–1.

[185] *Ibid.*

[186] Walker, *The Nariokotome Homo Erectus Skeleton*, p. 424.

[187] David Begum and A. Walker, *The Nariokotome Homo Erectus Skeleton*, p. 328.

[188] Walker, *The Nariokotome Homo Erectus Skeleton*, p. 424.

There is much confusion and disagreement among paleo-anthropologists concerning not only the status of the various fossils of *H. erectus* (Phillipps provides a complete list),[190] but also the supposed pathway that led from *H. erectus* to *H. sapiens*. There are some who do not believe that *H. erectus* was ancestral to *H. sapiens*.[191]

From Three-foot Australopithecus to Six-foot Homo erectus in No Time Flat

If the fossils classified as *Homo erectus* represent creatures that evolved from *Australopithecus* (*A. afarensis—A. africanus—Homo habilis*) the change was extremely dramatic both morphologically and chronologically. As described earlier, the alleged age of *A. africanus* ranges from four million years to as recent as one million years. Leakey's Skull 1470, which he classifies as *H. habilis* (others classify this and all other putative *H. habilis* creatures as *Australopithecus*) is dated at about 1.7–1.9 million years. OH 62, classified by Johanson, et al.,[192] and by Hartwig-Scherer and Martin[193] as *H. habilis*, was dated at 1.8 million years. According to these investigators OH 62 was a female about 3½ feet tall and was even more apelike than "Lucy." The Nariokotome *H. erectus* juvenile was dated at about 1.5 million years, and recently Swisher et al. have reported dates of 1.66 million years and 1.81 million years for some of the Asian *H. erectus*.[194] If we believe all that we have been told, then, we have *H. erectus* overlapping the austrlopithecines by almost one million years and just as old, or nearly so, as *H. habilis*. We thus have the australopithecines occupying the earth allegedly for three million years with little or no morphological change and then suddenly we have these creatures dramatically changing in a blink (or less) of geological time from an extremely apelike morphology into a creature with a cranial capacity double that of his alleged predecessor and whose facial skeleton "seems remarkably

---

[189] David L. Phillipps, M.A. Thesis (Northridge: California State University, January 1991), p. 28.

[190] *Ibid.*, p. 22-26.

[191] Walker, *The Nariokotome Homo Erectus Skeleton*, p. 418; and by J. E. Cronin et al., *Nature* 292:115 (1981).

[192] D. C. Johanson et al., *Nature* 327:205-209 (1987).

[193] S. Hartwig-Scherer and R. D. Martin, *Journal of Human Evolution* 21:439-449 (1991).

[194] C. C. Swisher, III, et al., *Science* 263:1118 (1994).

modern in many aspects," even resembling that of the Neanderthals (*H. sapiens*), and whose postcranial skeleton was essentially that of a modern day human.

It is first to be noted that there is thus a vast gulf between the australopithecines (including the so-called *H. habilis*) and those creatures classified as *Homo erectus*. There is no proposed evolutionary mechanism (except the "hopeful monster" mechanism, which is no mechanism at all but a mere scenario), not even the punctuated equilibrium scenario, that could account for such dramatic changes with essentially no time span.

Secondly, with the exception of those few who would classify all *H. erectus* fossils as *Homo sapiens*, almost all evolutionary paleoanthropologists classify all the fossils in question as *Homo erectus*. In spite of this fact, it is very possible that those creatures in Africa characterized as "early" *H. erectus*, such as the Nariokotome fossil juvenile, were true humans, *Homo sapiens*, with no relationship whatsoever to the Asian fossils classified as *H. erectus*. This is the opinion of creationist Marvin Lubenow, who actually characterizes all *H. erectus* creatures as "archaic" *Homo sapiens*.[195] As noted earlier, the features of the Nariokotome juvenile were remarkably human, with few exceptions. On the other hand, the Asian *H. erectus* fossils were apparently very different in many respects, if Boule and Vallois and others are correct in their assessments of these creatures. It is a curious fact that the designation *erectus* was given to the Asian fossil *Pithecanthropus erectus* (subsequently renamed *Homo erectus*) because it was assumed that the human femur and apelike skull Dubois had found were owned by the same creature. Yet today many, if not most, paleoanthropologists believe that the femur was probably from a true man with no relationship to the creature whose skull cap was found.

As noted earlier, Boule and Vallois, with reference to Java Man (*P. erectus*) had stated that:

> If we possessed only the skull and the teeth, we should say that we are dealing with beings, if not identical with, at least

---

[195] Marvin Lubenow, *Bones of Contention* (Grand Rapids: Baker Book House, 1992).

closely allied to the Anthropoids. If we had only the femora,
we should declare we are dealing with Man.[196]

They also had serious doubts about the humanlike status of Peking
Man (*Sinanthropus pekinensis*, also brought into the taxon
H. erectus). With reference to the belief that Peking Man was a
humanlike creature who manufactured tools, used fire, and practiced
cannibalism, Boule and Vallois, as described earlier, stated that,

> To this hypothesis, other writers preferred the following,
> which seemed to them more in conformity with our whole
> body of knowledge: the hunter was true Man, whose stone
> industry has been found and who preyed upon
> *Sinanthropus*.[197]

As recalled, earlier it was noted that Swisher et al. have now
claimed they have dated some of the Asian *H. erectus* fossils from
about 1.6 to 1.8 million years. Supposedly the stone industry found on
the site where the Peking Man fossils were excavated had been
manufactured and used by Peking Man. Yet Breuil, an expert on
Paleolithic tools and who had made two trips to China to study the
tools found with Peking Man, had declared that these tools were not
primitive at all (as they surely would be for creatures more than
1.5 million years old), but were of fine workmanship, having many
features associated with tools found in France in the Upper Paleolithic.
The Upper (Late) Paleolithic supposedly began no more than about
35,000 years ago. If all of this is correct, then these Asian creatures
could not possibly have made the tools found at Choukoutien, but
must have been the victims, as Boule and Vallois surmised, on whom
the tools were applied. This controversy over the tools found with
so-called Peking Man continues today. Jia Lanpo and Wang Jian
published their opinion that the stone artifacts found there were too
advanced to be representative of the earliest human industry. That
earliest human history must therefore be sought elsewhere.[198] These
facts seem to place these Asian creatures in a very different category
than the creatures in Africa associated with the Nariokotome juvenile.

---

[196] Boule and Vallois, *Fossil Men*, p. 126.

[197] *Ibid.*, p. 145.

[198] Jia Lanpo and Huang Weiwen, *The Story of Peking Man* (Beijing:
Foreign Language Press, 1990).

These conclusions tend to find some support from those who use cladistic studies to compare the Asian with the African *erectus* fossils. Cladistic studies attempt to compare unique derived characteristics shared by different creatures in order to establish similarities, without necessarily assuming any ancestral-descendant relationship. The results of the cladistic study revealed major differences between some of the African *H. erectus* fossils and the Asian *erectus* fossils. The study did not find any shared derived features that can link the African creatures with those of Asia.

The discoveries reported by Thorne and Macumber[199] are of an entirely different nature than that by Walker and Leakey just described. Walker and Leakey claim to have discovered the fossil of a young *Homo erectus* dating back at least 1.5 million years. As we have just related, however, the fossil in its postcranial skeleton is essentially identical to a modern human and the skull is sufficiently human-like to look very much like Neanderthal Man. Thorne and Macumber report the recovery of the remains of over thirty individuals from the Kow Swamp area in northern Victoria, Australia, which similarly have a number of *Homo erectus* features in their cranial morphology. These specimens, however, are dated at only 10,000 years! *Homo sapiens*, a fully modern type, are reported to have made their appearance in Europe at least 25,000 years ago, or 15,000 years earlier, and Neanderthal Man, or *Homo sapiens*, is supposed to have made his appearance in Europe at least 100,000 years ago, or about 90,000 years before the existence of these Kow Swamp individuals.

Thorne and Macumber report that the skulls have a number of archaic features that are typical of early *sapiens* (by "early *sapiens*," it is presumed they mean Neanderthal Man) including cranial size, vault bone thickness, the form of the face and the mandibles, and, to a lesser extent, the occipital region.

They report, however, that the frontal bones are especially archaic, preserving an almost unmodified Javan pithecanthropine form. Since no mention was made in the article concerning the postcranial skeleton of these creatures, it is assumed that it was altogether modern.

It appears that the fossil discovered by Walker and Leakey in Kenya may be very similar to the Kow Swamp individuals, many of

---

[199] A. G. Thorne and P. G. Macumber, *Nature* 238: 316 (1972).

which were recovered from the undisturbed graves. If this turns out to be the case, we will have fossils of these individuals, some supposedly 1.5 million years old, and some presumed to be only 10,000 years old or less, and thus overlapping *Homo sapiens* by at least 90,000 years. Thus, there seems to be a strong likelihood, to say the very least, that these individuals were no more than racial variants of *Homo sapiens*.

As we have described in the earlier section on *Australopithecus*, Louis Leakey had established the contemporaneity of *Homo erectus*, *Australopithecus*, and a creature he designated *Homo habilis*, all of whose remains were recovered from Bed II of the Olduvai Gorge. Richard Leakey has recovered the remains of *Australopithecus*, *Homo habilis*, and *Homo erectus* from geological formations near Lake Turkana, all of which are supposed to be 1.5 million years old, and thus contemporary. Furthermore, as also described earlier, Louis Leakey had found the remains of a circular stone habitation hut, a product of man still fabricated in Africa today, in Bed I underneath, and thus older than Bed II. We repeat the questions we asked earlier: If the fossil creatures which have been labeled *Australopithecus, Homo habilis* and *Homo erectus* lived together at the same time, how could any one be ancestral to any other? And if the artifacts of modern man are found in a geological formation older than the one in which these fossil creatures were found, how could any of them be the ancestors of man?

Now we may ask a further question: If the creature whose fossil remains were found by Walker and Leakey in Kenya is the same, or very nearly so, as the creatures whose buried remains were found in the Kow Swamp area of Australia, and the latter postdated the first appearance of *Homo sapiens* by at least 90,000 years, how could these creatures have been ancestral to man?

At this time, it is our opinion that some specimens attributed to *Homo erectus*, such as Java Man and Peking Man, are definitely from the ape family with no link of any kind to man. In other cases (some of which have not been described here), specimens have been attributed to *Homo erectus* which otherwise would have been attributed to Neanderthal Man if the authorities making this decision had not believed that the fossil creature was too old to have been Neanderthal Man. In these instances, as, for example, the very recent find by Walker and Leakey near Lake Turkana, it may be that the creature was fully human, *Homo sapiens*. If some creature, such as *erectus*, evolved into *sapiens*, then, as Phillipps has remarked, the details of when, where, and how such a transformation took place remain unknown.[200]

Neanderthal Man

Neanderthal Man was first discovered over a century ago in a cave in the Neander Valley near Dusseldorf, Germany. He was initially classified as *Homo neanderthalensis* and portrayed as a semi-erect brutish sub-human. This misconception of Neanderthal Man was most likely due to the bias of evolution-minded paleoanthropologists plus the fact that the individual on whom this assessment was made had been crippled with arthritis. Furthermore, it is known that these people suffered severely from rickets, caused by a deficiency of Vitamin D. This condition results in softening of bone and consequent malformation. It is now known that Neanderthal Man was fully erect and in many details was indistinguishable from modern man.[201] His cranial capacity even exceeded that of modern man. It has been said that if he were given a shave, a haircut, and a bath, and dressed in a business suit, and were to walk down one of our city streets, he would be given no more attention than any other individual. Today he is classified *Homo sapiens*—fully human. It is believed that the Neanderthal people appeared abruptly in Europe about 100,000 years ago. No one has the faintest notion where they came from. They then disappeared just as abruptly about 35,000 years ago, it is said, and were immediately replaced by the Cro-Magnon race, which is essentially indistinguishable from modern Europeans. Again, no one is able to offer any information concerning their origin. It is now known that modern humans were contemporary with Neanderthal people and even preceded the Neanderthals in some cases by thousands of years.[202]

Other fossil remains which are undoubtedly varieties or races of *Homo sapiens* include the Swanscombe, Steinheim and Fontechevade fossils.[203] Swanscombe Man has been dated to almost 250,000 years.[204]

---

[200] Phillipps, M.A. Thesis, p. 28.

[201] F. Ivanhoe, *Nature* 227:577 (1970); E. Trinkaus and W. W. Howells, *Scientific American* 241(6): 118 (1979).

[202] Ofer Bar-Yosef and Bernard Vandermeersch, *Scientific American* 268:94-100 (1993); F. McDermott et al., *Nature* 363:252-255 (1993).

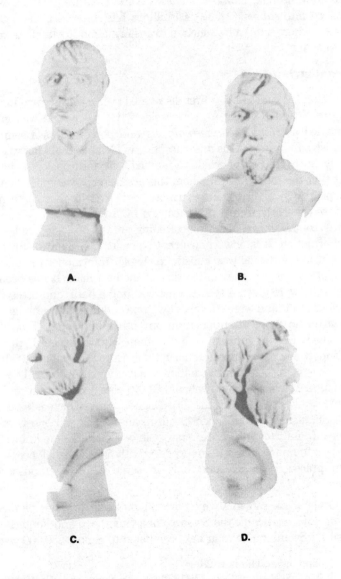

Figure 33. Two flesh models of Neanderthal Man (Skhul V). From
Rusch's "Human Fossils," in *Rock Strata and the Bible Record*, P.
A. Zimmerman, Ed., Concordia Publishing House.

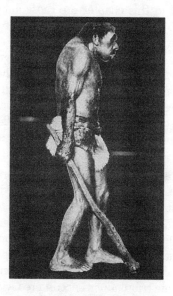

Figure 34. An early model of Neanderthal Man no longer considered valid. Neg. No. 338558, Photo copy by J. Beckett. Courtesy of the Department of Liberary Services, American Museum of Natural History.

Figure 35. Modern day model of Neanderthal Man. Neg. No. 333607. Courtesy of the Department of Library Services, American Museum of Natural History.

The dates mentioned in this chapter are those judged to be at least approximately correct by evolutionary geologists. At the present time, it is assumed that the Pleistocene Epoch (to which most of the fossils which are thought to be hominids have been assigned) began about 1,800,000 years ago. Earlier it had been estimated that the duration of the Pleistocene was only a fraction of that (Sir Arthur Keith believed the duration to be about 200,000 years), but stretching out the Pleistocene has given evolutionists the time they believe is required for the evolution of man from his supposed ape-like ancestor.

If a fossil is found in what is assumed to be the early Pleistocene, it is assigned an age of about 1.8 million years or less. If it is thought to be of middle Pleistocene age, it would be estimated to be about one million years in age. It would, of course, be assigned to a younger age if found in formations believed to be of late Pleistocene times. Various time spans within the Pleistocene are estimated on the basis of the supposed ages of various glacial or interglacial periods which are believed to have occurred during the Pleistocene. The methods involved as well as some tribulations encountered with this system are described by Pilbeam[205] and may be found in many standard works on anthropology.

Evolutionist Suggests Monkeys and Apes Evolved from Man!

When Richard Leakey announced the discovery of Skull 1470 and made the claim that he had found a man-like creature as old, or older than, some of our supposed ape-like ancestors, he quite predictably stirred up much controversy and generated considerable speculation as well. As related earlier, some paleoanthropologists attacked Leakey's bold claims and maintained that the individual represented by Skull 1470 was essentially the same as the australopithecines. Others were much impressed and called for a reassessment of current theories, some even suggesting a radical departure from present-day notions about human origins.

---

[203] McDermott et al., *Nature*, 363:252-255 (1993); M. H. Day, *Guide to Fossil Man*, 3rd ed. (Chicago: The University of Chicago Press, 1977).

[204] R. B. Eckhardt, *Scientific American* 226(1): 94 (1972).

[205] D. R. Pilbeam, *The Evolution of Man* (New York: Funk & Wagnalls, 1970).

One primatologist who declared that Leakey's evidence demanded a radical change in theory was Geoffrey Bourne, then the director of the Yerkes Primate Research Center of Emory University in Atlanta, Georgia. Ever since Darwin, evolutionists have maintained that man has evolved from some ape-like creature. Accepting at face value the claims of Richard Leakey, Bourne declared that it is now evident that evolutionists have been wrong all along—man did not evolve from the apes, but apes and monkeys have evolved from man!

An article published in *Modern People* (Vol. 1, p. 11, April 18, 1976) states:

> For, whereas Darwin popularized the theory that man descended from the primate family, Dr. Bourne believes the exact opposite—that monkeys, apes, and all other lower primate species are really the offspring of man.

Bourne cites as evidence for this incredible theory the findings of Richard Leakey and evidence from embryology. The article states:

> Another argument the doctor, who is considered one of the world's leading experts on primates, uses to support his theory, is the fact that an ape fetus looks like a human fetus

during the early stages of development before birth. It is
only in the later stages of gestation that the unborn ape
starts developing typical ape-like characteristics.

This means the development of an ape infant recapitulates
his origin; he goes from a human-like to an ape-like animal
in the fetus.

The latter statement contradicts earlier claims by evolutionists that
just the opposite is true, that the human embryo recapitulates its
evolutionary history in such a way that the embryo looks more like an
ape in its earlier development and looks more human-like as it
develops further. Furthermore, the entire idea of embryological
recapitulation has been discredited by modern embryologists (see
Chapter VIII).

Bourne's theory also contradicts the Darwinian idea of survival of
the fittest, or natural selection, as the driving force of evolution, for the
article further relates that:

In speaking about man, the doctor claims that it is man's
superior brain, formation of his hands and arms, and his
position in walking that have made him the most dominant
animal on Earth.

If this is true, apes and monkeys are obviously inferior to man.
How, then, did natural selection bring about the evolution of apes and
monkeys from man?

Bourne, in a personal communication, confirmed the accuracy of
the article. How can it be that evolutionists, looking at exactly the
same data, arrive at theories that are diametrically opposed to one
another—in one case that man has evolved from an ape-like animal,
and in the other that apes have evolved from man? Incredible!
Incredible unless the basic assumption on which their entire system of
belief is based—evoution—is wrong.

As incredible as this idea may seem, Bourne has received support
from at least two other evolutionist theorizers. John Gribbin and
Jeremy Cherfas in an article entitled "Descent of Man—or Ascent of
Ape?"[206] suggest that a creature first evolved the ability to walk

---

[206] J. Gribbin and J. Cherfas, *New Scientist* 91:592 (1981).

habitually upright, something perhaps similar to Johanson's "Lucy," or a descendant of it. Some of these creatures then decided to abandon the hard life on the plains and to return to the good life in the trees. The chimpanzee and the gorilla are the products of this return to an arboreal way of life. Gribbin and Cherfas thus say:

> . . . when pressed the popular mind would admit that what it really thinks is that man and the chimp are descended from something very ape-like, very like a chimp. To translate our suggestion into that form of speech, we think that the chimp is descended from man, that the common ancestor of the two was much more man-like than ape-like. Whatever the small genetic changes needed to accomplish the anatomical reshuffling that produced an upright ape, they could surely have been equally easily reversed . . . perhaps the genetic changes that produced early man from an ape were cleanly reversed to produce early chimps and gorillas from man.

Lord Zuckerman, himself an evolutionist, has, as noted earlier, expressed his conviction that there is really no science at all in the search for man's fossil ancestry. He has arranged various scientific endeavors in a spectrum beginning with what he considered to be pure science and moving toward endeavors he considered to be less and less scientific. He began with chemistry and physics, then moved into the biological sciences, and then into the social sciences. He then goes on to say:

> We then move right off the register of objective truth into those fields of presumed biological science, like extrasensory perception or the interpretation of man's fossil history, where to the faithful anything is possible—and where the ardent believer is sometimes able to believe several contradictory things at the same time.[207]

---

[207] S. Zuckerman, *Beyond the Ivory Tower* (New York: Toplinger Pub. Co., 1970), p. 19.

Can Apes learn Language?

Of all the creatures on the earth, only man has the ability to use language. Not only does man have the ability to remember the past, to cope with complicated problems in the present, and to plan for the future, but he has the ability to express all of these thoughts both verbally and in written form. Man is equipped with a vocal apparatus that allows him to verbalize a great number of sounds. The human brain, with its twelve billion brain cells and 120 trillion (12×10^{12}) connections, is the most complex arrangement of matter in the universe. Thus endowed, man's ability to express himself verbally and in written form is truly incredible.

Neither the fossil record nor a comparative study of man and the apes provides any information that would allow the construction of a theoretical pathway for the acquisition of speech by man.[208] Nevertheless, evolutionary anthropologists and linguists, convinced that man has evolved from an ape-like creature, have valiantly attempted to demonstrate at least an incipient ability to use language in apes. We have all thus become familiar with Lana, a chimpanzee that supposedly has learned at least the rudiments of sign language.[209] The same has been said for Washoe, a chimpanzee, Koko, a gorilla, and Sarah, another chimpanzee. Such claims are highly controversial and are rejected by a number of the leaders in this field.

J. L. Mistler-Lachman and R. Lachman, for example, declare that "Lana (a chimpanzee) has not been shown to use language by any criterion strong enough to exclude rats, worms, or any other conditionable animal."[210]

In an article entitled "Ape-talk: Two Ways to Skinner Bird,"

> The flap over whether or not apes really can use symbols to communicate with one another has reached new heights with the entry into the picture of two Carneaux pigeons—Jack and Jill. In what could be interpreted as a compliment to pigeons, but is more like a slap at primate

---

[208] George Gaylord Simpson, *Science* 152:477 (1966).

[209] D. M. Rumbaugh, E. V. Hill, and E. C. von Glaserfeld, *Science* 182:731 (1973).

[210] J. L. Mistler-Lachman and R. Lachman, *Science* 185:871 (1974).

intelligence, famed Harvard behaviorist B. F. Skinner reports that his two birds have rather easily duplicated what was billed as a major accomplishment for apes: symbolic communication.[211]

Skinner and his colleagues report that their pigeons are able to transmit information to one another using symbols.[212] Skinner suggests that the reported use by apes of sign language may be nothing more than a result of a conditioning response that is achievable even in the lowly bird brain.

In his report on a conference attended by those involved in ape "language" studies,[213] Wade states:

> It was amazing that any of the ape language researchers should even have considered stepping into such a lions' den. The very framework of the conference implied that their work fell into the category either of circus tricks or of self delusion. Only the Rumbaughs, foster-parents to chimpanzee Lana, appeared in New York to defend the faith. The one other chimp-raiser present was ape language apostate Herbert Terrace.

> Terrace's loss of faith (see *Science*, 21 March, 1980) has dealt a serious blow to ape language research. In brief, Terrace's nemesis was Nim Chimpsky, whom he expected would develop the same abilities in sign language as those claimed for Washoe and other chimps. . . . Chimpsky learned signs, like the other apes, and also started using them in strings. . . . Terrace, after a crisis of doubt, decided that Chimpsky, and indeed the other pointing pongids, were not using the signs in a way characteristic of true language. Rather they were probably making monkeys out of their keepers by imitating or clever-Hansing them.

Sir Edmund Leach expressed similar convictions. He states:

> I am aware of course that some primatologists question the uniqueness of human speech, claiming that the circus

[211] Anonymous, *Science News* 177:87 (1980).
[212] R. Epstein, R. P. Lanza, and B. F. Skinner, *Science* 207:543 (1980).
[213] N. Wade, *Science* 208:1349 (1980).

tricks learnt by Washoe the chimpanzee, Koko the gorilla and their various expensively trained companions represent an embryo form of speech. This is a highly technical matter, but as far as I can judge, almost all the psychologists and linguists who have studied the evidence closely are quite satisfied that there is a major discontinuity between human speech and the sign-making capacities of apes.[214]

Psycholinguist Clifford R. Wilson, in his book *Monkeys Will Never Talk—or Will They?*[215] lists numerous fundamental differences between human language and the sign-making abilities of apes. Wilson is convinced that apes lack both the physical and the mental abilities required for true language, and thus a vast gulf exists between the abilities of man and apes in this respect.

The immense gulf between man and the apes in their ability to generate and use language is yet another indication that man is a special creation, distinctly set apart from the apes and all other creatures.

Are Some Humans Born with Tails?

An article entitled "Evolution and the Human Tail" by Dr. Fred D. Ledley appeared in the May 20, 1982, issue of *The New England Journal of Medicine*. The publication of this article apparently served as a source of a whale of a tale, for newspaper articles based on Ledley's publication appeared all over the United States. One of these articles had a headline typically associated with this story: "Baby's Tail Lends Evolution Support." The article stated that "The birth of a child with a tail is a rare glimpse of 'the relation between human beings and their primitive ancestors,' a doctor says." Later on, Ledley is quoted as stating:

> Even those familiar with evolution are rarely confronted with the relation between human beings and their primitive ancestors on a daily basis. The caudal appendage brings this reality to the fore and makes it tangible and inescapable.

---

[214] E. R. Leach, *Nature* 293:19 (1981).
[215] C. R. Wilson, *Monkeys Will Never Talk—or Will They?* (Colorado Springs: Creation-Life Publishers, 1978).

Thus, the reality of the fact of evolution is made tangible and inescapable, according to Dr. Ledley, by the birth of a baby with a tail. This is indeed the final conclusion stated by Ledley in his article. One needs only to read this article, however, to learn that Ledley himself has admitted that this may not be so. Earlier in the article (p. 1213), after quoting Darwin who said that "We thus learn that man is descended from a hairy quadruped furnished with a tail," Ledley states:

> When the caudal appendage is critically examined, however, it is evident that there are major morphologic differences between the caudal appendage and the tails of other vertebrates. First of all, the caudal appendage does not contain even rudimentary vertebral structures. . . . Secondly, the appendage is not located at the caudal terminus of the vertebral column. *It is possible that this structure is merely a dermal appendage coincidentally located in the caudal region. This possibility cannot be excluded* [Emphasis added].

How can it be said that the presence of this "tail" brings us tangibly and inescapably to the reality of evolution if we cannot exclude the possibility that it is nothing more than a "dermal appendage coincidentally located in the caudal region"? As a matter of fact, even a superficial reading of Ledley's article makes clear that this so-called tail was no tail at all, but was nothing more than an anomalous growth coincidentally located in the caudal region.

Case Description

The infant was normal in every way except for the presence of the appendage. The appendage was slightly more than two inches long, and had a diameter at the base of about ¼ inch. It was located adjacent to the sacrum and was offset from the midline about ½ inch. The appendage had a soft fibrous fatty core and was covered with skin of normal texture. There were no bony or cartilaginous elements in the appendage, and it was found to have no connection to vertebral structures. X-rays of the spine were normal. The appendage was removed surgically under a local anesthetic.

Ledley's Interpretation of the Appendage

The biochemistry of man is remarkably similar to that of the apes and, in fact, is very similar to that of all other living creatures (this is, by the way, precisely what creation scientists would predict). What, then, accounts for the profound morphological differences between man and the apes and all other creatures? Obviously, the differences do not reside in the genes that code for proteins, but must reside in other genetic characteristics.

In seeking to explain evolution, many evolutionists are now suggesting that much of evolution is due to mutations in regulatory genes, genes that do not affect the structures of proteins but which are believed to control the temporal, spatial, or proportional relations between developmental structures and events. Ledley apparently believes that the human "tail" results from such a mutation. Ledley states:

> In modern theory the parallels between ontogeny and phylogeny derive from the ability to trace the phenotypic expression [external morphological change] of developmental mutations to specific stages of embryonic development at which differentiation occurs between largely homologous molecular and morphologic structures.

Later, Ledley goes on to say:

> The modern understanding of teratology [the study of anomalous malformations] and tail formation finds nothing unhuman or reversionary about the tail-like structure. . . .

> The child with a tail is striking not because the tail is a "reversion" but because it is *not* a reversion—because it is entirely consistent with our understanding of ontogeny and phylogeny, which places us in the midst of primate evolution. The occurrence of the caudal appendage, as well as the presence of a well-formed embryonic tail in a child, are testimony to the preservation of the structural elements necessary for tail formation in the human genome.

What is Ledley saying? What he seems to be saying is this: Although humans do not ordinarily have tails, and thus the genes for tails in humans are usually suppressed, yet humans still retain genes for tails—"structural elements necessary for tail formation in the human genome." According to Ledley, then, though the genes are not expressed and thus are useless baggage, we humans for many millions of years have been carrying those genes and faithfully reproducing them even though they are totally without function.

Presumably, then, we would also be carrying along in our human genetic apparatus other genes that are responsible for all other characteristics seen in our monkey-like ancestors but not seen in man. Following this thinking to its logical conclusion, the human genetic apparatus should still be carrying every gene ever possessed by any of our ancestors, even the genes that make a worm a worm, if indeed a worm was the ancestor of vertebrates. Even from an evolutionary perspective, this would seem to be terribly wasteful in energy and other cellular resources. According to evolution theory, then, such genes would long ago have been completely eliminated by natural selection. We would not thus predict that Ledley's theory would find general acceptance in evolutionary circles.

Alternative Explanations

We would like to emphasize once again the fact that this appendage was not a tail. We have already quoted Ledley's own testimony that the "tail" did not contain even rudimentary vertebral structures. Ledley states in his article that there is no precedent for a vertebral tail without caudal vertebrae. The "tail" was offset from midline with no connection to vertebral structures, and contained a soft fibrous fatty core. The resemblance to a tail was highly superficial.

Ledley reports that there are at least thirty mutations known in laboratory mice that affect tail morphology. Most mutant tails contain caudal vertebrae, but a particular mutant frequently has no caudal vertebrae, leaving a shortened boneless tail filament containing only loose connective tissue, blood vessels, and nerve fibers. Ledley compares this to the human "tail." These two conditions are in no way comparable, however. The normal mouse has a tail, and the mutant condition represents the *loss* of a normal structure. The human has no tail, and the caudal appendage represents the *gain of* an abnormal structure. Furthermore, the condition in the mouse in unquestionably due to a mutant gene and is, of course, inheritable. As Ledley states in his article, however, the caudal appendage in the human is a benign lesion which has never been reported to recur in families. If this caudal appendage were due to a mutation, the mutant gene would be passed on to offspring and would eventually be reexpressed in some of those offspring. This has never been known to occur. The anomaly is thus not due to a mutation but to some disarrangement that occurred during embryological development.

Rijsbosch describes a similar anomalous growth in a newborn male.[216] He refers to it as an "unusual tumor in the sacrococcygeal area" with a core that consists entirely of highly vascularized fatty tissue. He reported that no osseous, cartilaginous, or muscular tissue was encountered and that the structure was in complete accord with the caudal formations in man described in medical literature. He reviewed the myths that had been associated with these and other anomalous growths, particularly in the Middle Ages.

Rijsbosch reviews a report by Schaeffer[217] in which Schaeffer emphasized that "tail" formation is not necessarily an isolated phenomenon but may be associated with numerous other congenital anomalies. Schaeffer was able to derive from the medical literature a list of thirty-five deformities and anomalies which may exist concurrently with the caudal appendage. If, as Ledley maintains, "some malformations may in fact represent back mutations to an ancestral state" (see p. 1214 of his paper in *The New England Journal of Medicine*) and the caudal appendage is one of these, we should also be able to associate many of the thirty-five deformities reported by Schaeffer with other ancestral states. No such relationship can be inferred, however. These, as well as the caudal appendage, are nothing more than anomalous malformations not traceable to any imaginary ancestral state.

Rijsbosch also notes that M. Bartels[218] had collected 116 reports of "tail" formation in humans. In cases where the sex was reported, fifty-two were males and sixteen were females. If the caudal appendage represents a back mutation to an ancestral state, the human male must thus be somewhat closer to his monkey ancestor than the female,

---

[216] J. K. C. Rijsbosch, *Archivum Chirurgicum Neelandicum* 29:261 (1977).

[217] O. Schaeffer, *Archaeological Anthropology* 20:189 (1891/1892).

[218] M. Bartels, *Archaeological Anthropology* 15:45 (1884).

since the condition occurs three times more frequently in males than in females!

Warkany reports that while most persons with caudal appendages showed normal general development, caudal appendages have been associated with such malformations as meningocele, spina bifida, chondrodystophy, cleft palate, hemangiomas, syndactyly, hypodactyly, and heterotopic anus.[219] Can evolutionists identify ancestral states with any of these malformations?

If malformations may possibly be due to the expression of genes inherited from distant ancestors but long suppressed, one can think of interesting suggestions. For example, some human females are born with mammary glands under the armpits. Some bats normally have their mammary glands in that region. Does that mean that human females are carrying long-suppressed genes for mammary glands under the armpits and we humans have a bat in our ancestry? Some human females are born with mammary glands in the groin region. Mammary glands normally occur in the groin region of whales. Does that mean that human females still possess genes for mammary glands in the groin region that have been inherited from a whale ancestor? Mammary glands, as a matter of fact, have developed in humans in many places, including the back, arms, and legs. How can evolutionary theory help us explain that?

In their reports, both Rijsbosch and Warkany describe some of the mythical stories that have been generated by the appearance of anomalous malformations that occur in humans. Ledley is a professor in the Division of Clinical Genetics, Department of Pediatrics, Children's Hospital Medical Center, Harvard Medical School, and is no doubt a very capable physician to whom any one of us would entrust the care of our children. He is deeply devoted, however, to faith in evolution. His paper in *the New England Journal of Medicine* thus represents simply another contribution to the mythology generated by the occurrence of malformations in the newborn.

---

[219] J. Warkany, *Congenital Malformations* (Chicago: Yearbook Medical Pub., 1971), p. 925.

Modern Humans One Million Years Old?

Beginning in 1932 Louis Leakey's team recovered the fossilized remains of several anatomically modern humans in the Kanjera Formation in the foothills of Homa Mountain on the Homa Peninsula of Lake Victoria, Kenya.[220] Based on the fossils of animals found with the human remains in the same formation, Leakey proclaimed that he had found modern human fossils from the middle Pleistocene. The middle Pleistocene is dated at almost one million years, older than some of the alleged ages for *Homo erectus* and almost as old as some of the ages given for a few of the australopithecines. These facts render Leakey's assessment unacceptable to most evolutionists, and so Leakey's conclusions have been under attack by his fellow evolutionists ever since. Leakey, however, never surrendered his belief in the antiquity of these human remains and his conviction that he had found fossils of fully developed humans in the middle Pleistocene.[221]

P. G. H. Boswell, a geologist who accompanied Leakey on a later expedition to the area, made a scathing attack on Leakey, claiming that the archaic fauna and the modern human remains had been brought together by sediment slumping.[222] In a paper published in 1995, Thomas Plummer and Richard Potts review all of the evidence collected by Leakey and by a number of subsequent expeditions to the area.[223]

According to the review by Plummer and Potts, there is no question that the fossils found by Leakey and subsequent expeditions were of anatomically modern humans. Some had been collected on the surface, but there was no question that those fossils designated Hominids 2 and 3 had been collected *in situ* in Kanjera Beds. Since Hominid 3 had become the cornerstone of Leakey's stratigraphic

---

[220] Louis S. B. Leakey, *Nature* 130:578 (1932); L. S. B. Leakey, *The Stone Age Races of Kenya* (London: Oxford University Press, 1935).

[221] L. S. B. Leakey, in *The Origin of Homo Sapiens*, ed. F. Bordes (Paris: UNESCO, 1972), pp. 25-29; L. S. B. Leakey, *By the Evidence* (New York: Harcourt Brace Jovanovich, 1974).

[222] P. G. H. Boswell, *Nature* 135:371 (1935).

[223] T. Plummer and R. Potts, *American Journal of Physical Anthropology* 96:7-23 (1995).

placement of all of the hominid fossils, they focused their attention on this fossil, which consisted of several cranial fragments, including frontal, parietal, and occipital pieces. Most of the crania collected at the site were thicker walled than modern human skulls. Leakey assumed this was evidence for their antiquity, but Plummer and Potts hypothesized that this may have been due to one of the side effects of parasites and/or hereditary or acquired anemia.

Several fragments, including some from Hominid 3, were subjected to an energy dispersive study. Plummer and Potts claim that the low elemental concentrations of the entire hominid sample indicates that they were deposited subsequent to the deposition of the Kanjera Formation, although the absolute age of the fossils could not be determined. They reported that research by subsequent expeditions had revealed that no sediment slumping had occurred at the site of Leakey's find, thus repudiating the basis for Boswell's attack on Leakey's claims.

Plummer and Potts conclude that the fossils found by Leakey were undoubted modern humans, that the Kanjera Formation included early to middle Pleistocene sedimentary deposits and that Hominid 3 was found *in situ* at a depth of several feet in an early Pleistocene deposit. They reconcile Leakey's discovery of Hominid 3 in an early Pleistocene bed by suggesting that this and other human fossils found there were the result of intrusive burial into the outcrops of the locality.

It is evident that no matter how good the evidence might be, any such evidence that would suggest that modern humans were contemporary with their alleged ancestors will be rejected out of hand by evolutionists, and every effort will be used to explain away the evidence. The facts are the fossils were found in early and middle Pleistocene deposits. There is no doubt that Hominid 3 was recovered *in situ* in an early Pleistocene bed at a depth of several feet. Had the reverse been true, and evolutionists wished to establish a date of one to two million years for this fossil, they would have accepted this evidence as proof. The low elemental concentrations of the hominid samples is very poor evidence concerning their provenance (origin or original level of deposition). Many factors could affect elemental levels during thousands of years, but this was the only evidence that the fossils were not of early to middle Pleistocene age, other than that they were modern humans, which in itself constitutes proof in the eyes of evolutionists the fossils could not have been contemporary with the early and middle Pleistocene. It will be duly reported in the evolutionary literature that Plummer and Potts have established that the hominid fossils found by Leakey were not of middle Pleistocene age as Leakey staunchly maintained. Nothing of the kind has been established, and the weight of the evidence is still on Leakey's side. He had the evidence. His opponents have their theories. Leakey's evidence, if true, is a death blow to all theories on an evolutionary origin of man.

More evidence is accumulating that documents the existence of *Homo sapiens* in the so-called middle Pleistocene. Juan-Luis Arsuaga et al. report the discovery of the remains of twenty-four humans which fit well within the "archaic *Homo sapiens*" group.[224] These human remains have been dated, it is said, in excess of 300,000 years, and the site has been judged to be middle Pleistocene. The fossils were found in a cave site called Sima de los Huesos (Sierra de Atapuerca), Burgos, Northern Spain. They had many features in common with the Neanderthals.

Chen, Yang, and Wu have reported the recovery of a well-preserved skull of what they call "early" *Homo sapiens* from a cave deposit at the Jinnuishan site, Yingkow County, Lianing Province, China.[225] The cranial capacity of the skull was about 1400 c.c., equal to that of modern humans. Some characteristics of the skull led them to believe it was close to the skull of archaic *Homo sapiens*. The animal fossils found with the skull suggest an antiquity of middle Pleistocene and on the basis of early work they had assigned an age of 230–300 thousand years, although now, since they believe this age is too old based on geological and archaeological evidence, they lean toward an age of 200 thousand years. Even with the younger age, they state that the dating results suggest the possible coexistence in China of *Homo sapiens* and *Homo erectus*.

Where Did Cain and Abel Get Their Wives?

Let us go back now to the very beginning of the human race to answer a question that is often asked: Where did Cain and Abel, as

---

[224] J. L. Arsuaga et al., *Nature* 362:534-537 (1993).
[225] Chen Tiemel, Yang Quan, and Wu En, *Nature* 368:55 (1994).

well as Seth, get their wives? From among their sisters, of course—where else? This intermarriage was an absolute necessity to propagate the human species. It was ordained of God, or else He would have created more than a single couple. Furthermore, since Adam and Eve were genetically perfect when created, and harmful, crippling mutations had not yet had time to form, at least to a significant extent when such intermarriage was necessary, no harmful biological results would occur from such intermarriage. Today almost 3000 crippling conditions, such as juvenile diabetes, sickle cell anemia, and phenylketonuria, are caused by harmful mutant genes. Chances of inheriting such a mutant gene from both father and mother (which is usually necessary for expression of the defect) is increased by intermarriage with cousins or closer relatives. Thus came prohibition against such intermarriage.

Some may object that the Bible mentions nothing about the other children of Adam and Eve. Genesis 5:4, however, states clearly that Adam "begot sons and daughters." As mentioned above, wives for Cain and Seth could only have been obtained from among their sisters. Furthermore, the Bible records the fact that Cain, after slaying Abel, feared that others in turn would take his life (Genesis 4:14). It is evident, then, that, as expected, Adam and Eve had many children—scores, perhaps even hundreds—during their long fruitful lifetime. Only Cain, Abel and Seth are mentioned by name because of certain important events involving these three.

The Origin of Races

Where did cave men, such as the Neanderthal, Cro-Magnon, and Swanscombe men come from? They were descendants of Noah's family, scattered throughout parts of Africa, Europe, Asia, and elsewhere, as they dispersed from the site of their ancestral home. They are believed to have been descendants of post-flood man because all of these remains have been discovered in the so-called Pleistocene deposits, which are believed to be post-flood.

Genesis, Chapter 11, records the fact that there was an early concentration of post-flood man in the land of Shinar (Babylonia). By this time, he had multiplied sufficiently and had developed adequate skills to contemplate building a great city, later called Babel (Babylon in the Greek), along with a great tower, or ziggurat. This has been shown to be quite plausible, even if no gaps are invoked to stretch out the genealogies of Genesis 11.[226]

This portion of Scripture contains the account of God's intervention by confounding the language of these people into a multiplicity of tongues. The event forced an acceleration of the process that God had ordained—"Be ye fruitful, multiply; bring forth abundantly in the earth, and multiply therein" (Genesis 9:7). It in turn caused a much more rapid migration of people into various parts of the world than had been occurring.

Whether God preserved in the eight survivors of the Flood a sufficient genetic potential, or gene pool, to give rise to the various human races existing today, or whether He created this potential via genetic engineering at the time of the event recorded in Genesis 11, we do not know. Nevertheless, the potential was there. As the various branches of the human family scattered and became increasingly isolated from one another and no longer interbred to a significant extent, these incipient races gave rise to ancient races, some of which we find in the form of fossils, but most of which have survived to the present time.

As members of a species disperse in small groups, such that they become geographically isolated, they become reproductively isolated as well. Each such group will carry with it only a fraction of the total gene pool, or genetic characteristics, of the population from which it split off. Being a small group, a high degree of in-breeding will result. Such a process may result in the rapid surfacing of genetic traits that were previously suppressed in the large population due to dilution through intermarriage throughout the entire population. As a result, "tribes" or "races" arise.

As this dispersal occurred from the original center of population, these small groups may have carried few skills with them or they eventually may have lost some of their original skills. Scattering in small groups may contribute to this loss via several factors. Lack of population pressure results in a reduction of the need for weapons to defend territory and to defend against predatory raids. Weapons may thus be abandoned. Lack of population pressure may also result in the abandonment of the practice of agriculture, since simple food gathering

---

[226] A. Courville, *The Exodus Problem and Its Ramifications*, vols. I and II (Loma Linda, California: Loma Linda Publ, 1971).

may suffice to feed the group. Furthermore, ideas and skills are no longer interchanged with neighboring groups. "Progress," as we generally understand it, could be severely retarded, and even a "degeneration" into a more "primitive" state might result.

Thus, while civilization was developing relatively rapidly in the heavily populated portions of Asia and Europe, peoples in the sparsely settled areas of Europe, the Americas, Australia, and southern Africa continued in a relatively primitive state, some even to this day. It is not surprising, therefore, that the remains of fossil man and associated artifacts, scattered as early man was, indicate that he lived in an "uncivilized" state. They manufactured rather sophisticated tools and weapons of stone. They were a religious people, as evidenced by the burial of their dead with flowers and various objects they believed would be useful in a life to follow.

That evolution theory, in view of known genetic data, produces no satisfactory explanation for the origin of races is evident from the following statement made in 1972 by the famous evolutionist, the late Theodosius Dobzhansky:

> It is almost incredible that a century after Darwin, the problem of the origin of racial differences in the human species remains about as baffling as it was in his time.[227]

In other words, there is no way of correlating the genetic data associated with the various races within an evolutionary framework. It is an amazing thing that evolutionists insist that they can explain how the universe evolved, how life evolved, how fishes, amphibians, reptiles, birds, and mammals evolved, how primates evolved from earlier mammals, and how apes, monkeys, and men evolved from earlier primates, and yet they must admit that they cannot explain the origin of races within the species *Homo sapiens*! If evolution theory cannot even explain the origin of races in the light of the known scientific evidence, how then can one pretend to use this theory to explain the most profound mysteries of all? Apparently, the closer the theory approaches the actual scientific data, the more untenable it becomes.

One obvious racial difference is skin color. It has sometimes been suggested that the Negroid race became black as an adaptation to the

---

[227] T. Dobzhansky, in *Sexual Selection and the Descent of Man*, ed. B. Campbell (Chicago: Aldine Publishing Company, 1972), p. 75.

more intense ultraviolet light from the sun in the tropics. This idea leaves unanswered why people equally black are not found in other areas of equally intense ultraviolet light, such as South America. Creationists believe that skin color variations developed as a natural sorting out of preexisting genetic traits during the formation of races as described in the section above. According to this view, blacks tended to migrate into those areas where their black skin offered protection from intense sunlight, while the fair-skinned, blue-eyed Scandinavian race naturally migrated to the far north to escape the more intense ultraviolet light encountered near the equator.

It is possible, as Parker has shown,[228] for a man and woman of the appropriate genetic mix to have sixteen children, one of whom could be black, one of whom could be white, and the other fourteen children could be of various mixed shades of color. A report documenting an occurrence of somewhat the same nature was published in Parade, a newspaper weekly magazine.[229] According to this report, Tom and Mandy Charnock of Leigh, a city near Manchester, England, had parented fraternal twin boys, one of whom has white skin, blue eyes, and blond hair, and the other has dark skin, brown hair, and brown eyes. The mother was the daughter of a Nigerian father and a white English mother, while the father was of white English parents.

A Pig's Tooth, an Ape's Jaw, A Dolphin's Rib and a Donkey's Skull

There is an old saying, "Could 50,000 Frenchmen be wrong?" In today's context, that could be translated into: "Could 50,000 evolutionists be wrong?" Absolutely! It has already been noted that for nearly fifty years, based on fragments of the jaw and a few teeth, evolution paleoanthropologists insisted that *Ramapithecus* was an intermediate between ape and man, but it turned out to be essentially the same as a modern orangutan. For nearly 100 years the Neanderthal people were believed to be our subhuman ancestors, *Homo neanderthalensis*, but have now been elevated to full human status, *Homo sapiens*. Two other famous supposed subhuman ancestors of man were touted by evolutionists, one of which turned out to be a fraud, and the other was based on a pig's tooth!

---

[228] Gary Parker, *Impact*, no. 89 (El Cajon, Calfornia: Institute for Creation Research, November 1980).

[229] Lloyd Shearer, Intelligence Report, "Mixed Twins," *Parade* (1983).

In 1922, a tooth was discovered in western Nebraska which was declared by Henry Fairfield Osborn, one of the most eminent paleontologists of that day, and several other authorities, to combine the characteristics of the chimpanzee, *Pithecanthropus*, and man.

Osborn and his colleagues could not quite decide whether the original owner of this tooth should be designated as an apelike man or a manlike ape. He was given the designation *Hesperopithecus haroldcookii* and become known popularly as Nebraska Man. An illustration of what this creature and his contemporaries supposedly

Figure 36. The picture of Nebraska Man (*Hesperopithecus*) published in *The Illustrated London News*, 24 June 1922.

looked like was published in the *Illustrated London News*.[230] In this illustration, *Hesperopithecus* looks remarkably similar to modern man, although brutish in appearance. In 1927, after further collecting and studies had been carried out, it was decided that *Hesperopithecus* was neither a manlike ape nor an apelike man, but was an extinct peccary, or pig![231] This is a case in which a scientist made a man out of a pig, and the pig made a monkey out of the scientist!

In 1912, Arthur Smith Woodward, Director of the Natural History Museum of London, and Charles Dawson, a medical doctor and amateur paleontologist, announced the discovery of a mandible and part of a skull. Dawson had recovered these specimens from a gravel pit near Piltdown, England. The jawbone appeared very simian-like except for the teeth, which seemed to show the type of wear expected for humans rather than that for apes. The skull, on the other hand, appeared to be very man-like.

These two specimens were combined into a single individual and designated *Eoanthropus dawsoni*, "Dawn Man." He became known popularly as Piltdown Man. He was judged to be about 500,000 years old. Although a few experts, such as Boule and Henry Fairfield Osborn, objected to the association of this very ape-like jaw with a humanlike skull, the consensus of the world's greatest authorities was that Piltdown Man was indeed an authentic link in the evolution of man.

By 1950 a method had become available for assigning a relative age to fossil bones. This method is dependent on the amount of fluoride absorbed by bones from the soil. When the Piltdown bones were subjected to this test, it was discovered that the jawbone contained practically no fluoride and thus was no fossil at all. It was judged to be no older than about the year it was found. The skull did have a significant amount of fluoride, but was estimated to be a few thousand years rather than 500,000 years old.

With this information at hand, the bones were subjected to a thorough and critical examination. It was discovered that the bones had been treated with iron salts to make them look old, and scratch marks were detected on the teeth, indicating that they had been filed. In other words, Piltdown Man was a complete fraud! A modern ape's

[230] *Illustrated London News*, 24 June 1922.
[231] W. K. Gregory, *Science* 66:579 (1927).

jaw and a human skull had been doctored to resemble an ape-man, and the forgery had succeeded in fooling most of the world's greatest experts.

In his article[232] on the Piltdown forgery, Stephen Jay Gould candidly reveals this tendency of the experts to find what they are looking for even though it is not there, and to not find what is there if they are not looking for it. Gould relates that:

> Piltdown's champions . . . modeled the "facts" . . . another illustration that information always reaches us through the strong filters of culture, hope, and expectation. As a persistent theme in "pure" description of the Piltdown remains, we learn from all its major supporters that the skull, although remarkably modern, contains a suite of definitely simian characters! . . . Grafton Elliot Smith . . . concluded: "We must regard this as being the most primitive and most simian human brain so far recorded; one, moreover, such as might reasonably have been expected to be associated in one and the same individual with the mandible which so definitely indicates the zoological rank of its original possessor." . . . Sir Arthur Keith wrote in his last major work (1948): "His forehead was like that of the orang, devoid of a supraorbital torus; in its modeling his frontal bone presented many points of resemblance to that of the orang of Borneo and Sumatra." . . . Careful examination of the jaw also revealed a set of "remarkably human features" for such an apish jaw (beyond the forged wear of the teeth). Sir Arthur Keith repeatedly emphasized, for example, that the teeth were inserted into the jaw in a human, rather than a simian, fashion.

In commenting on this tendency of allowing preconceived ideas to govern one's scientific conclusions, anthropologist Jaquetta Hawkes remarks that

> Accepting this as inevitable and not necessarily damaging, it still comes as a shock to discover how often preconceived ideas have affected the investigation of human origins.

---

[232] S. J. Gould, *Natural History* 88(3): 96 (1979).

There is, of course, nothing like a fake for exposing such weaknesses among the experts. For example, to look back over the bold claims and subtle anatomical distinctions made by some of our greatest authorities concerning the recent human skull and modern ape's jaw which together composed "Piltdown Man," rouses either joy or pain according to one's feeling for scientists.[233]

Have things changed much today? Two recent examples tend to indicate that tendencies of authorities have not really changed much at all. An article in *Science News* relates the charges of Tim White that Noel Boaz has mistaken a dolphin's rib for the clavicle (shoulder bone) of a hominoid.[234] White jests that the fossil should be designated *Flipperpithecus*! Boaz had claimed that the specimen resembles the clavicle of a pygmy chimpanzee and had suggested that the curve of the bone may even indicate habitual bipedalism. White argues that Boaz has misinterpreted the data. Alan Walker is quoted in this same article as stating that there is a long tradition of misinterpreting various bones as hominoid clavicles; in the past, Walker says, skilled anthropologists have erroneously described the femur of an alligator and the toe of a three-toed horse as clavicles!

A UPI press release published May 14, 1984,[235] revealed that a skull fragment which had been hailed by experts one year earlier as the oldest human fossil ever found in Europe may have come from a donkey! The fossil had been found in the Andalusia region of Spain, and a three-day symposium had been scheduled so that participants could examine and discuss the fossil, dubbed "Orce Man" for the southern Spanish town near which it had been found. When French experts revealed the fact that "Orce Man" was most likely a skull fragment from a four-month old donkey, embarrassed Spanish authorities sent out 500 letters canceling invitations to the symposium.

An ape's jaw in 1912, a pig's tooth in 1922, a dolphin's rib and donkey's skull in the 1980's—the script is the same, only the actors and props have changed. Perhaps Lord Zuckerman was right when he declared that it is doubtful whether there is any science at all in the search for man's fossil ancestry.[236]

---

[233] Jaquetta Hawkes, *Nature* 204:952 (1964).

[234] W. Herbert, *Science News* 123:246 (1983).

[235] Moline (Illinois) *Daily Dispatch*, 14 May 1984.

Summary

Recent research on living tree shrews and on primates has shown that there is no genetic relationship between primates and tree shrews, as had long been supposed. As we have also documented here, when the fossil record of primates is thoroughly and objectively evaluated, it is clear that the basically different types among the primates, as, for example, the lemurs, tarsiers, lorises, various types of monkeys, various kinds of apes, and man, have appeared fully formed in the fossil record without transitional forms, just as would be expected on the basis of creation.

Lord Zuckerman had spent a major portion of his scientific career investigating fossil specimens allegedly related to the origin of man. He had utilized the talents of an outstanding team of anatomists and had employed the best methods of analysis available. Since he was not a creationist, it cannot be said that his views were biased or distorted towards the creationist position. His work has been thorough, and his conclusions have been as objective as is humanly possible. In the book he published in 1970, *Beyond the Ivory Tower*, Lord Zuckerman has candidly stated his conclusions concerning the fossil record as it relates to man. He states:

> For example, no scientist could logically dispute the proposition that man, without having been involved in any act of divine creation, evolved from some ape-like creature in a very short space of time—speaking in geological terms—without leaving any fossil traces of the steps of the transformation.[237]

Thus, according to Lord Zuckerman, if we exclude the possibility of creation, then obviously man must have evolved from an ape-like creature, but if he did, there is no evidence for it in the fossil record.

There is thus no evidence, either in the present world or in the world of the past, that man has arisen from some "lower" creature. He stands alone as a separate and distinct created type, or basic morphological design, endowed with qualities that set him far above all other living creatures.

---

[236] Zuckerman, *Beyond the Ivory Tower*, p. 64.
[237] *Ibid.*

Chapter VIII

Evolution: The Fossils Say NO!

In the preceding chapters, we have cited example after example of failure to find transitional forms where evolutionary theory predicts such forms should have been found. Some might suspect that we have biased our choice of examples in such a way that only those cases have been cited where transitional forms have not yet been found, while failing to mention many other examples where transitional forms between basically different kinds of animals or plants are known. Nothing could be further from the truth.

The examples cited in this book are in no way exceptions, but serve to illustrate what is characteristic of the fossil record. While variations at the subspecies level are observable, and some at the species level may be inferred, the absence of transitional forms between higher categories (the created types of the creation model) is regular and systematic. We now propose to document this statement by citing published statements of evolutionists.

The Ubiquitous Absence of Transitional Forms

We wish to cite first the world's foremost evolutionary paleontologist, George Gaylord Simpson. In his book, *Tempo and Mode in Evolution*, under the section entitled "Major Systematic Discontinuities of Record," he states that nowhere in the world is there any trace of a fossil that would close the considerable gap between *Hyracotherium*, which most evolutionists assume was the first horse, and its supposed ancestral order Condylarthra. He then goes on to say:

> This is true of all thirty-two orders of mammals. . . . The earliest and most primitive known members of every order

already have the basic ordinal characters, and in no case is an approximately continuous sequence from one order to another known. In most cases the break is so sharp and the gap so large that the origin of the order is speculative and much disputed.[1]

Later on (p. 107), Simpson states:

This regular absence of transitional forms is not confined to mammals, but is an almost universal phenomenon, as has long been noted by paleontologists. It is true of almost all orders of all classes of animals, both vertebrate and invertebrate. *A fortiori*, it is also true of the classes, and of the major animal phyla, and it is apparently also true of analogous categories of plants.

In his book, *The Meaning of Evolution*, Simpson, with reference to the appearance of new phyla, classes, or other major groups, states that:

The process by which such radical events occur in evolution is the subject of one of the most serious remaining disputes among qualified professional students of evolution. The question is whether such major events take place instantaneously, by some process essentially unlike those involved in lesser or more gradual evolutionary change, or whether all of evolution, including these major changes, is explained by the same principles and processes throughout, their results being greater or less according to the time involved, the relative intensity of selection, and other material variables in any given situation.

Possibility for such dispute exists because transitions between major grades of organization are seldom well recorded by fossils. There is in this respect a tendency toward systematic deficiency in the record of the history of life. It is thus possible to claim that such transitions are not

---

[1] G. G. Simpson, *Tempo and Mode in Evolution* (New York: Columbia University Press, 1944), p. 105.

recorded because they did not exist, that the changes were not by transition but by sudden leaps in evolution.[2]

If phyla, classes, orders, and other major groups were connected by transitional forms rather than appearing suddenly in the fossil record with basic characteristics complete, it would not be necessary, of course, to refer to their appearance in the fossil record as "radical events." Furthermore, it cannot be emphasized too strongly that even evolutionists are arguing among themselves whether these major categories appeared *instantaneously* or not! It is precisely the argument of creationists that these forms *did* arise *instantaneously* and that the transitional forms are not recorded because they never existed. Creationists thus would re-word Simpson's statement to read:

> It is thus possible to claim that such transitions are not recorded because they did not exist, that these major types arose by creation rather than by a process of gradual evolution.

In a more recent work, Simpson stated that "it is a feature of the known fossil record that most taxa appear abruptly." In the same paragraph, he states further that "Gaps among known species are sporadic and often small. Gaps among known orders, classes, and phyla are systematic and almost always large."[3]

Although we intend to do so, it would hardly be necessary to document further the nature of the fossil record. It seems obvious that if the above statements of Simpson were stripped of all presuppositions and presumed evolutionary mechanisms to leave the bare record, they would describe exactly what is required by the creation model. This record is woefully deficient, however, in the light of the predictions of the evolution model.

No one has devoted himself more whole-heartedly than Simpson to what Dobzhansky has called "the mechanistic materialist philosophy shared by most of the present establishment in the biological sciences."[4] Simpson asserts that most paleontologists "find it logical, if

---

[2] G. G. Simpson, *The Meaning of Evolution* (New Haven: Yale University Press, 1949), p. 231.

[3] G. G. Simpson, in *The Evolution of Life*, ed. Sol Tax (Chicago: University of Chicago Press, 1960), p. 149.

[4] T. Dobzhansky, *Science* 175:49 (1972).

not scientifically required, to assume that the sudden appearance of a new systematic group is not evidence for creation. . . .["5]

Simpson has thus expended considerable effort in attempts to bend and twist every facet of evolution theory to explain away the deficiencies of the fossil record.[6] One needs to be reminded, however, that if evolution is adopted as an *a priori* principle, it is always possible to imagine auxiliary hypotheses—unproved and by nature unprovable—to make it work in any specific case. By this process biological evolution degenerates into what Thorpe calls one of his "four pillars of unwisdom"—mental evolution that is the result of random tries preserved by reinforcements.[7]

In reference to the nature of the record, Arnold has said:

> It has long been hoped that extinct plants will ultimately reveal some of the stages through which existing groups have passed during the course of their development, but it must freely be admitted that this aspiration has been fulfilled to a very slight extent, even though paleobotanical research has been in progress for more than one hundred years.[8]

The following remarks of E. J. H. Corner of the Cambridge University botany school were refreshingly candid:

> Much evidence can be adduced in favor of the theory of evolution—from biology, biogeography, and paleontology, but I still think that to the unprejudiced, the fossil record of plants is in favor of special creation.[9]

This evolutionist frankly states that the fossil record of plants does not support evolution, but rather supports creation.

---

[5] G. G. Simpson, *The Major Features of Evolution* (New York: Columbia University Press, 1953), p. 360.

[6] *Ibid.*, pp. 360-376; Simpson, *Tempo and Mode in Evolution*, pp. 105-124; Simpson, *The Evolution of Life*, pp. 149-152.

[7] W. Thorpe, *New Scientist* 43:635 (1969).

[8] C. A. Arnold, *An Introduction to Paleobotany* (New York: McGraw-Hill Publishing Company, 1947), p. 7.

[9] E. J. H. Corner, in *Contemporary Botanical Thought*, ed. A. M. MacLeod and L. S. Cobley (Chicago: Quadrangle Books, 1961), p. 97.

The origin of flowering plants (angiosperms), which Darwin termed "an abominable mystery," is still today, for evolutionists, an abominable mystery. Concerning the problem, Hughes has this to say:

> The evolutionary origin of the now dominant land-plant group, the angiosperms, has puzzled scientists since the middle of the nineteenth century. . . .

After describing several attempts to explain why the evidence for their evolutionary origin cannot be found, Hughes says,

> . . . with few exceptions of detail, however, the failure to find a satisfactory explanation has persisted and many biologists have concluded that the problem is not capable of solution by fossil evidence. . . . [10]

Beck has stated that,

> Indeed, the mystery of the origin and early evolution of the angiosperms is as pervasive and as fascinating today as it was when Darwin emphasized the problem in 1879. . . . We have no definitive answers, because we are forced to base our conclusions largely on circumstantial evidence, and they must usually, of necessity, be highly speculative and interpretative. [11]

Flowering plants burst upon the scene in bewildering variety. Forty-three families of the angiosperms abruptly appear with no trace of ancestors or intermediate forms. No wonder evolutionists describe their origin as an abominable mystery.

Olson has said:

> A third fundamental aspect of the record is somewhat different. Many new groups of plants and animals suddenly appear, apparently without any close ancestors. Most major groups of organisms—phyla, subphyla, and even

---

[10] N. F. Hughes, *Paleobiology of Angiosperm Origins: Problems of Mesozoic Seed-Plant Evolution* (Cambridge: Cambridge University Press, 1976), pp. 1-2.

[11] C. B. Beck, in *Origin and Early Evolution of Angiosperms*, ed. C. B. Beck (New York: Columbia University Press, 1976).

classes—have appeared in this way. . . . The fossil record,
which has produced the problem, is not much help in its
solution. . . . Most zoologists and the majority of
paleontologists feel that the breaks and the abrupt
appearances of new groups can be explained by the
incompleteness of the record. Some paleontologists disagree
and believe that these events tell a story not in accord with
the theory and not seen among living organisms.[12]

In regard to the remark concerning the alleged incompleteness of
the record, we refer to the statement by George recorded earlier in this
book about the richness of the record. Further refutation of that
explanation for the discontinuities may be deduced from Newell's
statement that, "Many of the discontinuities tend to be more and more
emphasized with increased collecting."[13]

In their book on the principles of paleontology, Raup and Stanley
have remarked:

Unfortunately, the origins of most higher categories are
shrouded in mystery: commonly new higher categories
appear abruptly in the fossil record without evidence of
transitional forms.[14]

Du Nouy has described the evidence in this way:

In brief, each group, order, or family seems to be born
suddenly, and we hardly ever find the forms which link
them to the preceding strain. When we discover them they
are already completely differentiated. Not only do we find
practically no transitional forms, but in general it is
impossible to authentically connect a new group with an
ancient one.[15]

---

[12] E. C. Olson, *The Evolution of Life* (New York: The New American
Library, 1965), p. 94.

[13] N. D. Newell, *Proceedings of the American Philosophical Society*
(April, 1959), p. 267.

[14] D. M. Raup and S. M. Stanley, *Principles of Paleontology* (San
Francisco: W. H. Freeman and Co., 1971), p. 306.

[15] L. du Nouy, *Human Destiny* (New York: The New American
Library, 1947), p. 63.

Kuhn has remarked:

> The fact of descent remains. However, descent beyond the typologically circumscribed boundaries is nowhere demonstrable. Therefore, we can indeed speak about a descent within types, but not about a descent of types.[16]

Concerning the major groups or phyla, Clark has stated:

> No matter how far back we go in the fossil record of previous animal life upon earth, we find no trace of any animal forms which are intermediate between the various major groups or phyla.[17]

Later on in this same volume (p. 196), he says:

> Since we have not the slightest evidence, either among the living or the fossil animals, of any intergrading types following the major groups, it is a fair supposition that there never have been any such intergrading types.

A review of the book, *Evolutionary Biology, Volume 6*,[18] states that

> Three paleontologists (no less) conclude that stratigraphic position is totally irrelevant to determination of phylogeny and almost say that no known taxon is derived from any other.[19]

Richard B. Goldschmidt, a German geneticist who later served as professor of zoology at the University of California, Berkeley, in contrast to Simpson and the majority of evolutionists, accepted the discontinuities in the fossil record at face value. He rejected the neo-Darwinian interpretation of evolution (the modern synthesis in today's term) which is accepted by the majority of evolutionists. The neo-Darwinian interpretation supposes that all evolutionary changes

---

[16] O. Kuhn, *Acta Biotheoretica* 6:55 (1942).

[17] A. H. Clark, in *The New Evolution; Zoogenesis*, ed. A. H. Clark (Baltimore: Williams and Wilkins, 1930), p. 189.

[18] T. Dobzhansky, M. K. Heck, and W. C. Steere, *Evolutionary Biology*, vol. 6 (New York: Appleton-Century-Crafts, 1972).

[19] L. Van Valen, *Science* 180:488 (1973).

took place slowly and gradually via many thousands of slight mutations. Goldschmidt instead proposed that major categories (phyla, classes, orders, families) arose instaneously by major saltations or systemic mutations.[20]

Goldschmidt termed his mechanism the "hopeful monster" mechanism. He proposed, for instance, that at one time a reptile laid an egg and a bird was hatched from the egg! All major gaps in the fossil record were accounted for, according to Goldschmidt, by similar events—something laid an egg, and something else got born. Neo-Darwinists prefer to believe that Goldschmidt is the one who laid the egg, maintaining that there is not a shred of evidence to support his "hopeful monster" mechanism. Goldschmidt insists just as strongly that there is no evidence for the postulated neo-Darwinian mechanism (major transformations by the accumulation of micromutations). Creationists agree with both the neo-Darwinists and Goldschmidt—there is no evidence for *either* type of evolution. Goldschmidt's publications do offer cogent arguments against the neo-Darwinian view of evolution, from both the field of genetics and the field of paleontology.

No one was more wholly committed to evolutionary philosophy than was Goldschmidt. If anybody wanted to find transitional forms, he did. If anybody would have admitted that a transitional form was a transitional form, if indeed that is what it was, he would have. But concerning the fossil record, this is what Goldschmidt had to say:

> The facts of greatest general importance are the following. When a new phylum, class, or order appears, there follows a quick, explosive (in terms of geological time) diversification so that practically all orders or families known appear suddenly and without any apparent transitions.[21]

Now, creationists ask, *what better description of the fossil record could one expect, based on the predictions of the creation model?* On the other hand, unless one accepts Goldschmidt's "hopeful monster" mechanism of evolution, this description contradicts the most critical

---

[20] R. B. Goldschmidt, *The Material Basis of Evolution* (New Haven: Yale University Press, 1940); R. B. Goldschmidt, *American Scientist* 40:97 (1952).

[21] *Ibid.*

prediction of the evolution model—the presence in the fossil record of the intermediates demanded by the theory.

Some critics might complain that the publications by Goldschmidt espousing the "hopeful monster" mechanism are from forty to fifty-five years old, and, furthermore, his ideas have been discredited by modern evolutionists. The important question is, however, why did Goldschmidt feel forced to propose such an incredible mechanism in the first place? Goldschmidt felt forced to propose this mechanism because transitional forms between basic types cannot be found, each type appearing in the fossil record fully formed. Intense searching of the fossil record during the past half century has produced nothing that would have caused Goldschmidt to change his mind.

Furthermore, one of America's best known evolutionists has rallied to the defense of Goldschmidt's ideas. Stephen Jay Gould, a professor at Harvard University teaching geology, biology, and the history of science, among his many publishing activities writes articles which appear in each issue of the journal, *Natural History*, a publication of the American Museum of Natural History. He published an article in that journal entitled "The Return of the Hopeful Monsters."[22]

After recounting the "official rebuke and derision" poured out on Goldschmidt by his fellow evolutionists because of his "hopeful monster" mechanism, Gould says: "I do, however, predict that during the next decade Goldschmidt will be largely vindicated in the world of evolutionary biology." A little later he states: "The fossil record with its abrupt transitions offers no support for gradual change. . . ."

Somewhat later in this same article, Gould says:

> All paleontologists know that the fossil record contains precious little in the way of intermediate forms; transitions between major groups are characteristically abrupt.

Gould is thus arguing that the fossil record, just as Goldschmidt argued, does not produce evidence of the gradual change of one plant or animal form into another and that, again, just as Goldschmidt argued, each kind appeared abruptly.

Gould then introduces another argument against gradual change that was used by Goldschmidt. Gould says:

---

[22] S. J. Gould, *Natural History* 86(6): 22-30 (1977).

> Even though we have no direct evidence for smooth
> transitions, can we invent a reasonable sequence of
> intermediate forms, that is, viable, functioning organisms,
> between ancestors and descendants? Of what possible use
> are the imperfect incipient stages of useful structures? What
> good is half a jaw or half a wing?

The argument here, that gradual evolutionary change of one form
into another is impossible because the transitional forms, being
incomplete, could not function, is an argument that has long been
suggested by creationists. This was one of Goldschmidt's key
arguments against the neo-Darwinian mechanism of evolution and is
now being echoed by Gould.

Gould argues, as did Goldschmidt, that most large evolutionary
changes are brought about by small alterations in rates of
development. In the first place, there is not one shred of empirical
evidence to support such an idea. Even Goldschmidt admitted that no
one had ever seen anything like that happen (that is, a new type
arising by the postulated hopeful monster mechanism). Gould, in the
article referred to above, cited Goldschmidt's work that allegedly
showed that large differences in color pattern in caterpillars resulted
from small changes in the timing of development. Of course, to cite this
as evidence in support of the hopeful monster mechanism is sheer
nonsense. The only change produced was in the color of the caterpillar.
It remained the same species, as did the butterfly that was produced
from the caterpillar. Are such processes supposed to explain the origin
of the caterpillar and butterfly in the first place? Of course not. In fact,
the clear thrust of Gould's article is that major evolutionary changes
were *not* produced by such minor variations. Variations in the color
patterns of caterpillars, then, offers no support whatsoever for the idea
that major evolutionary changes occur through small variations in
rates of development.

According to Goldschmidt, a reptile laid an egg from which the first
bird, feathers and all, was produced. How, one may ask, were entirely
new and novel structures, such as feathers, produced all at once by
small variations in rates of development of entirely different
structures? A feather is an amazingly complex structure with many
elements marvelously designed to function together in such a way that
the feather performs its task in an optimal fashion. Its very existence

speaks of deliberate design. To believe that a feather, an eye, or a kidney, let alone a completely new plant or animal, could be produced *do novo* by small variations in rates of development is absolutely incredible.

But, according to Gould, this appears to be what evolutionists must believe. On the final page of the article cited above, Gould says:

> Indeed, if we do not invoke discontinuous change by small alteration in rates of development, I do not see how most major evolutionary transitions can be accomplished at all. Few systems are more resistant to basic change than the strongly differentiated, highly specified, complex adults of "higher" animal groups. How could we ever convert a rhinoceros or a mosquito into something fundamentally different? Yet transitions between major groups must have occurred in the history of life.

It seems evident that if such a well-established present-day evolutionist as Stephen Jay Gould feels forced to postulate that evolution has occurred by something similar to Goldschmidt's hopeful monster mechanism, then indeed there is no actual empirical evidence that evolution is occurring in the present via the mechanism postulated by neo-Darwinists. If there were such evidence, no one would feel forced to adopt the incredible hopeful monster mechanism. But, on the other hand, certainly no one has ever witnessed the birth of a hopeful monster. Sewall Wright, well known for his part in developing certain aspects of the neo-Darwinian mechanism of evolution, has stated that while recording over 100,000 births of guinea pigs he has seen many monsters, but never a hopeful monster.[23]

Just as obvious is the fact that there is no evidence for the existence of transitional forms, for it is the *absence* of such transitional forms the hopeful monster mechanism was invented to explain! Although evolutionists are seeking some way out of the dilemma caused by the embarrassing absence of transitional forms, they are not embracing the hopeful monster concept as an escape mechanism. We are nearing the close of two decades which began in 1977 with the publication of the article by Gould, "The Return of the Hopeful Monsters." By the end of that decade, Gould predicted, Goldschmidt would be largely

---

[23] S. Wright, *Evolution* 36:440 (1982).

vindicated in the halls of evolutionary biology. Whatever else can be said concerning the unique abilities of Professor Gould, he appears to be a poor prophet, for with very few exceptions biologists have not rushed forward to rehabilitate Goldschmidt's reputation as an evolutionary biologist.

In the pages of *Discover* in 1981, Gould published an attack against creationists and creation science.[24] I asked the editor of *Discover* for permission to publish an essay of equal length in answer to Gould's article. This request was refused, but I was permitted to publish a reply in the form of a one-page letter-to-the-editor.[25]

In his essay, among other things, Gould took exception to the description of Goldschmidt's hopeful monster mechanism and of Gould's support which I had included in the 1979 edition of this book.[26] He accused me of creating a distorted caricature of Goldschmidt's hopeful monster mechanism.

Gould wrote:

> Duane Gish writes, "According to Goldschmidt, and now apparently according to Gould, a reptile laid an egg from which the first bird, feathers and all, was produced." Any evolutionist who believed such nonsense would rightly be laughed off the intellectual stage. . . .

In my letter-to-the-editor, I documented that is precisely what Goldschmidt did believe by quoting from Goldschmidt's book, *The Material Basis of Evolution* (p. 395), where he stated:

> I need only quote Schindewolf (1936), the most progressive investigator known to me. He shows by examples from fossil material that the major evolutionary advances must have taken place in single large steps. . . . He shows that the many missing links in the paleontological record are sought for in vain because they have never existed: "the first bird hatched from a reptilian egg."

[24] S. J. Gould, *Discover* 2(5): 34 (1981).

[25] D. T. Gish, *Discover* 2(7): 6 (1981).

[26] D. T. Gish, *Evolution: The Fossils Say No!* (San Diego: Creation-Life Publishers, 1979).

I went on to state that therefore, according to Gould's own statement, his hero of the next decade should be laughed off the intellectual stage.

In a subsequent letter-to-the-editor,[27] Gould maintained that Goldschmidt had intended for this to be understood only as a metaphor. Gould's fellow evolutionists, however, apparently agree with my understanding of what Goldschmidt had proposed. Futuyma, a fervent anti-creationist, in reference to Goldschmidt's suggested mechanism, states:

> He pushed his conclusion to extremes, and theorized that each major taxonomic group had arisen as a macro-mutation, a "hopeful monster" that in one jump had passed from worm to crustacean, or reptile to bird.[28]

Steven Stanley, a paleontologist at Johns Hopkins University and well known for his advocacy of the "punctuated equilibrium" mechanism of evolution to be discussed shortly, states:

> During the present century the idea that adaptive innovations arise by rapid speciation has appeared sporadically in paleontology without taking hold. Otto Schindewolf (1936, 1950) was a prime mover here, but as described earlier, his views were extreme, in part reflecting the influence of De Vries and Goldschmidt. Schindewolf believed that a single *Grossmutation* could instantaneously yield a form representing a new family or order of animals. This view engendered such visions as the first bird hatching from a reptilian egg.[29]

Stanley thus characterizes Schindewolf's views as extreme, engendering such visions as the first bird hatching from a reptilian egg, and credits Goldschmidt and De Vries for the influence that led to these extreme views.

John R. Turner, professor of genetics at Leeds University, states:

---

[27] S. J. Gould, *Discover* 2(10): 10 (1981).

[28] D. J. Futuyma, *Science on Trial* (New York: Pantheon Books, 1983), p. 65.

[29] S. Stanley, *Macroevolution* (San Francisco: W. H. Freeman Pub. Co., 1979), p. 35.

The biggest mistake that any punctuationist could make would be to assume, as Goldschmidt did, that this "hopeful monster," if that is what one wishes to call it, would be perfect, to the point of undergoing no further modification. Goldschmidt did his better ideas a disservice by attaching them so firmly to this perverse view.[30]

It is thus clear that I have neither misunderstood nor selectively misquoted either Goldschmidt or Gould in this matter. Gould, apparently embarrassed by his rather hasty and overenthusiastic support of the hopeful monster notion which he had voiced in his 1977 article, was attempting to extricate himself by denying that Goldschmidt really meant what he had said. We do agree with Gould, however, when he later wrote that to believe that the first bird hatched from a reptilian egg is scientific nonsense. To either voice such a suggestion or to endorse those who hold such views is an admission that the evidence is very embarrassing for evolutionary theory.

Gould has made a number of revealing statements in other articles in *Natural History*. He has said, for example:

> The extreme rarity of transitional forms in the fossil record persists as the trade secret of paleontology. The evolutionary trees that adorn our textbooks have data only at the tips and nodes of their branches; the rest is inference, however, reasonable, not the evidence of fossils.[31]

Later in the same article, he states:

> The history of most fossil species includes two features inconsistent with gradualism: 1. *Stasis*. Most species exhibit no directional change during their tenure on earth. They appear in the fossil record looking much the same as when they disappear; morphological change is usually limited and directionless. 2. *Sudden Appearance*. In any local area, a species does not arise gradually by the steady

---

[30] J. R. Turner, in *Dimensions of Darwinism*, ed. Marjorie Grene (Cambridge: Cambridge University Press, 1983), p. 158.

[31] S. J. Gould, *Natural History*, 86(5): 13 (1977).

transformation of its ancestors; it appears all at once and "fully formed."

In an article discussing taxonomical classifications, Gould said:

The three-level, five-kingdom system may appear, at first glance, to record an inevitable progress in the history of life that I have often opposed in these columns. Increasing diversity and multiple transitions seem to reflect a determined and inexorable progression toward higher things. But the paleontological record supports no such interpretation. There has been no steady progress in the higher development of organic design. We have had, instead, vast stretches of little or no change and one evolutionary burst that created the whole system.[32]

Eliminate the words "evolutionary burst" and substitute the words "burst of creation," and one would think he was reading an article by a creationist.

In an article in which he was discussing the relationship of paleontology and the theory of evolution, including the problem of the gaps in the fossil record, David B. Kitts, professor in the Department of Geology at the University of Oklahoma and an evolutionist who received his training in vertebrate paleontology under George Gaylord Simpson, said:

Despite the bright promise that paleontology provides a means of "seeing" evolution, it has presented some nasty difficulties for evolutionists, the most notorious of which is the presence of "gaps" in the fossil record. Evolution requires intermediate forms between species and paleontology does not provide them. . . .[33]

One may ask, just why then is Kitts an evolutionist? Whatever else motivates Kitts to accept evolution, it appears obvious that he is an evolutionist not because of the fossil record, but in spite of the fossil record. We certainly do agree with Kitts' statement that, first, evolution does require intermediate forms, and, secondly, that the fossil record (paleontology) does not produce them.

---

[32] S. J. Gould, *Natural History*, 85(6): 37 (1976).
[33] D. B. Kitts, *Evolution* 28:467 (1974).

Macbeth says flatly:

> Darwinism has failed in practice. The whole aim and
> purpose of Darwinism is to show how modern forms
> descended from ancient forms, that is, to construct reliable
> phylogenies (genealogies or family trees). In this he has
> utterly failed.[34]

He then goes on to quote other authors to the effect that the
phylogenies found in textbooks are based on unsupported assertions,
imaginative literature, speculations, and little more.

Francisco Ayala, a professor of biology at the University of
California, Davis, and well known in evolutionary circles for his
defense of the neo-Darwinian mechanism of evolution, has
nevertheless expressed puzzlement over the origin of new basic types,
or the higher categories. Along with his co-author, James Valentine,
Ayala states:

> The evolutionary origins of taxa in the higher categories
> are poorly known. . . . Most orders, classes, and phyla appear
> abruptly and commonly have already acquired all the
> characters that distinguish them.

After discussing and rejecting several suggestions as to how this
evidence might be accommodated within a theory that involves slow
gradual change over long stretches of time, Ayala and Valentine
conclude, "We are forced to the conclusion that most of the really novel
taxa that appear suddenly in the fossil record did in fact originate
suddenly."[35]

Ayala and Valentine, while admitting that the empirical evidence
does indicate that the higher categories have originated suddenly, are
still seeking, of course, some mechanistic, evolutionary process to
account for this. Creation scientists, on the other hand, point out that
an evolutionary process, dependent as it is on randomly produced
changes, by its very nature would require vast stretches of time,
certainly sufficient in extent to leave fossils of many transitional forms.

---

[34] N. Macbeth, *American Biology Teacher* (November 1976), p. 495.

[35] F. J. Ayala and J. W. Valentine, *Evolving: The Theory and Process
of Organic Evolution* (Menlo Park, California: Benjamin/Cummings
Publishing Company, 1979), pp. 266-267.

This would be especially true for the production of the higher categories, that is, families, orders, classes and phyla. Their sudden appearance, fully formed, is remarkable support for creation.

Colin Patterson is a senior paleontologist at the British Museum of Natural History in London and a lifelong evolutionist. There at this famous natural history museum he has available one of the greatest collections of fossils found anywhere in the world. Surely with this vast collection of fossils available, derived from an intense search that has spanned the 125 years since Darwin, and with a bias, if any, towards the evolutionary viewpoint, Patterson should be able to find hundreds, if not thousands of undoubted transitional forms, if evolution has actually occurred.

Patterson has published an excellent book on evolution.[36] In his book Patterson invites comments from the readers. One reader wrote to Patterson and asked him why he had not included any examples of actual transitional forms in his book. Patterson, in his reply, stated that he agreed with the reader's comments concerning the lack of direct illustrations of evolutionary transitions in his book, but that if he had known of any, fossil or living, he certainly would have included them.[37]

A report on a radio program broadcast by the British Broadcasting Corporation that featured Dr. Patterson was published in the BBC publication, *The Listener*.[38] In the article Patterson is quoted as saying:

> As it turns out, all one can learn about the history of life is learned from systematics, from the groupings one finds in nature. The rest of it is story telling of one sort or another. We have access to the tips of the tree; the tree itself is theory, and people who pretend to know about the tree and to describe what went on it—how the branches came off and the twigs came off—are, I think, telling stories.

Indeed, all we have of the theoretical evolutionary phylogenetic trees are the tips of the branches—evolutionists have never been able to find the transitional forms required for the trunks and the branches

---

[36] C. Patterson, *Evolution* (London: Natural History Museum, 1978).

[37] Personal communication to Luther Sunderland, Appalachin, New York, 10 April 1979.

[38] Brian Leith, *The Listener* 106:390 (1981).

of the trees. All these evolutionary trees we see in textbooks are just pretense, according to Patterson. Patterson's candidness is certainly highly commendable.

In his review of the book by Steven Stanley, *Macroevolution, Pattern and Process,*[39] David Woodruff states, "But fossil species remain unchanged throughout most of their history and the record fails to contain a single example of a significant transition."[40]

Sometimes it is stated by evolutionists that yes, the absence of transitional forms was a problem for Darwin, but since then many have been found, and more and more are being found all the time. Other evolutionists state just the opposite, however. Sir Edmund Leach has said, for example:

> Missing links in the sequence of fossil evidence were a worry to Darwin. He felt sure they would eventually turn up, but they are still missing and seem likely to remain so.[41]

David Raup, previously Curator of Geology at the Field Museum of Natural History in Chicago and now Professor of Geology at the University of Chicago and a strong advocate of evolutionary theory, has candidly stated:

> Darwin's theory of natural selection has always been closely linked to evidence from fossils, and probably most people assume that fossils provide a very important part of the general argument that is made in favor of darwinian interpretations of the history of life. Unfortunately, this is not strictly true. . . . The evidence we find in the geologic record is not nearly as compatible with darwinian natural selection as we would like it to be. Darwin was completely aware of this. He was embarrassed by the fossil record because it didn't look the way he predicted it would and, as a result, he devoted a long section of his *Origin of Species* to an attempt to explain and rationalize the differences. . . . Darwin's general solution to the incompatibility of fossil evidence and his theory was to say that the fossil record is a

---

[39] S. M. Stanley, *Macroevolution, Pattern and Process* (San Diego: Freeman, 1979).

[40] D. S. Woodruff, *Science* 208:716 (1980).

[41] E. R. Leach, *Nature* 293:19 (1981).

very incomplete one. . . . Well, we are now about 120 years after Darwin and the knowledge of the fossil record has been greatly expanded. We now have a quarter of a million fossil species but the situation hasn't changed much. The record of evolution is still surprisingly jerky and, ironically, we have even fewer examples of evolutionary transition than we had in Darwin's time. By this I mean that some of the classic cases of darwinian change in the fossil record, such as the evolution of the horse in North America, have had to be discarded or modified as a result of more detailed information—what appeared to be a nice simple progression when relatively few data were available now appears to be much more complex and much less gradualistic. So Darwin's problem has not been alleviated. . . .[42]

Earlier we mentioned that Gould had stated that the extreme rarity of transitional forms was a trade secret of paleontologists. This is certainly a testimony to the effectiveness of the censorship of the views of creation scientists by the establishment. Perhaps the persistence of creation scientists is helping to betray the secret, however, for even those who write for the popular press now seem to be aware of the problem. In an article significantly entitled "Is Man a Subtle Accident?" published in *Newsweek*, it is stated:

The missing link between man and the apes, whose absence has comforted religious fundamentalists since the days of Darwin, is merely the most glamorous of a whole hierarchy of phantom creatures. In the fossil record, missing links are the rule: the story of life is as disjointed as a silent newsreel, in which species succeed one another as abruptly as Balkan prime ministers. The more scientists have searched for the transitional forms that lie between species, the more they have been frustrated.[43]

The situation has become so embarrassing to evolutionists that some seek to disavow the importance of the fossil record to evolution theory. British zoologist and evolutionist Mark Ridley is now claiming:

---

[42] D. M. Raup, *Field Museum of Nat. Hist. Bull.* 50:22 (1979).
[43] "Is Man a Subtle Accident?" *Newsweek*, November 3, 1980.

... the gradual change of fossil species has *never* been part
of the evidence for evolution. In the chapters on the fossil
record in the *Origin of Species* Darwin showed that the
record was useless for testing between evolution and special
creation because it has great gaps in it. The same argument
still applies. . . . In any case, no real evolutionist, whether
gradualist or punctuationist, uses the fossil record as
evidence in favor of the theory of evolution as opposed to
special creation.[44]

That indeed is a surprising statement if evolution is really true. If
millions of species have evolved over a span of hundreds of millions of
years, billions times billions of transitional forms must have lived and
died during that vast stretch of time. As Professor Raup has stated,
over 250,000 different fossil species rest in museum collections. They
no doubt are represented by many millions of catalogued fossils. The
fossil record is almost immeasurably rich. What better evidence for
evolution, then, should one find than this record of the history of life?
What more conclusive evidence could an evolutionist wish for with
which to defend evolution against creation scientists? But no, Ridley
tells us—no real evolutionist should use the fossil record to defend
evolution versus special creation. In contrast to this advice, creation
scientists do not hesitate to use the fossil record to defend creation
versus evolution.

Pierre Grassé is the most distinguished of all French zoologists. It
has been said that his knowledge of the living world is encyclopedic. He
sharply rebukes the claim that the fossil record is unimportant as
support for evolution. He states:

Naturalists must remember that the process of evolution
is revealed only through fossil forms. A knowledge of
paleontology is, therefore, a prerequisite; only paleontology
can provide them with the evidence of evolution and reveal
its course or mechanisms. Neither the examination of
present beings, nor imagination, nor theories can serve as a
substitute for paleontological documents. If they ignore
them, biologists, the philosophers of nature, indulge in

---

[44] M. Ridley, *New Scientist* 90:830 (1981).

numerous commentaries and can only come up with hypotheses.[45]

Unfortunately for Grassé and his fellow evolutionists, the paleontological record does not provide that much needed evidence for evolution.

In spite of the testimony in the preceding pages concerning the embarrassing lack of evidence for evolution in the fossil record, almost all textbooks on evolution include several examples of supposed transitions provided by fossils. In some cases, they do appear impressive, and certainly seem so to students. With the passage of time, however, we find that each example withers under the weight of accumulated evidence. Derek Ager, the late Professor of Geology at Swansea, Wales, and a fervent anti-creationist, had said:

> It must be significant that nearly all the evolutionary stories I learned as a student, from Trueman's *Ostrea/Gryphea* to Carruther's *Zaphrentis delanouei*, have now been "debunked." Similarly, my own experience of more than twenty years looking for evolutionary lineages among the Mesozoic Brachiopoda has proved them equally elusive.[46]

Our advice is, not to worry, for while the present generation of evolutionists are debunking the evolutionary stories of the previous generation, they are just as busy generating their own evolutionary stories, which will be debunked by the next generation, etc.

Evolution by Punctuated Equilibrium

Stephen Jay Gould, Niles Eldredge, an invertebrate paleontologist at the American Museum of Natural History, and Steven Stanley, a paleontologist of Johns Hopkins University, have been the main proponents of a new notion about evolution that has become known as punctuated equilibrium.[47] These theorists, as well as a growing

---

[45] P. Grassé, *Evolution of Living Organisms* (New York: Academic Press, 1977), p. 4.

[46] D. V. Ager, *Proceedings of the Geological Association* 87:132 (1976).

[47] Stanley, *Macroevolution, Pattern and Process*; S. M. Stanley, *The*

number of others, have finally begun to admit that there is no evidence for gradual change in the fossil record.

Charles Darwin, the great high priest of evolution, had proclaimed that evolution had taken place slowly and gradually, during which very small, almost imperceptible changes accumulated in each evolving line, causing species to evolve into new species over long stretches of time. This idea is termed phyletic gradualism, and became supreme as the dogma of the establishment by the mid-1900's through the powerful influence of Julian Huxley, G. G. Simpson, Theodosius Dobzhansky, Ernst Mayr, G. L. Stebbins and John Maynard Smith, its main architects. Phyletic gradualism was the concept dominating this neo-Darwinian mechanism of evolution, also known as the synthetic theory.

Gould has now declared, however, that it is time for the funeral of the neo-Darwinian, or synthetic theory of evolution. He writes:

> ... but if Mayr's characterization of the synthetic theory is accurate, then that theory, as a general proposition, is effectively dead, despite its persistence as textbook orthodoxy.[48]

The advocates of the punctuated equilibrium notion point out that species appear in the fossil record fully formed, generally persist for long periods of time, and then disappear from the record looking very much as they did at their first appearance. This stability of form is called stasis and is a very real part of the record, according to Gould and his fellow punctuationists. Other species then appear in the record, fully formed, presumably related to preceding forms, but no transitional forms can be found to link one species to another. This evidence is obviously contradictory to the neo-Darwinian mechanism of evolution. How can evolutionary theory be bent to accommodate this fact?

The punctuationists have come up with a jerky mode of evolution as the answer. According to this scheme, once a species has developed, it proliferates into a large population and persists relatively unchanged for one, two, five, or ten million years, or even longer. Then for some

New Evolutionary Timetable (New York: Basic Books, 1981); S. J. Gould and N. Eldredge, *Paleobiology* 3:115-151 (1977).

[48] S. J. Gould, *Paleobiology* 6:121 (1980).

unknown reason a relatively small number of the individuals of the population become isolated, and by some unknown mechanism rapidly evolve into a new species (by rapid is meant something on the order of tens of thousands of years). Once the new species has evolved, it then either becomes rapidly extinct or proliferates into a large population. This large population then persists for one or more millions of years. The long period of stasis is the portion of the process referred to as the period of equilibrium, and the interval characterized by rapid evolution is the punctuation—thus the term, punctuated equilibrium.

According to the punctuationists, a large population persisting for many hundreds of thousands or millions of years provides an adequate opportunity for the deposition of fossils. The period of rapid evolution, on the other hand, especially since it involves a relatively small population, does not provide opportunity for fossilization. Thus, no transitional forms between species are found.

This notion of punctuated equilibrium, which is being hailed by many as the solution to the problem posed by the fossil record, is actually no solution at all. First of all, punctuated equilibrium is not a mechanism. No one knows why or how a species could rapidly evolve into a new species. In fact, this notion is contrary to our knowledge derived from the science of genetics. The genetic apparatus of a lizard, for example, is devoted 100% to producing another lizard. The idea that this indescribably complex, finely tuned, highly integrated, amazingly stable genetic apparatus involving hundreds of thousands of interdependent genes could be drastically altered and rapidly reintegrated in such a way that the new organism not only survives but actually is an improvement over the preceding form is contrary to what we know about the apparatus and how it functions.

Furthermore, this notion is without empirically observable scientific evidence. The only evidence for it is the absence of transitional forms. According to the punctuationist, since obviously one form did not slowly and gradually evolve into another, then just as obviously it must have rapidly evolved into the new form.

Ever since Darwin, creation scientists have insisted that the absence of transitional forms is evidence for special creation, but now the punctuationists, following the oft-proven advice, "if you can't beat them, join them," are claiming that the absence of transitional forms is evidence for evolution—according to a punctuational mode.

The most damaging indictment of the punctuationist scheme of evolution, however, is the fact that it offers no solution whatever for the really serious problem that the fossil record poses for evolution theory. The serious problem is the absence of transitional forms between the higher categories—families, orders, classes and phyla. For example, while the absence of transitional forms between various species of single-celled organisms, and the absence of transitional forms between, say, various species of sea urchins, does pose a serious problem, the vast gulf engendered by the total absence of transitional forms between single-celled organisms and the complex invertebrates, such as the sea urchins, is a problem of monumental proportions. Again, the absence of transitional forms between, say, various species of herring may be viewed by evolutionists as a problem for evolution theory, the lack of a single transitional form between the invertebrates and fishes, or between fishes and amphibia, poses problems of insurmountable magnitude.

The idea of punctuated equilibrium was invented to explain the absence of transitional forms between species, but does not even address, let alone solve, the problem of the really big gaps in the fossil record. Perhaps this is the reason that Gould, one of the architects of the punctuated equilibrium mode of evolution still feels compelled to predict a "return of the hopeful monsters." The rising popularity of the punctuated equilibrium notion of evolution is just another indication of the bankruptcy of evolution theory.

Creation, Evolution, and the Fossil Record: Summary

The major predictions of the creation model are:

1. The abrupt appearance of highly complex and diverse forms of life with no evidence of ancestral forms.

2. The sudden appearance of basic plant and animal types without evidence of transitional forms between these basic types.

The fossil record reveals:

1. The abrupt appearance of a great variety of highly complex forms of life. No evolutionary ancestors for these animals can be found anywhere on the earth.

2. The sudden appearance of the higher categories of plants and animals with no evidence of transitional forms between these basic types.

The historical, or fossil, record thus provides excellent support for special creation, but contradicts the major predictions of evolution theory. In answer to the question, did evolution really occur, the fossils shout a resounding NO!

Embryology, Vestigial Organs and Homology

What about other evidence for evolution, such as that from embryology, homology, and vestigial organs? Almost all evolutionists used to believe (and many still do) that the human embryo (and all other embryos), during its development, takes on, successively, the appearance of its evolutionary ancestors in the proper evolutionary sequence. Ontogeny (embryological development) is said to recapitulate phylogeny (evolutionary development or "family tree"). This claim is still found in most high school and college texts, although most embryologists now believe this theory to be completely discredited.

Over fifty years ago Waldo Shumway of the University of Illinois said, with respect to the theory of embryological recapitulation (also called the "biogenetic law"), that a consideration of the results of experimental embryology "seem to demand that the hypothesis be abandoned."[49] Walter J. Bock of the Department of Biological Sciences of Columbia University says:

. . . the biogenetic law has become so deeply rooted in biological thought that it cannot be weeded out in spite of its having been demonstrated to be wrong by numerous subsequent scholars.[50]

Many similar quotes to this effect may be cited (see, for example, the excellent section by Davidheiser on the theory of embryological recapitulation[51]).

---

[49] W. Shumway, *Quarterly Review of Biology* 7:98 (1932).

[50] W. J. Bock, *Science* 164:684 (1969).

[51] B. Davidheiser, *Evolution and Christian Faith* (Philadelphia: Presbyterian and Reformed Publishing Company, 1969), p. 240.

One of the more popular ideas expressed by those who believe in embryological recapitulation is the idea that the human embryo (as well as the embryos of all mammals, reptiles, and birds) has "gill slits" during early stages of its development. The human embryo does have a series of bars and grooves in the neck region, called pharyngeal pouches, which superficially resemble a series of bars and grooves in the neck region of the fish which do develop into gills. In the human, however, (and in other mammals, birds, and reptiles), these pharyngeal pouches do not open into the throat (they thus cannot be "slits"), and they do not develop into gills or respiratory tissue (and so they cannot be "gills"). If they are neither gills nor slits, how then can they be called "gill-slits"? These structures actually develop into various glands, the lower jaw, and structures in the inner ear. Langman states, "Since the human embryo never has gills—branchia—the term pharyngeal arches and clefts has been adopted for this book."[52]

If the human embryo recapitulates its assumed evolutionary ancestry, the human heart should begin with one chamber and then develop successively into two, then three, and finally four chambers. Instead, the human heart begins as a two-chambered organ which fuses to a single chamber, which then develops directly into four chambers. In other words, the sequence is 2–1–4, not 1–2–3–4 as required by the theory. The human brain develops before the nerve cords, and the heart before the blood vessels, both out of the assumed evolutionary sequence. It is because of many similar contradictions and omissions that the theory of embryological recapitulation has been abandoned by embryologists.

Furthermore, in recent years, an instrument called a fetoscope has been developed which, when inserted into the uterus, permits the observation and photographing of every stage of the human embryo during its development. As a result, it is now known that at every stage of its development, the fetal developmental process is uniquely human.[53]

Evolutionists at one time listed about 180 organs in the human body considered to be no more than useless vestiges of organs that were useful in man's animal ancestors. With increasing knowledge,

---

[52] Jan Langman, *Medical Embryology*, 3rd ed. (1975), p. 262.

[53] S. Schwabenthan, *Parents* (October 1979), p. 50.

however, this list has steadily shrunk until the number has been reduced practically to zero. Important organs such as the thymus gland, the pineal gland, the tonsils, and the coccyx (tail bone) were once considered vestigial. The thymus gland and the tonsils are involved in defense against disease. The appendix contains tissue similar to that found in the tonsils and is also active in the fight against foreign invaders. The coccyx is not a useless vestige of a tail, but serves an important function as the anchor for certain pelvic muscles. Furthermore, one cannot sit comfortably following removal of the coccyx.

Evolutionist S. R. Scadding, a zoologist at the University of Guelph, Ontario, lists two main arguments against the notion that so-called "vestigial organs" offer support for evolution. He points out, first of all, that practically every supposed vestigial organ has been shown to have a useful function. Secondly, Scadding emphasizes that it is impossible to demonstrate conclusively that an organ has no function. Scadding concludes that "vestigial organs" provide no evidence for the theory of evolution.[54]

Evolutionists cite the fact that many different kinds of animals have structures, organs (called homologous structures), and metabolisms that are similar. That this is true is quite evident. Is it surprising that the biochemistry (life chemistry or metabolism) of the human is very similar to that of a rat? After all, do we not eat the same food, drink the same water, and breathe the same air? *If* evolution were true, similarities in structure and metabolism would be a valuable aid in tracing evolutionary ancestries, but it is worthless as evidence *for* evolution. These types of similarities are predicted by both the creation and the evolution models. Such similarities are actually the result of the fact that creation is based upon the master plan of the Master Planner. Where similar functions were needed, the Creator used similar structures and life chemistry to perform these functions, merely modifying these structures and metabolic pathways to meet the individual requirement of each organism.

Much of the morphological and genetic evidence related to homologous structures, in fact, directly contradicts predictions based on evolution theory. Much of this contradictory data is discussed by Sir Gavin de Beer, a firm advocate of evolution theory, in his Oxford

---

[54] S. R. Scadding, *Evolutionary Theory* 5:173 (1981).

Biology Reader entitled *Homology, an Unsolved Problem.*[55] Sir Gavin
chose this title because the evidence is contradictory to what he, as an
evolutionist, would expect.

After citing much of this contradictory evidence, Sir Gavin
mentions the cruelest blow of all—the contradiction between the
genetic data and the concept of inheritance of homologous structures
from a common ancestor. After some discussion, Sir Gavin says:

> It is now clear that the pride with which it was assumed
> that the inheritance of homologous structures from a
> common ancestor explained homology was misplaced; for
> such inheritance cannot be ascribed to identity of genes. The
> attempt to find "homologous" genes, except in closely
> related species, has been given up as hopeless.

If homologous structures exist because animals (or plants) which
possess these similar structures have inherited them through
evolution from a common ancestor which possessed the structure,
then certainly these creatures should share in common the genes each
inherited from the common ancestor which determined the
homologous structure. In other words, the set of genes in each one of
these creatures which determines the homologous structure should be
nearly identical (thus "homologous"). But this is not the case. When
the homologous structure is traced back to the genes which determine
it, these genes are found to be completely different in the animals (or
plants) possessing the homologous structure.

Evolutionists believe that structures change (or evolve) because
genes change (or evolve). Thus, if genes change, certainly the structure
or function governed by these genes should change. Conversely, if the
structure or function has remained unchanged, then the genes
governing this structure or function would remain unchanged. These
are clearly the predictions that would be made if evolution were true.
The actual genetic data, however, directly contradicts these
predictions.

Because of this fact, evolutionists are forced to postulate an
incredible situation. Thus, as cited by Sir Gavin, S. C. Harland has
stated:

---

[55] G. R. de Beer, *Homology, An Unsolved Problem* (Oxford: Oxford
University Press, 1971).

> The genes, as a manifestation of which the character develops, must be continually changing. . . . We are able to see how organs such as the eye, which are common to all vertebrate animals, preserve their essential similarity in structure or function, though the genes responsible for the organ must have become wholly altered during the evolutionary process.[56]

What an incredible suggestion! Genes, for example, those governing the eyes, evolve into entirely different genes, but the structure (the eye) governed by these genes remains unchanged! In their attempt to resolve the contradictions between the genetic data and evolution theory, evolutionists are forced to postulate the most preposterous hypotheses. No naturalistic, mechanistic process could accomplish such an amazing physical arrangment—the structures being nearly identical, but the genes being completely different. The evidence certainly indicates that the genetic engineer that brought about such an incredible arrangement was an omnipotent Creator.

Although Sir Gavin can think of no alternative to the suggestion of Harland, he evidently feels very uncomfortable about it, for he says:

> But if it is true that through the genetic code, genes code for enzymes that synthesize proteins which are responsible (in a manner still unknown in embryology) for the differentiation of the various parts in their normal manner, what mechanism can it be that results in the production of homologous organs, the same "patterns," in spite of their not being controlled by the same genes? I asked that question in 1938, and it has not been answered.[57]

It has not been answered, because no answer is available that is compatible with evolution theory. It is highly recommended that those interested in the creation/evolution question obtain copies of both the Oxford Biology Reader and the 1938 publication by Sir Gavin. The 1938 publication discusses both homology and embryology and the problems these generate for evolution theory.[58]

---

[56] *Ibid.*, p. 16; see also S. C. Harland, *Biological Reviews* 11:83 (1936).

[57] de Beer, *Homology, An Unsolved Problem*, p. 16.

[58] G. R. de Beer, in *Evolution: Essays Presented to E. S. Goodrich*, ed.

The suggestion of Harland that structures can remain unchanged while the genes governing them become completely altered, in addition to the contradiction to evolution theory mentioned above, contradicts another basic assumption of evolution theory—that is, that evolution occurs through natural selection. In this case, it is obvious that, while the genes have become wholly altered, and thus have evolved drastically (according to evolutionists), natural selection could not possibly have been involved, since the structure (in this case, the eye) remains unchanged.

Natural selection, according to evolution theory, involves an interaction between the environment and the structures and functions (the phenotype) of plants and animals. There is no way the genes (the genotype) can be involved in this interaction without involving the phenotype. That is, the genotype can become involved only by its effect on the phenotype. If this is the case, then in the supposed evolutionary transformation of the genes suggested by the above by Harland, how could natural selection preserve and enhance the percentage of the mutant versus the original or unchanged variety throughout the series of changes required, since the structure itself remains unchanged? Obviously, natural selection is excluded. Furthermore, this has occurred numerous times, according to Sir Gavin, because, he says, the attempt to find "homologous" genes, except in closely related species (thus all derived from a single created kind according to creationists) has been given up as hopeless. Repeatedly, then, according to evolution theory, genes have become wholly altered with no change in the structure or function governed by these genes, the process thus being wholly independent of natural selection, the supposed driving force of evolution!

Sir Gavin de Beer's publication appeared in 1971, and twenty-five years later biologists are failing just as miserably in their attempts to explain homology on the basis of genetic, embryological, and morphological evidence from an evolutionary perspective. Rolf Sattler, in his article entitled "Homology—A Continuing Challenge"[59] admits that "As de Beer (1971) has pointed out, homology is still an 'unsolved problem.'" He believes, as de Beer did, that inheritance of homologous

---

G. R. de Beer (Oxford: Clarendon Press, 1938).

[59] R. Sattler, *Systematic Botany* 9(4): 382-394 (1984).

structures in different animals cannot be ascribed to the inheritance of the same or homologous genes, for he says:

> . . . in general the homology of structures such as organs or modules cannot be ascribed to inheritance of homologous genes or sets of genes. Consequently organ homology cannot be reduced to gene homology. . . . But what it is exactly, and how it is continuous, is still an unsolved problem.

Louise Roth is as frank to admit that evolutionary biologists have failed to provide a biological basis for homology. She says:

> It would appear that the title of de Beer's 1971 essay—"Homology, an unsolved problem"—remains an accurate description. . . . The relationships between processes at genetic, developmental, gross phenotypic, and evolutionary levels remain a black box.[60]

Roth also believes, as did de Beer and Sattler, that homologous structures in different animals are not controlled by the same genes. G. P. Wagner states that:

> The disturbingly many and deep problems associated with any attempt to identify the biological basis of homology have been presented repeatedly. . . . It is important to note the common theme in complaints of the inadequacy of developmental biology and genetics to account for homology.[61]

In his paper on homology, Wagner asks the plaintive question, "Why is it still difficult to find a biological basis of homology?" (p. 1157). Why, indeed. We believe the answer to their dilemma lies in the fact that they are seeking to reconcile homology with genetics, morphology, and embryology on the basis of evolutionary theory, and the facts simply cannot be made to fit. If homologous structures in different animals were controlled by identical or homologous genes, if these homologous structures originated from the same embryological

---

[60] Louise Roth, in *Ontogeny and Systematics*, ed. C. J. Humphrey (New York: Columbia University Press, 1988), pp. 1, 16.

[61] G. P. Wagner, *Evolution* 43(6): 1163 (1989).

structures, and if the developmental pathways were the same for homologous structures in different animals, then the facts would correspond to predictions based on evolutionary theory. None of these situations actually exist, however. The failure of predictions related to homology based on evolutionary theory is another indication of the total bankruptcy of the theory.

Earlier we referred to a program on BBC radio in which Colin Patterson had expressed some problems he had with evolutionary theory. In the article describing the program,[62] Patterson and others who hold his views on taxonomy (that taxonomists should ignore evolutionary theory in their work) are called "transformed cladists." The article states:

> So now we can see the full extent of the doubts. The transformed cladists claim that evolution is totally unnecessary for good taxonomy; at the same time they are unconvinced by the Darwinian explanation of how new species arise. To them, therefore, the history of life is still fiction rather than fact and the Darwinian penchant for explaining evolution in terms of adaptation and selection is largely empty rhetoric.

Later, Patterson is quoted as saying:

> Just as pre-Darwinian biology was carried out by people whose faith was in the Creator and His plan, post-Darwinian biology is being carried out by people whose faith is in, almost, the deity of Darwin. They've seen their task as to elaborate his theory and to fill the gaps in it, to fill in the trunk and twigs of the tree. But it seems to me that the theoretical framework has very little impact on the actual progress of the work in biological research. In a way some aspects of Darwinism and of neo-Darwinism seem to me to have held back the progress of science.

---

[62] Leith, *The Listener* 106:390 (1981).

Conclusion

Kerkut, although not a creationist, authored a notable little volume to expose the weaknesses and fallacies in the usual evidence used to support evolution theory. In the concluding paragraph of this book, Kerkut stated:

> ... there is the theory that all the living forms in the world have arisen from a single source which itself came from an inorganic form. This theory can be called the "General Theory of Evolution" and the evidence that supports it is not sufficiently strong to allow us to consider it as anything more than a working hypothesis.[63]

There is a world of difference, of course, between a working hypothesis and established scientific fact. The "fact of evolution" is actually the *faith* of evolutionists in their particular world view.

No less a convinced evolutionist than Thomas H. Huxley acknowledged that:

> ... "creation," in the ordinary sense of the word is perfectly conceivable. I find no difficulty in conceiving that, at some former period, this universe was not in existence, and that it made its appearance in six days (or instantaneously, if that is preferred), in consequence of the volition of some preexisting Being. Then, as now, the so-called *a priori* arguments against Theism and, given a Deity, against the possibility of creative acts, appeared to me to be devoid of reasonable foundation.[64]

R. D. Alexander, Professor of Zoology at the University of Michigan, and an evolutionist, as noted earlier in this book, believes that:

> No teacher should be dismayed at efforts to present creation as an alternative to evolution in biology courses;

---

[63] G. A. Kerkut, *Implication of Evolution* (New York: Pergamon Press, 1960), p. 157.

[64] T. H. Huxley, quoted in *Life and Letters of Thomas Henry Huxley*, vol. I, ed. L. Huxley (Macmillan, 1903), p. 241.

indeed, at this moment creation is the only alternative to evolution. Not only is this worth mentioning, but a comparison of the two alternatives can be an excellent exercise in logic and reason. Our primary goal as educators should be to teach students to think, and such a comparison, particularly because it concerns an issue in which many have special interests or are even emotionally involved, may accomplish that purpose better than most others.[65]

The refusal of the establishment within scientific and educational circles to consider creation as an alternative to evolution is thus based above all on the insistence upon a purely atheistic, materialistic, and mechanistic explanation for origins to the exclusion of an explanation based on theism. Restricting the teaching concerning origins to this one particular view thus constitutes indoctrination in a religious philosophy. Constitutional guarantees of separation of church and state are violated and true science is shackled in dogma.

After many years of intense study of the problem of origins from a scientific viewpoint, I am convinced that the facts of science declare special creation to be the only *rational* explanation of origins.

"In the beginning God created . . ." is still the most up-to-date statement that can be made about our origins.

---

[65] R. D. Alexander, in *Evolution versus Creationism: The Public Education Controversy*, ed. J. P. Zetterberg (Phoenix: Oryx Press, 1983), p. 91.

Now Evolution Is the Substance of Fossils Hoped For, The Evidence of Links Not Seen

Illustration Index

Glossary

agglutinated. Joined together by adhesion, as with glue.

algae. Any of various acquatic one-celled or multicellular plants that lack true stems, roots, and leaves but usually contain chlorophyll.

allometric. The study of the change in proportion of various parts of an organism as a consequence of growth.

amniote. A vertebrate, including reptiles, birds and mammals, having an amnion during the embryonic stage.

amnion. A thin, tough, membranous sac that contains a watery fluid in which the embryo of a mammal, bird or reptile is suspended.

anthropoid. Higher primates that include platyrrhine monkeys of the New World and humans and the catarrhine monkeys and apes of the Old World.

appendicular. Of, pertaining to, or consisting of an appendage or appendages, such as forelimbs and hindlimbs.

arboreal. Walking and running along branches; living in trees.

arthropod. Any of numerous invertebrate organisms of the phylum Arthropoda, which includes the insects, crustaceans, arachnids, and myriapods, characterized by a segmented body and jointed legs.

articular. Of or pertaining to a joint or joints; a bone in the jaw of some birds, reptiles and fishes, which, in reptiles, for example, articulates with the quadrate.

Aves. A class of animals composed of the birds.

biogenic. Produced by the actions of living organisms.

biota. The animal and plant life of a particular region considered as a total ecological entity.

bipedal. Balancing and moving the body atop two limbs; having two feet.

brachiopods. Any of various marine invertebrates of the phylum Brachiopoda, a class of bivalve mollusks having a pair of tentacled, armlike structures on either side of the mouth which they can protrude and withdraw.

caecilian. Any of a group of legless, burrowing, wormlike amphibians of tropical regions of the order Gymnophiona.

calcaneum. The "heel-bone," the quadrangular bone at the back of the tarsus.

canine. A conical tooth located between the incisors and the first premolars.

Canis. The genus of the dog family (Canidae), including dogs, wolves, coyotes and jackals.

carapace. A hard bony or chitinous outer covering, such as the fused dorsal plates of a turtle, or the covering of the armadillo, crab, etc.

carbonate. A salt or ester of carbonic acid.

Carboniferous. A division of the Paleozoic "era" following the Devonian and preceding the Permian, which thus includes Mississippian and Pennsylvanian rocks.

carnivorous. Belonging or pertaining to the order Carnivora; flesh-eating or predatory.

caudal. Of or near the tail or hind parts, posterior.

Cenozoic. Generally the uppermost, thus most recent geological deposits, divided into two "periods," Tertiary and Quaternary.

cephalopod. Any of the mollusks of the class Cephalopoda, such as an octopus or nautilus, having a distinct head, with large eyes and a beak, and an internal shell in some species, and prehensile tentacles.

cetacean. Of or belonging to the order Cetacea, which includes aquatic mammals such as the whale and porpoise.

choana. A funnel-shaped opening, especially one of the funnel-like nasal cavities.

chordate. Any of numerous animals belonging to the phylum Chordata, which includes all vertebrates and any animal having a notochord, gills, and a dorsal nerve cord at some stage of its development.

class. A taxonomic category ranking below a phylum and above an order.

clavicle. A bone that links the sternum and the scapula. Also called the "collarbone."

coelacanth. Any of various fishes of the order Coelacanthiformes, known only in fossil form until 1938, when a living species *Latimeria* was found in African marine waters.

condyle. A rounded articulatory prominence at the end of a bone.

congenital. A condition resulting from one's heredity or prenatal development.

conifer. Any of various predominantly evergreen, cone-bearing trees, such as a pine, spruce, hemlock, or fir.

coracoid. A small sharp bone or cartilage projecting from the scapula toward the sternum.

cranial capacity. The volume of the cranial cavity; the size of the brain.

cranium. The skull of a vertebrate.

crossopterygian. Of or belonging to the Crossopterygii, a group of mostly extinct fishes including the coelacanths and other lobe-finned fishes.

cynodont. Mammal-like therapsid reptiles of the Infraorder Cynodontia, assumed by evolutionists to have constituted the ancestor, or ancestors, of mammals.

dental arcade or dental arch. The curve formed by the cutting edges and masticating surfaces of the teeth.

dentary. One of two bones on each side of the lower jaw of mammals.

diastema. An abnormally large space between teeth.

dichotomy. Divisions into two usually contradictory parts or opinions; schism.

digital pad. The thickening of the skin on the underside of the toes of some animals.

distal. Anatomically located far from the origin or line of attachment.

ecology. The science of the relationships between living organisms and their environment.

ectothermy. The absorption of heat from external sources by an animal, which has a body temperature very close to that of the environment, thus characteristic of "cold-blooded" animals.

empirical. Relying upon or derived from observation or experiment; guided by practical experience and not by theory.

endoskeleton. An internal supporting skeleton characteristic of vertebrates.

endothermy. Production of heat in an animal from its own metabolism, which also employs devices to retard heat loss so that it is able to maintain its body temperature independent of its environment.

enzyme. Any of numerous proteins produced by living organisms and functioning as biochemical catalysts.

eukaryote. Living cells that possess organelles contained within membranes, such as chloroplasts, mitochondria, and nuclei.

family. The taxon in the taxonomical system, falling below the order and above the genus.

fauna. Animals collectively; especially, the animals of a particular region.

femur. The proximal bone of the lower or hind limb in vertebrates, situated between the pelvis and knee in humans; the thighbone.

fibula. The outer and smaller of two bones of the human leg or the hind leg of an animal, between the knee and the ankle.

flora. Plants collectively; especially, the plants of a particular region.

fluke. One of the two horizontally flattened divisions or branches of the tail of a whale or related animal.

fluvial. Of, pertaining to, or inhabiting a river or stream; formed or produced by the action of flowing water.

follicle. An approximately spherical group of cells containing a cavity; a vascular body in the ovary containing ova.

foramen. A small opening in a bone through which a nerve passes.

fossa. A hollow or depression, as in a bone.

gastropod. Any mollusk of the class Gastropoda, such as a snail, slug, cowry, or limpet.

genome. Totality of genetic material, or DNA, contained in a cell.

genotype. The genetic constitution of an organism, as distinguished from its physical appearance, or phenotype.

genus. Rank in the hierarchy of classification that lies below the family group (including tribes and subtribes) and above the subgenus and species.

glenoid cavity. A large depression in the scapula, which is part of the ball-and-socket joint of the upper arm in humans.

gnathostome. Of the group of the subphylum Vertebrata which possesses jaws and usually have paired appendages.

habitat. The area or type of environment in which an organism or biological population normally lives.

herbaceous. Pertaining to or characteristic of an herb as distinguished from a woody plant.

herbivorous. Feeding on plants; plant-eating.

hominid. The Hominidae is the Family of Man. Evolutionists include in the Hominidae not only humans but alleged interemediates between apes and man. All such creatures are referred to as hominids.

hominoid. Of or belonging to the superfamily Hominoidea, which includes the apes and man.

Hominidae. The family comprising humans and his alleged ape-like ancestors.

homologous. Features of organisms that by virtue of position, structure, or function seem to be comparable.

humerus. The long bone of the upper part of the arm, extending from the shoulder to the elbow.

ichthyosaur. Any of various extinct fishlike marine reptiles of the order Ichthyosauria.

ilium. The uppermost of three bones fused together within the pelvis of most land vertebrates; either of a pair of bones forming the superior portion of the pelvis bone in vertebrates.

incisor. A tooth designed for cutting, located at the apex of the dental arch.

innominate. A large flat bone forming the lateral half of the pelvis. Also called the "hipbone."

in situ. In its original place.

integumentary. Having an outer covering or coat, such as the skin of an animal or the coat of a seed.

invertebrate. An animal which has no backbone or spinal column.

ischium. The lowest of three major bones comprising each half of the pelvis.

isotope. One of two or more atoms, the nuclei of which have the same number of protons but different numbers of neutrons.

keratinous. Having a tough, fibrous protein forming the outer layer of epidermal structures such as hair, nails, horns and hoofs.

labyrinth. The internal ear, comprising the semicircular canals, vestibule, and cochlea.

lemur. A genus consisting for the most part of arboreal quadrupeds with a body weight of about 3 kg; any of several arboreal primates chiefly of the family Lemuridae, of Madagascar and adjacent islands, having large eyes, soft fur, and a long tail.

lemuroid. Of the suborder or subfamily of Primates including the lemurs, tarsiers, and lorises.

lineage. Direct descent from a particular ancestor; ancestry.

lithification. The process of turning to stone; conversion of a newly deposited sediment into rock.

lobate. Having lobes; resembling a lobe.

loris. Family of lower primates (Lorisidae) that includes both fossil and extant taxa; any of several small, nocturnal, arboreal primates of the genera *Loris* and *Nycticebus*, of tropical Asia, having dense, wooly fur and large eyes.

lungfish. Any of several tropical freshwater fishes of the order Dipnoi, having lungs as well as gills, and in certain species constructing a mucus-lined mud covering in which to withstand an extended drought.

mandible. The lower jaw in vertebrates.

marsupial. Any mammal of the order Marsupialia, including kangaroos, opossums, bandicoots, and wombats. The female of most species lacks a placenta and possesses an external abdominal pouch that contains mammary glands in which the young remain until fully developed.

mastodon. Any of several extinct mammals of the genus *Mammut*, resembling the elephant.

maxilla. One of a pair of bones forming the upper jaw in vertebrates.

metacarpal. That part of the hand or forefoot that includes the five bones between the phalanges and the carpus.

metatarsal. The part of the foot between the ankle and toes; the corresponding bones of an animal's hindlimb, between the tarsus and toes.

metazoa. A division of the animal kingdom, which includes all animals more complex than the one-celled protozoan; multicellular animals.

molar. A tooth with a broad crown for grinding food, located behind the premolars.

mollusk (mollusc). Any member of the phylum Mollusca, of largely marine invertebrates, including the oysters, snails, clams, squids, octupi, slugs, etc.

monodactyl. An animal having only one claw on each extremity.

monotreme. A member of the Monotremata, an order of egg-laying mammals restricted to Australia and New Guinea, and including the platypus and the echidna.

morphology. Shape; anatomy.

multivariate analysis. Statistical techniques for analyzing simultaneously many variables or characters measured on each individual unit.

mutant. An individual or organism differing from the parental strain as a result of mutation.

mutation. Any heritable alteration of the genes or chromosomes of an organism.

neo-Darwinism. The theory that the evolutionary development of plants and animals is principally determined by natural selection of slight variants produced by mutations.

newt. Any of several small, semiaquatic salamanders espcially of the genus *Trituris* and related genera.

notochord. A flexible rodlike structure in some lower vertebrates that provide dorsal support; a similar structure in embryos of higher vertebrates, from which the spine develops.

nuchal crest. A bony ridge along the back of the skull.

nucleic acid. Any member of either of two groups of complex compounds, ribonucleic acids and deoxyribonucleic acids found in all living cells, and composed of purines, pyrimidines, sugars, and phosphoric acid.

nucleotide. Any of various organic compounds consisting of a nucleoside (a compound of a purine or a pyrimidine and a sugar) combined with phosphoric acid. Nucleotides are the basic units of nucleic acids.

occipital. Pertaining to the curved, compound bone that forms the lower posterior part of the skull.

omnivorous. Eating both animal and vegetable substances.

ontogeny. Life history of an individual organism, beginning with conception and proceeding throughout embryonic development, when the formation of various structures and organ systems occurs.

order. A taxonomic category of plants and animals ranking above the family and below the class.

osteolepiformes. Of a primitive order of lobefin fishes, subclass Crossopterygii, generally characterized by two dorsal fins placed well back on the body, and a head covered with large dermal plating bones.

osteological. Pertaining to the bone structure or system of an animal.

otic. Pertaining to, or located near, the ear.

ozone. A blue, gaseous triatomic form of oxygen, O_3, derived or formed naturally from diatomic oxygen by electric discharge or exposure to ultraviolet radiation.

palate. The roof of the mouth in vertebrates forming a complete or partial separation of the mouth cavity and nasal passage, consisting of a bony front, backed by a fleshly soft palate.

paleoanthropologists. Scientists who study the fossils of manlike creatures.

paleontology. The study of fossils and ancient life forms.

Paleozoic. Of, belonging to, or designating the rock formations that include the Cambrian, Ordovician, Silurian, Devonian, Mississippian, Pennsylvanian and Permian formations.

parabolic. Of or having the form of a parabola.

parietal. Of or relating to the two bones between the frontal and occipital bones, thus forming part of the top and sides of the skull.

patella. A flat, triangular bone located at the front of the knee joint. Also called the "knee cap."

pectoral. Of or pertaining to the forelimbs of a vertebrate.

pelvic. Of, or near, or pertaining to the pelvis, a bone-shaped skeletal structure composed of the nominate bones on the sides, the pubis in front, and the sacrum and coccyx behind, that rests on the lower limbs and supports the spinal column.

pelycosaur. Of an extinct order of primitive, mammallike reptiles of the subclass Synapsida, characterized by a temporal fossa that lies low on the side of the skull.

permineralization. Mineral emplacement within wood, in which the dissolved minerals are carried by groundwater into the porous parts of buried wood (or shells or bones), where they crystallize out and settle, filling the pores.

phalange. One of the bones of the fingers or toes.

Phanerozoic. The part of geologic deposits for which there is abundant evidence of life, especially higher forms, in the corresponding rock, essentially post-Precambrian.

phenotype. Outward characteristics of an individual, usually the product of a complex interaction between the genetic constitution and the environment.

phosphate. Any salt or ester of phosphoric acid containing mainly pentavalent phosphorous and oxygen.

phylogeny. The supposed evolutionary development of any species of plant or animal.

phylum. A broad taxonomic division of the animal kingdom, next above class in size. For example, all vertebrates and chordates are included within the phylum Chordata.

placental. Pertaining to the vascular, membranous organ that develops in female mammals during pregnancy, lining the uterine wall and partially enveloping the fetus, to which it is attached by the umbilical cord.

plasma. The clear, yellowish fluid portion of blood, lymph, or intramuscular fluid in which cells are suspended.

Pongidae. The family of primates that includes the gibbons, orangutans, gorillas, and chimpanzees.

postcranial. That portion of the skeleton below the skull.

premolar. One of eight bicuspid teeth located in pairs on each side of the upper and lower jaws, behind the canines and in front of the molars.

proboscidean. Of the order Proboscidea, which includes one living family, Elephantidae, the elephants, which have columnar limbs, heavy bodies, tusks, and long prehensile snouts.

prokaryote. Small living cells that reproduce asexually by a process that does not involve mitosis, and include bacteria, blue-green algae, spirochetes, rickettsiae, and mycoplasma organisms. They have no cytoplasmic organelles such as vacuolles, mitochondria, endoplasmic reticulum, or photosynthetic plastids.

prosimian. Member of the lower primates, including the lemurs, lorises, galagos, and tarsiers.

Proterozoic. Of, belonging to, or designating the geologic deposits of the Precambrian era between the Archeozoic era and the Cambrian.

proximal. Near the central part of the body or a point of attachment or origin, as opposed to distal.

pseudosuchia. A suborder of extinct reptiles of the order Thecondontia comprising bipedal, unarmored or feebly armored forms.

pterodactyl. Any of various extinct flying reptiles of the family Pterodactylidae.

pterosaur. Any of various extinct flying reptiles of the order Pterosauria, including the pterodactyls, of the Jurassic and Cretaceous formations, characterized by wings consisting of a flap of skin supported by a very long fourth digit on each front leg.

pubis. The forward portion of either of the hipbones, at the juncture forming the front arch of the pelvis.

quadrate. A bone or cartilaginous structure of the skull, joining the upper and lower jaws in birds, fish, reptiles and amphibians.

quadrupedal. Using all four limbs for walking and running.

radius. A long, prismatic, slightly curved bone, the shorter and thicker of the two forearm bones, located on the lateral side of the ulna.

renal. Of, pertaining to, or in the region of the kidneys.

rhipidistian. Pertaining to the crossopterygian fish of the order Rhipidistia whose fossils are commonly found in Devonian and Carboniferous formations.

sacrum. A triangular bone made up of five vertebrae and forming the posterior section of the pelvis.

salamander. Any of various small, lizardlike amphibians of the order Caudata, having porous, scaleless skin and four legs that are often weak or small.

sarcopterygian. Of a subclass of Osteichthyes, including Crossopterygii and Dipnoi in some systems of classification.

scapula. Either of two large, flat, triangular bones forming the back part of the shoulder. Also called "shoulder blade."

Scuiromorpha. A suborder of the Order Rodentia that includes most so-called primitive rodent types and present-day squirrels.

sea urchin. Any of various echinoderms of the class Echinoidea, having a soft body enclosed in a round symmetrical, limy shell covered with long spines.

secondary palate. A shelf of bone forming the roof of the mouth, which separates the mouth from the nasal passages, and allows the mammal to breathe while chewing and gnawing on food.

serpentine. Of or resembling a serpent, as in form or movement; sinuous, winding.

sirenian. Any herbivorous aquatic mammal of the order Sirenia, which includes the manatee and the dugong.

squamosal. A bone lying external and dorsal to the auditory capsule of many vertebrate skulls. This is the bone to which the dentary bone of the mammal articulates.

stasis. A condition of essentially no change.

sympatric. Of a species, occupying the same range as another species but maintaining identity by not interbreeding.

Synapsida. The subclass of reptiles which includes all mammal-like reptiles.

tarsier. Any of several small nocturnal primates of the genus *Tarsius*, of the East Indies, having large round eyes and a long tail.

taxon. A group of organisms constituting one of the categories or formal units in taxonomic classification, such as a phylum, order, family, genus, or species, and characterized by common characteristics in varying degrees of distinction.

taxonomic. Pertaining to taxonomy.

taxonomy. Theory and practice of classifying organisms in established categories.

tectonics. The geology of the earth's structural deformation.

temporal. Either of two complex, three-part bones forming the sides and base of the skull.

teratology. The biological study of the production, development, anatomy, and classification of malformations.

therapsid. An order of mammallike reptiles of the subclass Synapsida which supposedly gave rise to mammals.

thorax. The part of the human body between the neck and the diaphragm, partially encased by the ribs; the chest.

tibia. The inner and larger of the two bones of the lower leg from the knee to the ankle. Also called the "shin," or the "shinbone" in the human.

tree shrew. Any of various members of the family Tupaiidae, of eastern
   Asia, generally resembling squirrels in habit and appearance.

tridactyl. Having three toes, claws, or similar parts.

trilobite. Any of numerous extinct marine arthropods of the class Trilobita,
   of the Paleozoic, having a segmented exoskeleton divided by grooves or
   furrows into 3 longitudinal lobes.

tuff. A rock composed of compacted volcanic ash varying in size from fine
   sand to course gravel.

tympanum. The tympanic membrane; eardrum.

ulna. The bone extending from the elbow to the wrist on the side opposite
   to the thumb.

ungulate. A mammal whose toes end in hooves made up of hardened skin
   tissue, which includes deer, camels, cattle, horses, elephants, and
   hyraxes.

vault. An arched anatomical part.

vertebrate. Any member of the subphylum Vertebrata, a primary division
   of the phylum Chordata that includes the fishes, amphibians, reptiles,
   birds, and mammals, all of which are characterized by a segmented bony
   or cartilaginous spinal column.

volant. Flying or capable of flying.

Subject Index

Author Index